DISORDERS OF THE INSTINCTS AND THE EMOTIONS

The Parapathiac Disorders

By

WILHELM STEKEL, M.D.

PATTERNS OF PSYCHOSEXUAL INFANTILISM

PATTERNS

OF

PSYCHOSEXUAL INFANTILISM

by

WILHELM STEKEL, M.D.

EDITED AND WITH AN INTRODUCTION BY

EMIL A. GUTHEIL, M.D.

Diplomate, American Board of Neurology and Psychiatry

LIVERIGHT
PUBLISHING CORPORATION
NEW YORK

Library of Congress Catalog Card Number: 52-9664

PRINTED IN THE UNITED STATES OF AMERICA

CONTENTS

vi　　　　　　　　*Contents*

INTRODUCTION

This book is written for physicians, psychologists, and those who deal with human maladjustments as a part of their profession. Although many of the cases cited in this book undoubtedly are "interesting" because they represent drastic deviations from normal patterns of behavior, they have been published because of the important underlying psychological components and the dynamic factors responsible for the deviations.

Many of the cases presented here belong to a group of disorders formerly designated as "perversions." We consider the term "perversion" as unscientific and, in addition, as carrying an unnecessary moralistic stigma, acquired through common usage. It is hard to see why we should use a word which derives from the concept of *version—per* or otherwise. We prefer to use the term *paraphilia* for all those conditions where the sexual attraction ("philia") is directed toward a goal that lies outside ("para") the normal, heterosexual object relationship.

The term *Psychosexual Infantilism* emphasizes the psychodynamic structure of the clinical entities described. It refers to conditions which are of *psychic* origin, pertain primarily to the *sexual* sphere, and represent effects of fixation on or regression to *infantile* levels of emotional development.

The psychotherapeutic task in these cases is often extremely difficult. The "Lost Paradise" of happy childhood days represents a powerful temptation, and many succumb to it, particularly when life confronts them with threats and frustrations. Klaus Groth expressed the longing for this lost paradise in a beautiful poem which was put to music by Johannes Brahms. It runs as follows: [1]

[1] We cite the German original alongside of a free English translation.— *The Editor.*

vii

O wüsst ich doch den Weg zurück,	I wish I knew the pathway back
Den lieben Weg zum Kinderland!	The path that leads to childhood's land!
O warum sucht' ich nach dem Glück	Oh, why did I, in search for gain,
Und liess der Mutter Hand?	Abandon Mother's guiding hand?
O wie mich sehnet auszuruh'n,	Oh, how I crave but to retire
Von keinem Streben aufgeweckt,	And not be roused by vain desire,
Die müden Augen zuzutun,	To shut my weary, tired eyes,
Von Liebe sanft bedeckt!	Be gently shielded by Her hand!
Und nichts zu forschen, nichts zu späh'n,	And not to search, nor to explore,
Und nur zu träumen leicht und lind;	And only dream in sweet delight;
Der Zeiten Wandel nicht zu seh'n,	To take no heed of passing tides,
Zum zweiten Mal ein Kind!	To be a child again!
O zeigt mir doch den Weg zurück,	Oh, show me, pray, the pathway back
Den lieben Weg zum Kinderland!	The path that leads to childhood's land!
Vergebens such' ich nach dem Glück,	I seek for happiness in vain,
Ringsum ist öder Strand!	See only wasteland round.

The success of psychotherapy in cases of psychosexual infantilism shows that the regressions and fixations underlying it are not irreversible, and that after the patients' anxieties have been allayed, it is possible to reconcile the patients with reality. Psychotherapy offers new hope to the disappointed and helps the anxious to work out constructive plans of adjustment. Thus the patients' impulse to seek refuge in reveries of childhood can be successfully overcome.

The editor wishes to express thanks to Dr. Nah Brind of Los Angeles, California, for his valuable help in the translation of this book.

E. A. G.

Chapter One

THE CHILD

Chapter One

THE CHILD

1. The Emotional Life of the Child

The manifestations of psychosexual infantilism can be understood only on the basis of a thorough knowledge of the child's emotional life. The latter has long been a *terra incognita* to us. Only recently have scientists such as Preyer, Freud, Stern, Tiedemann, Scupin, Saupp, Groos, Shin, and Hug-Helmuth given us some understanding of the emotional life of the child. We have gained insight into the earliest mental processes, into the growth of emotional patterns and into the development of cognitive faculties. However, it would by far exceed my immediate task if I attempted to go into all these problems at length. I will, therefore, touch only upon those psychic phenomena of childhood which will help us to comprehend the pathological configurations of the cases described in this book.

The child is at first completely dominated by primitive, elemental drives. These drives imply a perfectly egotistic make-up which includes also a hostile attitude toward the surrounding world.

The child's life is self-centered. In the adult, the selfish

11

tendencies are, to a greater or lesser extent, concealed; they break through only in certain forms of mental disorder. The child is not self-centered to the exclusion of the rest of the world; he is merely self-seeking. He rather conceives himself as the center of the universe. He responds only to those people around him who are sources of pleasure to him. If a wetnurse feeds him, he likes her as much as he likes his mother. He may like the governess better than his close relatives. The child's attitude is not different from that of a new-born animal which is capable of clinging with equal eagerness to the dam or the foster mother. The child's behavior disproves the existence of a feeling of hereditary kinship.

The child is hostile toward the world. Anything strange or new frightens him. Apparently this neophobia evolves from a hereditary instinct. Only when the child becomes aware of the pleasures received does he learn to love the carriers of pleasure.

The anger reaction to an unfulfilled wish emerges in the first year of life with but minor individual variations. The child, assuming himself to be the center of the household, displays tyrannical tendencies. He soon reacts with spells (respiratory cramps, wheezing, etc.) whenever subjected to anything displeasing. Progressively, the anger reactions become intensified. The child gasps for air (vocal cord cramps), goes into tantrums, inflicts wounds on himself, and turns aggressively against other people. With the passing of early childhood, manifestations of spite and defiance turn into more subtle forms of vengeance. If the child notices that his mother emphasizes the importance of food, he may refuse to eat or to chew on his food, or he may retard swallowing. Soon he will develop idiosyncrasies. At times, nervous vomiting will occur as an expression of his disgust and defiance.

The child's craving for love is insatiable. He wants the love of everyone around him, and, most strongly, that of his mother. Apparently love is a requirement essential to the growth and development of the child. In foundling homes, even in those operating under fair sanitary conditions, children do not prosper unless given love and care.

The child cannot stand to be ignored and is very ingenious at tricking the adults into giving him love and attention. He has a keen eye for other people's reactions and is very shrewd. At an early stage he discovers that sickness is profitable in terms of added care and attention. From such an observation to the shamming of sickness is only a step. He may complain of headaches, tummyaches, fears, and many woes, with the single purpose of arousing the sympathy and love of adults around him. The pampering of sickly children is especially apt to produce in them an abnormal longing for sickness which asserts itself in later life.

Psychosexual infantilism is but a re-emergence of this reaction formation. Characteristically enough, it appears in relation to people whose sympathy and love cannot be won otherwise. The procedure of physical care and handling, in itself, is a source of erotic stimulation and makes the child want to be sick. Mother again seats him on the toilet, washes him, feeds him, and generally handles him the way she did when he was a helpless baby.

The pleasure element of the care process may generate in the child a longing for illness. To him, being sick is then equivalent to being pampered. What the child looks for is not mere attention but an excess of it. Sickness also endows him with the power to dominate his environment, and it gives him a chance to have all his whims granted.

The child's illness always arouses envy in his siblings. Why should the *sick* one be so pampered? the other sibling asks himself. Why should he get the best of food? Why should he be free to do nothing? The sick sibling becomes the object of jealousy which may become the root of neurotic disturbances in the other children of the family. The dreadful game of "who is the sickest" among siblings often degenerates into intense mutual hatred. We shall have occasion to introduce a few cases of infantilism which can be traced to such childhood rivalries.

The prerequisite for simulating a disease is good acting ability. Children are born actors and their parents ordinarily foster these innate talents. I have repeatedly emphasized the fact that all neurotics are actors, that often they portray specific characters. Anyone who ever watched children knows that they are keen observers and splendidly imitate and even caricature the foibles of the adults. Hence the amazed statement of many neurotic parents that their children display the same symptoms as they do, and their frequent declaration that heredity is responsible for this coincidence.

One of my patients complained of gastric disturbances which prevented her from taking food. Her husband had to use much persuasion and sometimes force to make her eat. It was a turbulently dynamic case of hysterical anorexia. She had frequent attacks of violent cramps. There were days when she could not eat at all. The patient's four-year-old daughter soon began to display the same symptoms so convincingly that her mother firmly believed the girl was afflicted with her own ailment.

Children learn to use tears, pains, coughing spells, and any number of other dramatic complaints to frighten their parents into compliance. Experienced pediatricians and clever mothers know how often the child's woeful crying serves the sole purpose of fooling the adults.

The propensity to act leads the child to assume roles or to conceal facts from his parents. Hence the fact that so many parents contentedly believe that their children are naive and ignorant, when the latter have long since learned the facts of life.

A fellow physician told me the following story: When he was seven years old, he found a book of obscene jokes on his father's night-table. One of the jokes read: "A captain of the army was looking for a room at a carpenter's home; the lady of the house refused to let him in. She had only one room in the back and one in the front, she explained. The rear room was dark and dirty and the front one was usually occupied by her husband." Later the boy told the joke in the company of adults and although he understood the meaning perfectly, he kept asking naively what was funny about it.

Children carry within themselves secret schemes which they try to act out. I know a six-year-old girl whose mother had divorced her husband in order to marry another man. The child realized she would have to please her stepfather if she wanted to stay with her mother, and she acted friendly and kindly toward him. But she incited her mother against him and belittled him at every chance. They frequently had to wait for him to come home because he was a busy man. On such occasions, the girl never failed to ask her mother: "Why do you always have to wait for him, Mother? Why don't you make him wait for you once in a while?" One day her mother had tears in her eyes while cutting onions, and the girl said: "I wish he'd cut onions for once; he should cry! He should feel how it hurts!"

Children set their life goal (Adler) very early and select parts for themselves to be acted out later in their own social and sexual relations. Here lies the reason why unhappy marriages exert such a devastating influence on the children of the family.

Every child lives under the sign of the "Will to Power" (Nietzsche). He yearns to dominate—magically—not only his parents, but the entire world. In his imagination the world is his possession and everything in it belongs to him; to make his fantasy real is all the child craves in his day-to-day life. His fantasies of world cataclysms in which he is the only survivor are revealing (Tannenbaum's "Noah Complex").

The Robinson Crusoe story, with its motif of isolation from mankind and of building a world of one's own, steers the child's fantasy. In his early years he develops the missionary idea of being entrusted with a great historical task. He believes he is destined to surpass everyone. The craving for unlimited power drives him in his daydreams to challenge the Creator, to contest God's own dominion. This explains why we find so many Christ complexes among the parapathies and paralogies. They are expressions of the child's early duels with the Lord.

At some initial point, the child, in the isolation of his room, shyly utters a blasphemy and timidly waits for God's punishment. Yet no thunderbolt crashes, no divine arm strikes the rebel. The child may repeat the experiment to make completely sure; but whatever the procedure may be, it may dawn upon him that "there is no God," and that "God is just another lie of my father's."

And then he gets the idea of substituting for the missing Deity. He himself shall be God. He feels within himself great magic forces. He has the power to kill his enemies simply by wishing them to die. He is master over the life and death of every person around him.

When these childhood fancies coincide with a real mishap in the family, such as the death of a younger sibling or of the stern father, pangs of conscience and self-accusations undermine the child's mental strength. He shrinks from his desire to be God-like. The forces of conscience prevail; guilt feelings develop and grow and exert their regulative, restrictive and, at times, disastrous influence. The child becomes God-fearing again. He embarks upon a new phase of reactive piety of which I will have more to say in the next chapter.

It seems likely that at least some components of conscience have a hereditary basis. Others arise in the child in the process of his development, in the course of his mental inventory-taking, when he compares himself with the people about him and is horrified by the "abysmal wickedness" within himself. He considers others as kind and good. They have all—with rare exceptions—treated him lovingly, whereas he is ungrateful, selfish and wicked.

Obsessed with ideas of vengeance and the "death to the enemies" impulse, the child will soon succumb to the terror created by the admonitions that God is omiscient and omnipresent. He begins to live in constant fear of divine punishment. It is precisely this fear which drives the child back to accept faith and religion. He needs God's help and assistance in the fight against himself, and a mishap in the family, a spell of illness, a low mark at school are interpreted by the child as omens of the Almighty's wrath. The child seeks to win back God's favor through added, exaggerated devotion. He simply cannot do enough to live up to the divine will.

All neurotic manifestations reveal traces of this childhood struggle, of this accentuated childhood religiousness, but in some infantilistic repressions, suffering and pain appear as substitutes for faith. As a matter of fact, they may become in themselves a form of religious theory, while the parapathy serves the unconscious purpose of preserving the fiction of piety and devotion to the Commandments under an assumed appearance of liberalism and atheism.

The discovery of his own wickedness may lead the child to fear and distrust other people. "How do I know you are not a robber?" asked a five-year-old boy when a gentleman, who had been rather friendly to him, paid a visit.

Time and again I have had occasion to observe in the child the image of Primeval Man. The primitive emotions of both, in their refining process of cultural adjustment, can be reshaped only gradually and slowly.

The child's fear of the devil and the "bad man," like his love for cruel and thrilling stories, has a valid reason. The horror fiction is in accord with the criminal promptings within the child himself. The fairy tales and thrillers often contain at the same time the element of the miraculous, and the outcome is always the triumph of the weak, the small, and the oppressed—that is, symbolically, of the child himself —over the big and strong—the adults.

The dichotomy of Big and Small rules all childish emotions. The child has but one desire: to grow up soon, to become much bigger than the others. These notions of Big and Small are, of course, natural reflections of the child's own helplessness. And the only way for him to avenge himself at will on the big-sized outer world is to grow very big himself.

Every trained and unbiased observer can easily discover the primary sadistic tendencies in the child's make-up, but most of us are inclined to overlook them. Here are a few expressive utterances of a five-year-old girl: "When I grow up, I want to have many, many babies of my own, so that I can spank all of them." And after a visit to the dentist, "I am going to become a dentist, and I'll hurt everybody."

My observations on childhood criminal tendencies have been criticized by those who cannot conceive of a child's scheming to commit murderous acts. The very idea of a child brooding over criminal adventures, eagerly planning assassinations, poisoning, arson, seems preposterous.

Unfortunately, those unimaginable fancies are often translated into reality. Let this item, as reported by the daily *Neues Wiener Tagblatt* (May 5, 1913), serve as an illustration:

"Three-Year-Old Attempts Murder and Suicide.

"Mr. Emmerich Ehrenwald, a contractor, upon his return home from a hike last night, found his three-year-old son and his one-and-a-half-year-old daughter lying on the sofa. Both children were unconscious, and the room was filled with illuminating gas which came from an open burner on the stove. After the children were at last revived, the boy said that he wanted to kill his sister and himself because their mother had refused to take them for a walk. The boy's father recalled then that he had been telling at lunchtime the story of a man who had committed suicide in a gas-filled room. The tot had apparently absorbed the story thoroughly."

And here is a fellow physician's story:

Case No. 1: "A cousin of mine used to display a rather elaborate and fanciful criminal inclination. Once, after a spanking, he said to his mother, 'You are a bad mother and we don't like you a bit. I'll lock you up in a room without food until you die. And I won't bury you either. I'll just drop you into the garbage can.'"

I am in the habit of having my friends watch their children carefully for the earliest manifestation of erotic and criminal tendencies. Here are the observations of two highly intelligent parents, familiar with my work, whose report is thoroughly factual and unbiased.

Case No. 2: "I am sending you the notes on my boy, Otto," writes a father. "Please rest assured that we have tried to make the interpolated interpretations as objective as humanly possible.

"The notes and the quotations encompass a period of one-and-a-half years. Otto's present age is five years. Otto was three-and-a-half and completely unprepared when the second child came— also a boy. He stared speechlessly at the newcomer, who had arrived while Otto was away, and formulated no questions about the how and why of his little brother. Many of his subsequent side remarks, though, revealed that he was preoccupied with the problem. The feeling of amazement was succeeded by that of jealousy. He was angry with anyone who merely looked at the baby. As before, everybody's attention had to be concentrated upon him. Apparently he made some allowance for the baby as a future playmate and showed at times all the impatience of waiting, but the present rivalry was too much for him and he vented his displeasures in questions such as, 'What is he here for anyway?'

"Thereupon followed an interval of displeasure with the sibling's sex. 'I don't like him because he is a boy and has a dark skin. I only like blonde girls. I want him to be a girl.' As the younger boy grew, so grew Otto's dislike for him. Disquieting, destructive tendencies began to color Otto's remarks. When ordered not to tap the baby's head, he would say that it did not matter so much, because the baby was just a machine, or that he had no sensations, or he would say, 'If his head breaks, so what? He is not glass.' Or, 'Let's throw him out.'

"To justify his maltreatment of the younger brother, he advanced all sorts of theories about the baby's lack of sensitivity. According to Otto, the little boy was made of clay, just baked in a stove or factory-made. When told that the baby would not stand his ill-treatment very long, he wanted to order a new baby from the factory.

"A few remarks such as 'Chop the baby up' were bluntly murderous. One afternoon, while dinner was being discussed, he suggested, 'We could eat the baby.' Asked how he himself would like to be eaten, he said, 'Don't eat me; eat the baby. It's dead anyway.' And after thinking awhile, he added, 'Mommy, when the baby is four years old and wants to eat me, you'll throw it out of the house within fourteen days, won't you?' (Otto was at that time greatly preoccupied with the problem of time.) Otto makes strange mental jumps from the baby to the game he saw at the butcher's. In his opinion, the baby can be bought in the meat shop on Thursdays, or he says, 'The baby has been cleaned and he is ready to be served.' There is obviously some confusion in his mind about dead and live things, as many of his sayings show. At the sight of deer carcasses hanging in the store, he asks, 'When will they again run in the woods?' or, 'When people die, are they sold at the butcher's, too?'

"Alongside of the hatred toward the younger brother there is a great liking for him. Otto reacts violently against any visitor's joking pretense of taking the baby away. He often bursts into tears at the prospect of his little brother's being carried off. When the baby cries in pain or gets medical treatment, Otto is sad and full of sympathy, and often joins in the crying. Patiently and gleefully he teaches the younger one to talk and to sing.

He anticipates the time when the little boy will meet him on the street after school and play games with him. Lately, he went so far as to help the baby blow his nose, although ordinarily Otto is full of aversion against any uncleanliness of the human body.

"Yet all this does not deter him from alternate expressions of hatred toward the younger brother. The absorption with which he follows the younger one's rapid development points up Otto's wish to be just as small as his brother. He insists on talking like the younger one, violently demands to be treated and handled in the same way. He never really renounces, though, the prerogatives of an older child. Whenever we point out the exemplary behavior of some other boy, he willingly admits the latter's qualities, but with the never-failing qualification, 'Well, it's different with me.' "

As a rule, the stories we hear of children and their behavior omit any of the numerous manifestations of criminal propensities. Considerably greater attention and careful watching of what the child says is indicated if we want to form an adequate picture of the child. I have before me the notes of an observing lady.

Case No. 3: "I spent the summer months in the house of a farmer, father of an eight-year-old girl and three-year-old boy. One morning, when the farmer and his wife went off to town, I remained alone with the children. The girl had been ordered to watch over the unruly boy, but as it turned out, the young fellow refused to obey his sister. He cut loose and almost ran into a passing car. I caught him in time and gave him a few gentle slaps on his behind. The boy showed no reaction whatsoever and all day long never mentioned the incident. However, when his mother returned in the late afternoon, the boy seated himself in her lap and burst out violently, pointing at me, 'Mommy, if I had only had Daddy's big garden shears, I would have cut her head off because she hit me.' "

The following story may also serve as an illustration of childish cruelty:

Case No. 4: "Otto, age six, asked his grandmother where she expected to be buried, whether she wanted to be buried in Grandpa's grave. The old lady suggested that there might not be enough room for her, whereupon the boy hit upon an idea. 'Know what, Grandma, we'll roll you up tight like a herring. You'll have plenty of room.'"

Ludwig Schleich tells us in his *Memories:*

"It was Christmas time. Of all the toys my brother and I had received we liked best a papier-maché mechanical lion. When wound up, the lion, almost as big as a live puppy, would rush through the room and roar loudly. Only the threshold made the galloping imitation beast stop. Logically enough, we soon started to play lion-hunting, and I provided the game with lavish ideas of hiding and stalking behind the couch in the room. Our hunting equipment consisted of a barbecue knife and fork which we had taken surreptitiously from mother's silver, while a huge wooden ladle served as a protective weapon against the lion's possible assaults. The lion was wound up, and he came obediently roaring toward us, rolling along on the smooth surface of the floor. We gave out a jungle yell and threw ourselves upon the beast with knife, fork, and ladle. Suddenly, the lion lay motionless on his side, deep wounds gaping in his flanks, and the two of us, on an inspiration, plunged our hands into his entrails, like real hunters dressing a slain animal. At this point, the door was thrown open and father came into the room. He stared at us for a while in amazement, and said with a deep sigh, 'And I paid thirty talers for the toy.' He did not punish us too severely. Then, to get some gain out of the pitiful loss, he made us investigate the mechanism of the lion, its movements and roar. I can't help thinking that a rougher treatment would have been of greater use for me and my brother, the two young and mean killers!"

The child's propensity for daydreaming is enormous. He actually lives in an imagined world of his own; he converts all actuality into fancy. This dream-life, in which his ego expands beyond bounds, often serves the purpose of shaping the vague antisocial cravings into definite, palpable images.

Given the desire to see things as they really are, it is not hard at all to figure out the hidden thoughts behind the child's play. The child plays soldier or cowboy because, with his sword or gun, he can kill people. As a driver he can run down pedestrians; as an engineer he is master of a big deadly mechanism; as a fireman he can exploit his arsonist tendencies. Pfeiffer, in his "Reflections of Infantile Erotic Drives in Play and Game, A Psychoanalytic Interpretation of Play Theories" (*Imago,* Budapest), brings out very illuminating material on the subject. The following is an example:

Case No. 5: "The game most favored by N.J., between the ages of four and six, was hog-killing. He drove the point of an awl into discarded jar handles or sticks of wood (the hogs), kneeling as he did so, and shrieking in imitation of the animal that was being slaughtered. He piously arranged funerals for the carcasses, he himself usually being the clergyman or standard bearer. N.J. and his play have not been analyzed, but we obtained elucidation from the personal and family history of the boy. We know through Freud that play-killing and subsequent mourning, the death ritual, are typical transfigurations of incestuous and patricidal wishes, and we are not surprised to find in the family constellations of the boy a deep-seated antagonism between the pampering mother and the stern father. The boy's identification with his father, whom he wishes to eliminate, is seen in the use of the tool (father is a saddlemaker, and an awl is a basic instrument in his craft), and in the imitative character of the play (father, who is also a hog feeder, kills the animals in the winter months). Characteristically enough, the playing boy copied exactly his father's ways of stabbing. The standard-bearing at the mock funeral was an imitation of an activity of father, who was standard bearer at town ceremonials and church processions such as the Easter procession during which all the church bells rang. There can be no doubt that if the boy sub-

stitutes for his father in the fancied funeral procession, the one
in the hearse must be the corpse of the slain father. With much
psychological sense, although with little erudition, the living
father of N.J. always caught on to the idea. At the sound of the
'bells,' represented by noisy clapping on the fence, he always
rushed out of his workshop and gave his son a thorough spanking, although he never objected to any other noisy entertainment. We may also safely assume that the stabbing in the child's
play-killing was a sadistically colored reflection of the parental
sexual act which the child, in those crowded quarters, must have
observed at one time or another. As an additional detail of the
picture we want to mention the absolute inability of the father,
despite rigorous punitive measures, to make the boy stop using
a Hungarian curse which implies intercourse with the mother.
During adolescence, this boy committed suicide in despair over
unrequited love. We know from analytic experience that such a
suicide, too, reflects a fixation of the incestual drive combined
with death wishes toward the father (self-punishment)."

In the following childhood reminiscence, reported by
Schleich, the author obviously confuses curiosity with cruelty.

"I recall vividly the spot on that idyllic and childishly romantic playground where I once hammered away with a rock
at a watch my father had given me in his typically irresponsible naïveté! I was five then, and it must have been sheer curiosity that made me crush the watch between two rocks. At
least that's what I proffered as an explanation when everyone
in the family (Father included) scolded me for my foolish
prank. I remember saying with tears in my eyes: 'Don't boys
always want to know what's inside!'" (Schleich, I, page 16).

In one of his recent—and most remarkable—papers, Freud
analyzes the play of a one-and-a-half-year-old child. The tot
could speak only a few words, and these indistinctly; but his
parents and relatives understood him perfectly. While at play
he threw things and uttered a loud, protracted "O-o-oh."
Mother interpreted the sound as: "gone." At another time,
Freud watched the child play with a spool which had some

thread on it. The child never pulled the spool as if it were a carriage, but always drew it close only to throw it away again. When the spool was rolling away, the child shouted "O-o-oh!" and when he was pulling the spool back toward his bed he gleefully exclaimed, "Here!"

Freud considered this behavior in connection with the fact that the child's mother was temporarily absent from home. The child took the absence very hard. He had never cried, and his behavior had been generally brave, but it was obvious that his mother's absence, her being "gone," affected him strongly. And now he reproduced, in his play, her absence (*gone*) and return (*here*).

Freud quite rightly insists that the repetition compulsion seen in the child's game is a pattern which reappears also in the behavior of the neurotic. By means of turning his passive role into an active one, the child and the neurotic seem to solve a specific emotional conflict. The boy throws his mother (spool) away in order to draw her back. He transforms pain into play and consequently into joy. Turning the passive experience into active play, the child inflicts upon his partner the pain he has suffered and thus retaliates against this person who has caused him pain.

This observation explains many neurotic traits. The compulsion to re-enact his experience is an attempt to master it and to overcome it. We will return to this phenomenon later.

The child's curiosity and exploratory drive are boundless. Almost every fairy tale contains a passage dealing with a forbidden chamber and the illicit entry into it, a transgression which as a rule is punished severely. The child's early wakened sexual curiosity is the root of his exploratory drive (Freud). Children often play family, and, when left alone, enact sexual intercourse.

The child's propensity to imitate is extremely strong. Keen-eyed, he watches the adults and mimics them in his games which are partly his school of life (Groos), and partly atavistic reminiscences (Stanley-Hall). Not only man, but the beast, too, is the object of his imitation, and it is this latter form of mimicry that eventually re-emerges in those special forms of sexual disorders called zoanthropy.

To the child, miracles are real, and he indiscriminately endows all matter with life. For him, animals converse with each other and become human; trees are but enchanted people; and out of the wind come songs or certain words. All nature is alive. There is no parting line between life and death.

The child craves the Wonder World and is constantly waiting for miracles to happen. He would like to perform miracles himself and puts much effort into acquiring the skills of the magician. Above all, he believes that his mental powers are all-pervasive and that he can be the master of life and death. He broods over his origin, imagines himself a born prince or a nobleman exalted to the highest position. He foreshortens the distance to his mother and lengthens that to his father, thus reshaping the family romance to accord with his wishes (Freud). Or he fantasies himself as a foundling or as a child who was born by mistake, and then he waits for the Golden Carriage and the Silver Steeds to pull up one day before the house and deliver him from his lowly state.

Just as he has been probing into the power of the Almighty, he doubts and tests the omnipotence of his parents, and thus makes the first timid step toward a rebellion against all authority. Not before the guilt feelings arise will he again submit to it. ("The roots of weakness lie in our conscience.")

The richest source of guilt feelings and wicked thoughts is jealousy. The child's jealousy knows no limit, albeit he soon learns to conceal it rather cleverly. There is no joy for him in the tidings of the coming stork. Quite the contrary is true. He becomes hostile, and at the first observation of a lessening or diversion of parental attention, malign and vengeful urges obsess him and often burst out in frank expressions of hate.

When Father asks little Ann, "What will you do when you get a baby brother?" she replies, "I'll kill him." (Jung, *The Child's Mental Conflicts.*)

Fixation on one of the siblings goes hand in hand with increased jealousy. Listen for it in this remark of a seven-year-old girl toward her playmate: "If you so much as like my brother, I'll hate you." The girl and her brother were extremely jealous of each other and fought fiercely for their mother's attention, for the privilege of sitting near her. Once, when the girl snatched the seat near Mother, the boy said in a rage, "Let me sit near Mama or I'll smash your head with my feet."

In the pathogenesis and development of neurotic disturbances, the early relations with the older and younger siblings play an important part. Such relations often determine the course of a life. It is an undeniable fact that the child is basically an autocrat. The world has to be his exclusively. Stealing is often a symbolic expression of this inflated self-assertion. To the child there is no dividing line between his and someone else's possessions—everything belongs to him. Only external force makes him pull back his outgoing possessive drive, and then it grows even more violent in the inner realm of his thoughts and fancies. Everything belongs to the King. God is absolute master of the universe. The entire apartment is at the disposal of Father. The little anarchist obeys the restrictive orders reluctantly. In fact, every injunction generates in him the lust for transgression. The stolen candies are not just sweet, they are doubly sweet because they are consumed "in sin."

Here are the roots of spite, a reaction which plays such a tremendous part in the child's life. The more he is taught to tell the truth and nothing but the truth, the more he will be inclined to lie. The child's first attempts at insight into sex are, of course, the prime domain of falsehood, simply because it is there the child learns his first lesson of the dangers involved in being frank. We shall later have a chance to refer to the frankness of a boy named Hans, as reported by Freud. Lying is not only a way to self-exaltation, to putting one's parents to the test, but also a way to deflate authority and to skirt injunctions.

The child's acting ability manifests itself in imitation and mimicry as well as in the caricaturing and deriding of all authorities. Many neurotic disturbances develop from these childish tendencies to persiflage and represent belated self-punishment imposed by the conscience.

Of very early origin are the relative notions of Big and Small mentioned above, notions which under pathological conditions are apt to be transformed into the extremes of superiority and inferiority feelings. In their rudiments they are also present in "normal" men and women. The strong desire to be big leads to an absorptive growth of the child's imagination. The child does not grow up soon enough to suit his wishes. We rarely encounter a neurotic disturbance built around the express fear of growing old. The wish to grow old is the domain of normality. Moreover, the child, so naturally greedy, jealous, and righteous, projects into the future his hopes to avenge all his wrongs.

Two of the most frequent forerunners of possible neurotic disturbances in the child are accentuated lack of social sense and overemphasized moral inhibitions. Our virtues are but the bastards of our vices, according to Hebbel. Very indicative is the stubborn clinging to imperfect functional performances such as a "pidgeon-toe" walk, baby talk, mumbling, lisping, nasalization, stuttering (usually made worse through improper treatments), bedwetting, involuntary defecation, tics, fidgeting, restlessness, blinking, grimacing, slow chewing, vomiting, constipation, oversensitivity to light and noise, sucking, nailbiting, skinbiting, scratching, finger-sucking, bruxism. Early destructive trends are also often manifestations of a gradually developing neurotic disturbance. In contrast to the reasonably active normal child, the disturbed child soon tends to become either excessively restless or "dreamy" and "lazy." A child's exaggerated neurotic diligence in learning may lead his parents to the most absurd aspirations regarding his future.

The child may decide to beat his parents with their own weapons and become so "good" as to drive his mother and father to distraction. Such a child beats the best of actors in his performance of overobedience by which he hopes to placate and degrade his parents. Stealing, though primarily a manifestation of spite, shows also a distinct relation to sex, as we intend to demonstrate in the part of this book dealing with kleptomania. It is not sufficiently well known that nearly all children steal, and that often the urge to steal later becomes a reaction formation, the source of the exaggerated legalistic attitude toward property in general.

The tendency to perceive his world in symbolic images, and then to attribute to the symbols an autonomous reality, leads to the establishment of strange relations between the child and the objects around him, and to many purely symbolic gestures or patterns of behavior which are carried over into later periods. Masturbation is the most specific domain where objects substitute for live people. Here are a few illustrations of this aspect of behavior:

Case No. 6: A man of forty-five hugs the pillow and sucks at a pillow-point before falling asleep. He says that he acquired this habit in early childhood and has never been able to free himself of it. Further probing reveals that the pillow substitutes for the wetnurse who had been in the house until he was four and had always taken him into her bed to sleep beside her.

Case No. 7: Miss O.Z., twenty-six, office worker, given to masturbation since early youth, uses a fur muff as a stimulant. She puts the fur piece between her knees and presses until she reaches orgasm. Her favorite plaything when she was a child was one of her mother's old worn muffs. She could not be induced to part with it. To her the fur piece was an animate being. All her games revolved around the personified muff and its many incarnations (metamorphoses), so that her parents used to tease her, "One day you're going to marry a fur dealer." The muff has forever remained the focal point of her fancies. Now, this muff is obviously a mother image, and all her doings with it are re-enactments of one unforgettable situation. She was three or four years old at the time, and she was cold. Mother took her into her bed and put her legs around her until she was warm again. During this time, the child held her hands on her mother's pubic hair.

She had another important experience: when she was five, she once playfully put her dog between her legs. The animal performed a cunnilingus. The girl then knowingly staged this situation a few more times. Soon the dog became ill and was put to death. The scenes with the dog remained vivid for her, and for many years to come she could not go to bed without a muff.

The child's imaginative power is so strong that he is able to animate everything in his surroundings and, through symbolization, to create people out of small, insignificant objects. I shall quote many illustrative examples of this later. At this point I wish only to point out that although some children tenaciously cling to their pet objects and develop a rather monotonous imaginary world, others prefer variety and change. It is the former rather than the latter inclination which permits us to evaluate certain traits of psychosexual infantilism. Let us look at a few cases in each of which the specific situation and the specific fancy are located in the period of childhood.

Case No. 8: Mrs. T.W., thirty-nine, is still in the habit of playing with colored rags. Mother of grown children and soon to become a grandmother, she cannot resist opening her chest drawer and digging among the precious treasures of her childhood. While other people relish any childhood relic, she has readily dispensed with her toys, books, letters, old gifts and testimonials. She has kept only the rags which she started collecting when she was four. To get hold of a colored rag was at that age her favorite game. She could play with it for days in succession. She transfigured it into a human being or a life situation. The red rag was a professional man, the gray one a shepherd, the green one a meadow and so on. The collection of rags was a world of her own. She was a poor student and completely given to daydreaming; she spent all her leisure time with the rags. As a grownup she held on to her faded bits of cloth. As everybody began teasing her, she took refuge in the yard, or displayed her riches at night after everyone had gone to sleep.

She was married at the age of 19. She loved her husband dearly, but she was not sensitive to his embraces. She was an exemplary mother, and she enjoyed playing with her children as long as they were young and "cute." She then felt like a child herself. She still continues to play with other people's children, and is known in the neighborhood as "Play-auntie." But she really enjoys only those moments of her life when she can play with old rags.

Very few people confess fixations on specific situations and fancies. It is often by mere chance that we learn of such childhood fixations.

An appropriate illustration of such a chance discovery is the history of a boy, nearly fifteen, whom I had occasion to present at a medical conference.

Case No. 9: This was a peculiar case of sleep disturbance. G.R., going on fifteen, underdeveloped, with pronounced traits of somatic infantilism, had been suffering from a rare form of insomnia for the last nine months. Every evening at 6 o'clock, he felt acute pains in his legs, in the upper part of his arms, and sometimes in the shoulder region. He became restless and either tossed in bed or ran, groaning and moaning, up and down the room. The look in his eyes became glassy at times, and he seemed distraught. At other, more frequent, times, he uttered the name of his mother or of his sister. In the early morning hours he sank into a deep, cataleptic-like sleep and could only be wakened with difficulty. He rose only to eat, and then went back to sleep.

On February 15, the boy had been placed in the St. Luke Children's Hospital with the tentative diagnosis of diphtheria. The symptoms were breathing difficulties and high temperature, and he was complaining of heavy respiratory obstruction in his throat. This latter complaint was the main reason why the house doctor had the patient hospitalized. The boy displayed all the obvious signs of dyspnea and the recession of the fossa suprasternal was clearly visible. In addition, he was in a state of acute toxic delirium.

The hospital entry for February 15 read: "Small, thin boy, displaying chorea-like convulsions. Quiet during examination, but restlessness and incoherent talk returned after the examination was over. Heart and lungs negative. Temperature—C 37.5 (99.5 F). Reflexes—normal. All through the night the boy was restless, talked incoherently of his clothes and would not stay in bed. At 8 A.M. he began to gasp and complained of choking sensations. Corneal reflexes—weak; pharynx reflex—absent."

On the following night the picture of chorea became more emphatic. The boy asked many times to be permitted to go to Lena, his sister.

He stayed in the hospital a short time. He was discharged with the diagnosis: influenza, chorea, psychosis.

Soon thereafter he was brought back to the hospital by his parents. The boy had been sleeping days and crying nights; he was restless, unruly and so agitated that the parents could not cope with him.

I had seen him two weeks prior to this, in the forenoon, while he was sleeping. It was not a normal sleep; it rather resembled catalepsy. At the examination, I noticed that he held his hand close to the erected penis. I woke him and easily put him into a hypnotic trance. In a few minutes I induced cataleptic rigidity of his limbs. I ordered him to tell me the truth about everything. My first question was: "How long have you been masturbating?"

"Since February 15," was his quick reply.

On February 12, the boy's sister had been married, and as he adored her, it was quite natural to see some relation between the sister's wedding and the boy's illness, the more so since the sister played such an important part in all his deliria and nightly crying spells.

And then the boy, first in a state of hypnotic trance, then wide awake, related to me the following details:

Some years ago he had learned from friends that in sexual intercourse an immission of the penis into an opening of the female takes place. The friends illustrated their theory with pertinent games. When the boy's sister was married, he was greatly worried about what her husband was going to do to her. On the wedding day he was very agitated. It was also the first time that his parents permitted him to stay up past his regular bedtime. The wedding ceremony began in the morning, and the reception and dinner lasted until far after midnight. The boy's sister was very affectionate toward her groom. She danced with him and embraced him. At four o'clock in the morning the newlyweds said goodbye to the guests and withdrew to their apartment. It was then that the boy began to cry and whine inconsolably. He kept repeating, "I was crying because Lena left."

On the 15th, three days after the wedding, at noontime, he masturbated for the first time in the family's bathroom, thinking, in the act, of his sister and her husband. He remembered having heard from his friends that the man was supposed to eliminate some sort of mucus; the boys had called it "the nature." Suddenly, while the boy reached orgasm—an orgasm which was yet without ejaculation—he felt a lump of mucus in his throat. It was the kind of experience which Freud designates as displacement from below upward. It was a hysterical conversion symptom. The boy experienced in his mouth what he thought was happening at another orifice.

He ran to his mother, gasping for air. The family doctor noticed the symptoms mentioned at the beginning of this history and had the boy put into the hospital.

After his discharge from the ward, the boy went to confession. He has always been very religious, and a member of a

Catholic Youth Organization. He confessed among other things his sinful reflections on his sister, and the Father Confessor sternly admonished him to free himself of these thoughts and also to desist from unchastity practiced on his own body. He was told that his thoughts of his sister in that way were a grave sin. After that time the boy repressed all thoughts of his sister and, instead of these, the nightly pains appeared, tormented him, and made him cry.

It is obvious that the boy was obsessed by the idea of his sister's wedding (Janet). In his own way he annulled the wedding and yet constantly re-experienced it himself. In the same process he also experienced everything that followed the wedding. At the hour corresponding to the hour of arrival of the first wedding guests he would become agitated and—exactly as on the wedding night—stay awake until the early morning hours.

Before dawn, at the hour when, on the wedding night, he imagined that his sister had gone to bed, he too would retire. His constant erection betrayed his thoughts. After a short while he would masturbate and fall asleep. On the first day after the wedding he also slept nearly the whole day.

This condition has lasted now for nine months, and it threatens to retard the boy's mental development or to produce a lasting infantile fixation.

I attempted to exert a strong, hypnotic influence on him; he is, as I have said, a good hypnotic subject, and carries out promptly every command for hypnotic and post-hypnotic actions. I ordered him to get out of bed and to stay out all day, and he obeyed. He was somewhat groggy and slow in his motions, but he was out of bed, and busied himself with something in the room. Then I ordered him to go to bed at nine in the evening, to sleep well, and to get up at six. He again obeyed, and went to sleep at the designated hour, but a half hour later he awakened and began his usual troublesome routine. Subsequent hypnotic commands were of no avail. He leaves his bed in the daytime—he came to my office during the day twice—but he spends sleepless nights, and lives on in his wedding-day fixation. He relives in his neurosis this single experience.

The above case is a fair illustration of the tenacity with which neurotics cling to a definite morbid configuration. A stubborn fixation of this type may produce symptoms even in early childhood and cause parents, who do not know the mental origin of the phenomenon, no little consternation. A fully developed specific fixation may become the nucleus of a psychosis, especially of schizophrenia.

Catatonic symptoms without prognostic significance can be observed in every child. Some children repeat for months in succession one senseless phrase, one gesture or posture. Others, of a specifically responsive nature, may persist in their identification with a certain fairy-tale character.

Every game a child plays has a hidden meaning. The child's words and gestures are not nonsensical. Whether he identifies himself with his father and mimics him, or imagines himself to be an animal, or mumbles something indistinctly to himself, or echoes the words of the people about him, there is always meaning and sense to it.

The child's behavior is, at times, sheer rebellion against reality. He negates reality and reshapes it in his fantasy, where he recreates it in accordance with his autocratic whim.

We again encounter these tendencies in the poet who, in some aspects, shows traits of mental infantilism. Conversely, every child is a poet. Tolstoi once had the pupils of an elementary school tell him fairy tales of their own invention, and he was delighted with the result. He was of the opinion that no poet could have done better. However, it should be kept in mind that the child's fairy tales are not fictitious to him. He believes them. They are his world of reality.

Many aspects of psychosexual infantilism are but fixations on fairy-tale elements, as we shall see in the succeeding chapters of this book.

2. CHILDHOOD SEXUALITY

It is an amazing socio-psychological fact that until very recently the sexual life of the child has been completely overlooked. Even among the doctors of our time there are many who refuse to accept the idea of child sexuality, and stubbornly cling to their old faith in the child's "innocence." Every pertinent fact uncovered by analysts or by analytically trained teachers and parents is dismissed as an exception to the rule, as a consequence of a "morbid predisposition" and therefore without general validity. Parents, too, cherish a beautiful dream of the child's angelic purity, especially when the progeny is their own.

Concerning the reason behind this strange attitude, I have spoken at length elsewhere.[1] At this point I will merely introduce a few facts and data for the better understanding of what I call "psychosexual infantilism." Only a thorough knowledge of childhood sexuality will make it possible for us to comprehend that the aberrations and deviations of the sexual drive most commonly encountered are various forms of fixation and regression.

Man's sex life probably goes back to his fetal existence. It may be assumed that the fetus experiences some sexual sensations, although this assumption cannot be proved. It is a fact, however, that we find in neurotics manifold and fanciful preoccupations with father's abdomen and mother's womb. Whether such preoccupations are also present in "normal" minds, I do not know, although I am inclined to believe they are.

The intra-abdominal and intra-uterine fantasies of our neurotics can be thought of as retrospective and not necessarily related to any actual experiences which occurred during the

[1] *Conditions of Nervous Anxiety and Their Treatment* (New York: Liveright, 1950).

fetal existence.[1] However, quite a few male infants are known to have had erections only a few hours after birth. Moreover, gynecologists of my acquaintance have observed erections in infants immediately after they were born. An erection at the fetal stage of existence could be thought of as a consequence of some peripheral stimulation or of a purely physiological process, such as a vibrational stimulation of the spinal erection center. It is at least likely that the embryo has libidinous sensation. Motion as such might be experienced as a pleasurable sensation (muscle and skin erotism), and the rhythmical swing of the mother's walking or riding might transmit to the child a sensuous pleasure sensation.

Let us, however, turn from these hypotheses to facts. Newly born infants, whose occasional erections I have mentioned, can often be observed touching their genitalia in search of pleasure-sensations. It appears that the infantile self-gratification is not exceptional, but widespread; it involves a universal physiological need. The child requires an unlimited amount of love (pleasure) to be able to withstand the many dangers and threats of his early life.

The child derives his pleasure from two sources. First, there is the autoerotic titillation associated with playing with the genitals and with some kinds of motion. Secondly, there is the great stream of libido flowing from physical contacts with the mother or wetnurse. Breast-sucking in itself carries pleasurable sensations. If the child is not breast-fed, there is always the "pacifier" or its equivalents. The old polemic about the autoerotic significance of sucking has long since been decided in favor of Lindner and Freud.

The genital zone is not the only one the child has at his disposal. Indeed, the child is endowed with an enviable abundance of erogenous zones. The most important of these is, of

[1] A great deal of speculation on this problem arose in the course of time. Semon's "engram" theory and many intellectual gymnastics of his epigons belong here.—*E.A.G.*

course, the mouth. For the child, the intake of food is an act abounding in thrills, and Havelock Ellis has justly compared it with an erotic act.

Sucking and swallowing go on in an atmosphere of physical excitement. Doctors ought to be aware of the fact that mothers themselves may reach orgasm while feeding their babies. The good looks of many nursing mothers can often be explained by their intense and constant gratification. Such women show, as a rule, an erogenous preponderance of the mammillar zone.

That sucking is an inexhaustible source of pleasure is proved by the many people who cling to this "sweet" habit, or to modifications of it, all their lives. Within the child's life, with its uninhibited elemental drives, with its constant alternations between urges and their gratifications, sucking certainly has an important role.

Other pleasure sensations stem from the stimulations accompanying the handling of the child. Mother cleans the soiled parts of his body to prevent eczemas and skin infections; she washes, touches, rubs, oils and powders, soaps and bathes the child's genital and anal zones. All these actions must have the effect of potent sexual stimuli, as they indeed may provoke male babies to erections and induce girls to rocking, masturbatory motions.

At this point it may be pertinent to note that many mothers, driven by unconscious motives, lavish an excess of care on their babies and thus provoke in them a strong attachment to these early forms of pleasure gains. It happens more frequently than we care to admit that mothers actually play with the baby's genitalia. Mothers and wetnurses of the lower social strata sometimes resort to direct stimulation of the child's genitalia and his erogenous zones to calm the unruly and noisy "brats." Naturally, once this habit of soothing is introduced, a vicious circle is created. The child demands this erotic stimulation, and when the adults fail him he soon learns how to obtain this pleasure through masturbatory activities. Older children, while in the bathtub, often ask their mothers to soap and wash them some more "down there below," under some such pretense as an unendurable itch. Believe it or not, they actually "produce" eczemas in order to necessitate the desired handling and fondling.

Rocking, cradling, and being carried about are also sources of pleasure. The rhythmic vibrations mentioned in connection with fetal sexuality are very effective in promoting the child's enjoyment of vehicles of all sorts. The desire for rhythmic stimulation can be recognized in his urge for driving, riding, being carried in the arms, and many similar devices. This early way of moving along with the help of others may induce a fixation and later lead to specific forms of psychosexual infantilism. There are men who profess to feel potent only in a moving railway car, or on a boat. Some of these men actually undergo satyriastic or priapistic spells while on railroad trips and on sea voyages. Some women masturbate while riding. Many women, elsewhere prudish, easily succumb to sexual temptation while on a railway train.

Movement games with baby, such as exaggerated rocking, swinging, throwing into the air, are sexually provocative, and may lead to certain caricaturistic revivals in later paraphilias.

I have mentioned earlier a type of trainer who stimulates the crying child's genitalia in order to obtain a moment of peace; I should add here those mothers who make of their baby a sort of erogenous toy and overwhelm him with their own superabundant libido. These are the unhappy, disappointed mothers who convert all their ungratified desires into expressions of ardent "maternal love," which they lavish on their baby. Such women stroke, pet, and hug their babies excessively, kiss them constantly on cheeks, ears, "tummies," navels, and buttocks, while showering them with innumerable caressing words and pet names. I have heard many a mother assert, "My baby's little rear-end looks prettier than many faces I know."

Max Graf says somewhere, "I know an excellent poem, *L'Habitude des Caresses*, by August Dorchain, a French poet almost unknown in the German-speaking countries, which, in a most striking manner, establishes the connection between early-wakened sexuality and neurosis. The poem runs like this:

> Mothers, you love your little ones too much
> And soothe them with too many smiles.
> Don't make your sons as weak as we are now
> Through long, excessive kisses,
> Or you will mold their souls in your own image,
> And they will pay for it one day with pain.
> Their hearts will be like women's hearts,
> Easy to be hurt and slow to repair.
> Feather not their nests to be soft
> With all your embraces and caution and care,
> Lest the remembrance of your sweet caresses
> Make their lives weary, too hard to endure.
> Your balmy breath at present
> Hovers over their sleep and lingers on.
> They may, when it is gone,
> Hardly ever fall asleep again.
> Oh, mothers! when you hug your sons
> And rock them on your knees,
> Remember that the memory may haunt them
> When they're on their feet." [1]

What harmonious poetic form, what perspicacity! How true that the memory of the caresses received as a child may become indelible. The boy may develop jealousy and hatred toward his father, with whom he is forced to share this attachment, and his incestuous fancies may also block his love for his future wife. Both perils happened to coincide in the case

[1] From the collection *La Jeunesse Pensive*. Free translation.

of the famous Austrian dramatist, Grillparzer, to mention but one man reared under the care of a passionate mother who had turned the excess of her unrequited love on her son.

The anus is one of the main erogenous zones of the human being. Freud noted the importance of the anal zone, and he concluded that the children sometimes retard elimination in order to protract the pleasure induced by the pressure of the stool against the anal mucous membrane. Ordinarily, however, all the erogenous zones, including the anal, relinquish their importance to the genital zone at puberty (Freud).

Now, many mothers, through ignorance, often create situations which cause an overstimulation of the anal mucous tissues. The absolutely unnecessary use of irrigations is one of the main malpractices applied to induce bowel movement. Some mothers imagine themselves to be particularly clever when they administer an enema to the baby whenever he cries. If the child, thanks to the stimulation, quiets down, the proud mother is sure she has helped the baby to get rid of the annoying "gas." Every bit of stool released by the enema is interpreted as proof that a dangerous accumulation of excrements in the body exists.

All superfluous treatments of this kind, as well as too frequent insertions of the thermometer, contribute to the development of anal erotism and may cause constipation and dependence on enemas for an entire lifetime. No child has ever died of constipation. Grown people, too, are ridiculously fussy about enemas, purging herbs, and other forms of irrigations, all designed to provide a masturbatory stimulation of the anal zone under the pretext of a hygienic measure.

But these are by no means all of mother's devices. Children are frequently taken into their parents' bed. The infant lies sandwiched between father and mother, and in some instances the practice goes on until the baby has become a child of six, or even ten. In cases like this, parents are usually guided by the principle that "the child has no idea of sex anyway." They are certain the little one does not know the meaning of the sexual act. They completely ignore the enormous plasticity of the child's mind which absorbs even those impressions not understood, only to reproduce and work them off inadequately in a neurotic pattern later in his life. Besides, ignorance can be pleaded only in reference to the earliest age of the child. Soon, very soon, the child catches on to what is taking place and learns, moreover, that he has to keep his knowledge to himself.

Such a child is sexually oriented to the exclusion of anything else. He represents, in this respect, the primitive, instinct-directed man. Freud designates the child as a "polymorphous pervert." I think that "panerotic" is a more precise term, for perversion implies something that deviates from the normal, whereas the sexual qualities in question are common to all children.

With varying degrees of frequency, nearly all children masturbate, and it comes almost as a surprise to discover that many pediatricians are unaware of this fact. Henoch described the infant's rocking motions as signals of masturbatory stimulations. Not all masturbation must be manual, though every infant also unfailingly reaches out his hand toward his genitalia. Masturbation is achieved most frequently by way of rocking motions, by pressing the thighs against each other, or through the sensation of tepid dampness coming from soiled diapers. Masturbating children may reach orgasm. They roll their eyes or stare glassily before them, their breath breaks, and they seem to lose consciousness briefly. These "fainting spells" were frequently interpreted as epileptic. In reality, they were masturbatory acts followed by a strong orgasm.

The child's sexuality manifests itself not only as panerotism or autoerotism, but also through forms of "primordial" gratification. Thus he may derive joy from the smell of excrements and urine. He strives, way past his infant stage, to put everything into his mouth and into all the other openings, such as nostrils, ears, and anus. The child has to be taught not to smear his feces all over his body and not to eat them. In the process of training, the excrements become the symbol of the taboo and the repulsive. "Bah, this is kaka," say the mothers of my country, and "kaka" is the word for anything that is disgusting, undesirable. The child, however, never really relinquishes the joy of organic eliminations. Surreptitiously, he tastes some of these forbidden secretions and excrements, desisting from such doings only gradually, some children sooner, some later. In another part of this book (Ch. 5) I discuss adults who have preserved a predilection for their eliminations and cannot free themselves from this infantilistic trait. Many an "indecent" gesture or act of our refined fellow men stems from this infantilistic attitude. Nose picking by otherwise properly behaved people is typical. Various little ways of bathroom behavior, like so many petrified fossil remnants, point toward that early age and its exaggerated attention to the secretions of the body.

The toilet generally occupies a central position in the sexual life of the child. To him the toilet-bowl is not just a contraption for the relief of certain needs, but a vehicle of erotic stimulation. It is all too easy to overlook the importance of elimination in the life of the child.

No mean source of childhood pleasure is the release of a flatus. The child accompanies the flatus with gay laughter, expressing the strong significance which flatulence has in man's life as a general phenomenon (Jones).

The child willingly lingers in the bathroom. He runs to it under any pretext. At times he is helped to it by his mother, for mothers are so afraid to leave their children without supervision that they take them along whenever they go to the toilet.

The child, attentive to the smells of his surroundings, soon learns to distinguish which member of the household has preceded him in the lavatory, and in some instances retains this ability until late in life.

The child goes to any length to watch adults in the act of elimination. As a byproduct of his observations, he also considers the adult's genitalia and compares what he has seen with what he himself has got, a procedure which often provokes in the child an inferiority feeling. Carryings-on of this kind have been observed in two- and three-year-old children. Excrement and toilets also play an important part in the child's games, unless parental admonitions have checked his uninhibited candor and he has learned to keep the things he knows to himself. Children take their dolls to the toilet and wash and clean them after they have "done their duty." Unavoidably, the child learns the pertinent "filthy" words, which he uses to embarrass his parents or to provoke merriment. I knew a girl who compulsively reiterated the German word for the backside and at times ran from the bathroom to the living room, turned 'round in the doorway and made her entrance walking backward and showing her exposed rear-end, to the consternation of the people in the room. Another child, a boy of three, when introduced to the guests of the house, always emitted a flatus. Some children ask to be taken to the bathroom whenever they sense a chance to embarrass the adults.

In response to parental threats or to faulty education, many children develop a fear of elimination—one of the earliest childhood phobias—which may linger on into adulthood and cause socially unacceptable peculiarities. Feces (anal erotism) and urine (urethral erotism—Sadger) often color the child's imagination. I have heard of two boys playing a game of "Pipi-Man" and "Kaka-man," both exalted deities. The first could drown the whole world in his urine; the second could cover the entire universe with his excrement. In endless games, the two deities combatted for supremacy.

The first thoughts regarding birth are often associated with elimination. The children believe that babies come into the

world the way excrement does (infantile sex theories—Freud).
I have known a child who called the feces "Baby."

It should be noted that many adults feel rather free to urinate in the presence of children, and thus expose their genitalia to the youngsters. The boy preferably watches mother
but does not disdain to watch his father, pays great heed to
the volume of sound, and weaves his fantasies around it. It
cannot be repeated too often that this childhood behavior can
reappear in the form of a neurosis or paraphilia in the adult.
There are men whose sexual potency is conditioned by the
partner's urination. There are prostitutes who know more of
these deviations than all the sexologists together.

In elimination games, children vie with each other; a longer
and stronger stream of urine, more stool, louder and more
frequent wind—all these are appraised and appreciated. Experienced psychologists know the weight and value of such
games. "Dad and Mom," "Family," "Marriage," "Doctor and
Patient" and many other games, often involving mutual exposure, are played absorbedly by most children.

The child's urge to expose himself is at first unrestrained.
Only the force of constant training makes bashfulness out of
shamelessness. The child is driven by two irrepressible urges:
to see (voyeurism, scoptophilia), and to expose himself (exhibitionism). Left to their own proclivities, five-year-olds will
do away with their clothes and show each other their genitalia.
Sometimes they touch each other. These habits are universal,
and no man's biography is clear of them, except for that of
certain neurotics who grew up under strict supervision and
subsequently developed a specific disturbance which is a combination of mental infantilism and precocious senility. Such
people have been cheated out of their childhood, and later,
through regression, they elect to remain eternal babies.

Children do not stop at mutual exposure, however. Left to
their own devices, sooner or later they will attempt sexual
intercourse. My observations lead me to believe that such at-

tempts occur as early as the second year of life. And while many adults are quite uncertain about the techniques of the sexual act (I know both men and women ignorant of them), the child is remarkably nearer to nature in this respect, and needs no instructions.

Coital attempts among children are not infrequent. The youngest sexual experimenter known to me was a boy of two who had a three-year-old girl playmate. Their attempt at intercourse was spontaneous.

Remarkably, children are aware of something illicit about this "play" and are secretive about it. (I have had occasion to present so many pertinent examples in my previous writings that I may well omit them here.) We find a realistic description of such an attempt in Liepman's excellent book, *Psychotherapie und Gynäkologie,* in the section dealing with "Confessions of Patients":

Case No. 10: "I grew up in a very poor house in a proletarian section of North Berlin. My father is a shoemaker, and both he and my mother are simple, uneducated people, devout Catholics. They fervently hoped that their children would live a better life than that they were able to offer. I don't recall ever having heard in our house an indecent word. We were five children, four boys and one girl, who was the youngest of us. I was the second child, and I spent the first years of my life in the company of my brother, the elder by two years. The two of us were rather free to do what we pleased because our mother was always busy with the smaller kids. Up to the age of nine the only restriction I knew was the rule—for my brother and me—to be back in the house by eight in the evening; on Sundays, though, we were allowed to stay out until nine P.M. My first sexual experience came when I was four. I remember the incident vividly. My brother, who was six, following the example of other boys, got hold of a six-year-old girl, a next-door neighbor, and in the twilight of the early evening steered her to a dark corner, unbuttoned her panties, and began to fondle her genitals. The boys called this game "Dad and Mom." The girl played willingly, lay on her back and seemed to enjoy everything. The same evening the incident blew up. The girl was not yet able to button her panties correctly, and her mother became suspicious and questioned her closely. Soon the lady ran into our house. My brother and I received a memorable spanking and from then on we treated the girl in a gentlemanly manner. My brother dug up other girls for the game, and went on in this fashion until the age of fourteen or fifteen, when he began working as a store clerk apprentice and took up sexual intercourse in the full meaning of the word. My parents heard of some of his doings with the girls of the neighborhood and beat him severely on every occasion, but my brother could not or would not desist. I partook only in the first games. Not that I did not enjoy the touch of a girl's body, but my fear of punishment was greater than my desire for the pleasure. While at it, I thought of nothing in particular, and I do not believe my brother did. We just petted with the girls for the pleasure connected with it, and because all the other boys did the same. It seems that in my neighborhood the children of this day still amuse themselves the same way. Only recently, I stumbled upon a seven-year-old boy and a five-year-old girl on the staircase, indulging in the game. When I asked them what they were doing, they said laughingly, 'Just playing.' And to my further remark that they must not do such things and that they would be punished if they did, the boy said, arrogantly, 'Well, doesn't my Dad do the same thing to Mom?' Now, this boy's father happens to be a simple factory worker, but I still do not believe that he would forget himself in the presence of the child to such an extent as to give him an object lesson."

Anyway, it is a fact that the less supervised children of the working classes often play this sort of game, and no amount of punishment can make them stop completely. The pleasure they derive must be stronger than the fear of punishment.

It also happens at times that children attack adults. The mother, the aunt, the maid, the wetnurse—any of these persons may be the object of the child's sexual aggression. But it is not known widely enough that such acts of aggression are often benevolently tolerated and at times lead to the establishment of a stable relation of sorts. The rejection of the aggressive urge plays an important part in the dynamics of the eventual neurosis. Most common are relations between siblings. Bad habits and the circumstances which necessitate putting two and more children into one bed facilitate the establishment of sexual relations which may persist for years. I know many instances where the coitus among siblings has begun at the earliest age and persisted until puberty, and even beyond.

It should be remembered that the child is essentially bisexual and that he is attracted both by his own sex and the opposite sex. Mutual contacts, therefore, may occur among brothers and/or sisters. Quite remarkable is the trend, among children, toward paraphilic gratifications. Uninstructed, the boys masturbate with each other. Cunnilingus and anilingus may also be practiced. I know of girls who, in early childhood, experienced cunnilingus with their brothers and retained forever a craving for this form of sexual gratification.

Sticking objects into the anus is also a widespread habit among children. I know the case of two brothers, ages six and seven, who used to shove the nozzle of a spray into the anus of their four-year-old sister and then blow air into it. Pencils, penholders, all kinds of pointed objects are used in these games.

I have repeatedly called the attention of my readers to the child's sadistic tendencies. The child's criminality which, of course, is not criminality in the ordinary sense but rather a sort of primitive human quality, can be understood only when the basic needs and urges of the child are carefully studied.

As stated above, the child is an absolute egotist, and his attitude toward the world is basically hostile. He likes only those people and things from which he derives pleasure. He is often preoccupied with murder ideas and desires to do away with his rivals (siblings, parents, house guests, relatives) who impede the gratification of his urges or oppress him with educational restrictions and provoke in him reactions of spite.

The sadistic tendency emerges clearly in the pattern of the erotic games. The playmate is gagged, stabbed, beaten, shackled, or simply knocked out. Slapping on the exposed buttocks is also a favorite pastime, and a fixation upon this play form may lead to sadistic or masochistic paraphilias. At times, such games cause bruises and wounds and thus come to the attention of the parents. Psychopathic children are especially apt to shock the adults through their display of brutality, through their accentuated selfishness and their lack of ability to establish social contacts.

In normal children the conversion of primitive urges under the influence of training begins early. These youngsters become over-bashful, hypersensitive to filth, and sentimental; they cannot stand the sight of blood or of cruelty toward animals, and they display the first signs of piety and maturity. It is mainly fear of God's punishment which turns these children into rueful moralists.

With individual variations, depending on the general intelligence level, the child's first period of conversion usually begins at about the age of five. Later, between eleven and fourteen, the second change of values takes place and is characterized by a similar rejection of former criminal urges.

Turning from these general observations to our specific subject, the child of three, we note that children of this age group usually take the adults about them under careful scrutiny. They absorb every word the adults utter, they spy and eavesdrop on the adults' sexual activities. If the child sleeps in a room adjoining that of his parents, his imagination elaborates on the sounds coming from the adjacent room (*Nebenzimmer-Erotia*). Often the child has a chance to eavesdrop on the sexual intercourse. Mother's groaning, her position during the act, which the child may occasionally observe, then become building stones for his sadistically determined infantile sex theory ("Father beats Mother"), a theory soon to be enriched by at first vague and obscure, later more elaborated rape fantasies.

At about the same time begins the speculation on the puzzle of gestation and birth. No hypothesis is too absurd to be rejected. "Mother kisses Father; his saliva runs down into her stomach and becomes a child," may be one theory. "Father and Mother go to the bathroom together, and out of their joint eliminations comes the child," is another theory. According to the child, the woman becomes impregnated when the man's navel touches hers, or when their flatus unites. The child is willing to believe that babies are knifed out of the "tummy," or that the abdomen bursts open for the baby to pop out. These are but a few samples of the childish constructions. There certainly are thousands more of such gestation and birth theories, all of them testifying to the child's intense preoccupation with things sexual.

When told of the coming little brother or sister, the child never fails to notice that his mother is getting heavier. He listens to stories of the stork and all the while spins his own ideas on the subject.

Children are extremely good at acting and pretending. As soon as they discover that their parents do not always tell the truth, they seriously begin to doubt their parents' omniscience, and put them to the test with little lies of their own. The initial fibs eventually may grow out of all proportion and into the *pseudologia fantastica* of adult hysterics.

Lies are the child's reaction to the experience that he is being cheated by his parents in sexual matters. Excessive truthfulness may emerge as a reaction formation and a compensation for the one great, central lie. Excessive truthfulness in a child is often connected with his surreptitious masturbation, an activity which most children carefully hide from the parental eye.

The child begins to test early, and to deride, the omnipotence of the adults around him. God Himself is put to all sorts of tests. The child utters blasphemies and waits to see what will happen. If nothing happens, the child begins to doubt God's power and discards the stories on the subject as fairy tales. Only in the course of further training, and as a product of guilt feelings, does the child's submissiveness and religiousness re-emerge. At times, the stages of doubt and re-assertion alternate, as though the child were forever attempting to rid himself of the feeling of guilt and to convert his fear of God into rebellion against God and authority.

I have referred to the child's propensity to conjure death upon his "enemies." He may wish death upon his older sister whom he believes to be the family favorite. (The "older brother" or the "older sister" is often present in the structures of neurosis.) Or his jealousy may be aroused at the announcement of the birth of a rival. Here is the typical response of a two-year-old at the sight of his baby brother, recently delivered by the stork: "Out with him!" Other children in similar situations speak of killing or doing away with the intruder, or they promise themselves simply to chop off their rival's head. In quiet children the reaction is barely perceptible and often compensated for by a display of excessive interest and affection. Girls frequently identify themselves with their mothers and manifest exaggerated care and love for the new baby. But children with strong impulses feel a real hatred toward their rivals, who rob them of parental love and attention. When in a competitive situation, the older children often become nasty in order to punish their mothers or to force their attention or to arouse feelings in them, even anger. What they can't stand is indifference.

The pattern of behavior toward the father is about the same, except for the additional fear of punishment, which, if combined with early masochistic tendencies, may grow into a desire for punishment. This is the more likely when the punishment is not too severe and the stimulation of the spanked buttocks makes the punishment appear rather pleasurable.

The child's belief in the omnipotence of his thoughts may become fateful for his whole life. Let us imagine that a child wishes secretly that his younger brother would die. If, by some timely coincidence, the younger sibling becomes ill, the older child's first reaction will be to expect that at last his innermost desire will be fulfilled. And if then the rival really dies, the older child will blame himself, will look upon himself as the prime and only cause of the brother's death. Feelings of guilt later may bring on a complete reversal of the child's state of mind. The spiteful, rough, unruly boy may become timid, pliable and obedient. He may also become pious, and even extremely so. The fear which his own "wicked" thoughts instil in him may develop into a childhood neurosis and manifest itself in an obsessive cleanliness, in compulsions to figure, count, collect, and keep order, and in the haunting fear of forgetting things.

Compulsion neurosis, this dreadful scourge of the man of our culture, ordinarily emerges after the age of five. Almost every child displays symptoms of a more or less pronounced compulsive nature, but under normal conditions these traits (grimacing, tics, looking at the clock, compulsive giggling and crying, counting, various bizarre gestures, elaborate ritualistic patterns, reiteration of meaningless words) soon disappear. Various phobias and idiosyncrasies are indicative of the mental struggle within the child of this age.

In order to understand the mental make-up of the child, we must recognize, no matter how shocking it may seem to us, that the child goes initially through the entire gamut of primitive sexuality and that he has to fight those primitive instincts to overcome them.

The child is esthetically indiscriminating. He loves any person who is kind to him, who thus offers pleasure, whether the person is pretty or ugly, young or old. Hence all those strange aberrations in later life, such as love for hunchbacks or for cross-eyed or aged people, and those generally repulsive attractions such as that for dirty and ugly servant maids with the stench of sweat and stool about them. It is through training that the child learns to make objective evaluations. At first, his father is "the strongest man in the world" and his mother "the most beautiful lady," and no comparison between anyone else and these two is possible. Sound esthetic sense among children is the exception and not the rule.

The child is strongly attracted by the odors of the human body and, at this early age, he delights in bad, pungent smells. He sniffs with pleasure at his own perspiration, and picks some of it from between his toes to carry it closer to his nose. He likes people with copious perspiration. The sweating feet of a cook in the child's house may be the origin of some of his subsequent foot fetishisms (Abraham). The child also likes the smell of the armpit perspiration on women, and whether he continues to like this odor as a grownup or goes to the opposite extreme of repulsion, his attitude stems from an early childhood predilection.

Very little study of the child's cannibalistic and necrophilic urges has been made as yet. But it is well known that children avidly listen to tales of giants devouring men and personify such monsters in their games. During the child's meal, some morsels of food are thought of as "babies," spaghetti becomes human fingers, while other foods have repressed connections with other parts of the human body. One twelve-year-old boy I know refused to eat plum dumplings because they looked to him like blown-up corpses. Fruit often represents human bodies, and the cutting and consumption of them may acquire a cannibalistic significance.

Soon, however, fear and disgust displace these primitive tendencies (to which we may safely add the so-called vampiristic trait). The child then begins to display a great aversion toward foods which remind him of excrements or of parts of the human body. Or he may hate liquids resembling urine or blood. For this reason some children abhor food tinged red (blood-like), such as red beets, red beet soup, rare meat, "blood sausages," crimson berries and syrups.

These idiosyncrasies vary with the individual, but nearly every child hates the thicker particles or the surface cream in unskimmed, unhomogenized milk, and often this distaste remains throughout the individual's life. Traits of cannibalism and vampirism can also be seen in the child's proclivity to bite people or to lick at his own or someone else's blood. The later neurotic transformation of these features appears as aversion toward meat (vegetarianism) or as an oversensitivity of the oral zone of anorexia proportions (Abraham).

The child's zoophilia is also worthy of mention. His general nearness to nature and the primitive level of his instincts determine his attitude toward animals, which is considerably more intimate than that of adults. He loves animals passionately and uses them consciously or unconsciously as love objects. Sexual stimulation through animals is frequent among children. The child's identification with animals appears clearly in his games. Children pretend to be dogs, cats, bears, wolves, poultry, lions, fish, and so on. In the chapter of this book devoted to zoanthropism we shall see the connection between zoophilia and sex, as well as the relation between the child's identification with animals and his criminal or sexual fancies. In such cases we must think in terms of the ability of dogs to bite, of cats to scratch, of cocks to peck the eyes, of wolves to suck the blood, and so on down the list. We encounter in the fairy tales, those mirrors of child mentality, all sorts of criminal and sexual motifs. The animal also figures largely as the carrier of death to others and the avenger of the child's ill-treated ego. On the other hand, guilt feelings may also lead to zoophobias, such as the one observed by Freud in "Little Hans."

Childhood zoophobias and zoophilias deserve most careful study, for they may bring us to a closer understanding of many forms of infantilism in adults. Masturbation fantasies are often connected with animal images, and just as frequent are the instances when a child, in orgasm, utters animal cries, such as crowing or barking.

There are children who begin masturbating when they are infants and continue the practice until puberty and beyond. As adults, they are apt to be found among "normal" people, that is, among those who remember well their childhood period. They show none of the specific amnesia characteristic of neurotics in relation to anything concerning early childhood.

Many children give up masturbation by the end of infancy and resume it after an interval which Freud calls "latency period," either in the wake of external seduction or through a spontaneous rediscovery. This second masturbatory period is closely connected with the child's play. If left without supervision, children of pre-puberty age will play erotic games. The usual procedure is for the older ones to instruct the younger playmates in the intricacies of masturbation. In this respect, the sixth year is a rather crucial one: the child meets for the first time in school many new friends, among whom are a number of experienced ones, and he is then able to add much exciting material to the store of his own fantasies. Up to that moment, the child has tried to learn the truth by his own devices: brooding, watching, and eavesdropping on conversations. Now he is in a position to exchange information and opinions. What he had only vaguely suspected about the ways that adults get their pleasures and beget their babies, he now learns in precise detail.

At first, the child is shocked by the idea that his parents could possibly do "such things." Many children who had already repressed their impressions and experiences would come to their mother, tell her what they had learned, and ask for clarification of the point. Naïve questioning, though, may also be a sham and only serve the purpose of testing the truth-fulness of parents. And then there are those, of course, who definitely part company with their parents and from then on cling to their friends who are so free with their knowledge and their theories.

At this point I should like to make clear that in my opinion this early enlightenment is both natural and harmless. The reaction of teachers and parents to the phenomenon is rather ludicrous. The child's soul is neither contaminated nor per-manently injured in the process, or else society would consist only of sick, perverted people. Quite the contrary is true. I found the most severe cases of neuroses among those who had never masturbated and had always been under the strictest supervision of parents or governesses. People reared under such conditions have no sense for reality; they live forever in a world of fantasy and are socially inadequate.

A certain alleviation of the guilt feeling comes to the child through insight into the "wickedness" of other children. He learns unconsciously the human quality of his problems, whereas the isolated child is crushed by his guilt feeling. "No-body does what I do. I am different from anyone else."

Two forces fight for supremacy in the child's mind. On one side, there is the child's self-adoration, the narcissism which boosts his ego to God-like proportions and makes him burn with the desire for power, for limitless authority and unblem-ished beauty. He wants to be bigger, stronger, and richer than anyone else. He listens breathlessly to the tales in which the small one, the weakling, the Tom Thumb, vanquishes the giant and marries the princess. He has faith in his own magic powers, and the praise of the family and of the guests of the house only tends to foster his aspirations. He is in love with himself and expects for and from himself the best. He is apt to look at himself in the mirror for hours, lost in the admira-tion of his features, which include also his genitals.

At some time or other, he is bound, of course, to think of

the genitals of adults which he has had a chance to see. He compares them with his own, and his megalomania at times collapses right then, to give way to an oppressive feeling of inferiority. This feeling feeds on the child's knowledge of his "wickedness," while from the outside the constant blows of the grownups fall upon him, reminding him of the undisputed superiority of adults. The child is torn between the narcissistic megalomania of his fantasies and inferiority feelings based on reality. A craving to grow up soon obsesses the child. All his desires converge into one: to be big. Boys crave a big penis, a large scrotum, moustaches; girls yearn for pubic hair, breasts, and elaborate hairdos. Bodily defects are either overlooked in blind self-adoration, or overemphasized.

The subsequent development of the child is extremely difficult to sketch, for no two children develop entirely alike.

The child's character is usually set by the time he reaches ten. His behavior pattern at this point is clearly determined either by rebellious challenge or by submissiveness. In boys, the comprehension of sex has by that time broken through to the fore, although they still choose objects in the immediate vicinity. The boy adores his mother, yet his father is even dearer to him. The homosexual attitude toward the father is too often completely overlooked. The Freudians point incessantly at the Oedipus Complex (the son's love for his mother) and neglect the homosexual component in the boy's rebellion against his father. This rebelliousness in itself may result in poor scholastic achievements and in obstreperous behavior. The situation is similar in the girl, whose jealousy may embrace father, mother, and siblings.

Soon, however, the child begins to look for his objects in a larger circle. We know from autobiographies of poets and from our own observations how early in life children become enamored. I had occasions to observe the phenomenon in connection with four-year-olds. Boys fall in love with their aunts, cousins, girl friends of their sisters, and with girls their own age or younger. A love of this kind may be vehement and persistent. The teacher at school may become the love object. The very significant friendship relations of that period reveal to every unbiased observer their sexual components. These friendships frequently verge on love. I have yet to find a man who before puberty had not been in love with another boy or a male adult. The age between ten and fourteen is characterized by the antagonism between homo- and heterosexual tendencies.

The children have an inkling of the unnaturalness of their "crushes" and try to fight them off without ever becoming completely aware of the nature of the struggle, because the sexual component is usually disguised. But it is there, just the same, and is very potent, revealing itself in boundless jealousy and in occasional physical contacts such as hugging and kissing. The love relation may not always remain completely platonic. Boys may indulge in homosexual practices. They may handle each other's genitalia; in a few instances *immissio in anum* or fellatio may take place. Girls, too, may resort to mutual manipulations when sharing one bed, or on other occasions.

The difference between boys and girls of this age—ten to fourteen—is very pronounced. Boys may never have given up masturbation (no "latency period"), or they may have resumed it. Their sexual eagerness is very great; they know many things about sex now and openly search for appropriate sex objects. Girls, on the other hand, have by then so thoroughly repressed all the sexuality of the earlier period that they may have to begin anew in their search for knowledge and information. They mature earlier and display a stronger rejection of sex. These remarks are, of course, of a general nature, for there is no rule applicable to all individuals. The struggle is between the woman and the child in the girl. The inclination toward the same sex is even more pronounced than in boys.

Girls get their information from fellow-students, books (encyclopedias), and often from maids. There is no lack of traumatic experiences, to which different girls respond differently. Remarkably enough, the sexual urge of the girl between the ages of thirteen and sixteen, conditioned by the physiological development, is so strong that this age group is especially susceptible to seduction. Loss of virginity is likely to occur in this period. Past this age, the inhibitions become much stronger, and the balance is established between urge and inhibition.

Among girls, puberty usually evokes a second masturbatory period, the first one with all its experiences having been most thoroughly forgotten. The girl needs a second set of elucidations, while her sexual urge grows so vehement that she can hardly wait for the first sexual experience. The girl's reaction to the drive may be excessive religiousness, prudishness, or a total rejection of sex. She swears eternal chastity, proudly proclaims her determination never to get married, pledges to join or does join a religious order. She is filled with all sorts of utopian, salvationist ideas. She shuns men, establishes rapturous relations with girl friends, and often rebels against her parents, who have not given up sex.

The discovery that the parents persist in having sexual relations fills the girls with disgust. They disdain their parents and simply refuse to understand how grown, mature people can still indulge in such filthy practices. They are afraid mother may become pregnant and bring shame on the whole family. To an actual happening of the kind, that is to the late arrival of a baby, a girl may respond with a severe neurosis. Given the older component of jealousy, she may be driven to homosexuality or to some other form of paraphilia. Or she may suddenly change her mind, submit to the first man who happens to come her way, and perhaps drive on to a suicidal end.

Puberty is a danger period for every girl. In cases where

a special constitutional predisposition exists and strong moral inhibitions are added through training, the first sexual experience may trigger off a psychotic reaction. Varying with each individual, puberty, which usually lasts for several years, definitely terminates the period of childhood for the girl.

Boys are less endangered through puberty, although they, too, undergo marked changes of personality. They display a spiteful, moody, alternately sentimental and cynical attitude. At the initial stage of puberty, and sometimes sooner, a second period of religiousness may set in, only to be discarded at the height of the period and to be replaced by an atheistic and materialistic outlook on life. Of course, the variability is as great among boys as among girls. Some boys vehemently fight their masturbatory habits and quickly pass on to regular sexual relations, usually at the age of thirteen to fifteen (country as well as city boys). My own observations tell me that such an early start is rather the rule than the exception.

I remember that most of my fellow students had their first regular sexual experiences in a brothel, at the age of fourteen or so. There were fifty boys of different social strata in our class. The older boys already had had sexual relations with the maids in their houses. At the age of thirteen to fifteen about half of the group knew sexual intercourse. The last one of our group experienced sex in the sixth grade. For a long while he was the only "chaste" boy. We celebrated his initiation with an improvised party.

All this may produce the impression that we were a gang of juvenile hoodlums. Far from it. We were an alert, intelligent group; we edited our own papers and formed a literary club with discriminatory admission practices, in order to have a "creative" membership. Most of the boys achieved high social positions in later life. None has gone wrong or done too badly.

Many boys are initiated into the mysteries of sex by maids, governesses, older cousins, and the like. Love for immature boys is a common sexual deviation among adult women. The diminution of the possibility of becoming impregnated or infected adds a great deal to the paraphilic preference given boy-lovers. Havelock Ellis was the first to point out the strange fact that on the whole more men are seduced by women than the other way around. The biographies of men willing to expose their sexual experiences confirm this fact. Many a ten-year-old boy is taken by his governess into her bed and trained to perform a coitus or to give her some other form of sexual gratification.

Dr. X. once talked before the Vienna Psychoanalytical Society of his boyhood experiences. When he was twelve he was seduced by the maid, who used to play with his penis until orgasm was induced. The relationship lasted six months. Then another maid came into the house. This time the boy persuaded the girl to join him in the game. Before he was nineteen, some twenty maids had served in the household, and, of them, only one refused to accommodate him.

This story throws light on a rather obscure subject. In the lower social strata, sexual freedom is much greater than we care to admit. Servants, especially, tend to compensate for the lack of social freedom by an abundance of sexual license. The moment of revenge on the employer through corruption of the progeny comes as an additional incentive. That is why maids delight in the seduction of the sons of the family, indulge in relations with the master of the house himself, and gladly enlighten the daughters of their employer. They willingly serve as helpers and protectors of the girls when these indulge in affairs of their own. The maids go even a step farther and help the seducer in breaking down the moral inhibitions of the girls.

Older women, even married women, may succumb to their deep-seated tendencies and look for love partners among young, well-built boys. Some eager lady friends of the mistress of the house, who expand their friendship to include the younger male generation, may be suspected of pedophilia.

I have nowhere seen evidence of any physical or psychological harm done by such early seductions of boys. Whereas girls of the higher social strata may be forever affected, uprooted, may become neurotic or psychotic, may renounce marriage because they have lost their virginity, boys usually experience no such consequences.

Very often the first experience determines the individual's choice of a partner. Literature furnishes us many examples of such decisive influences. Moll reports the case of a boy of thirteen who was seduced by a lady dressed for horseback riding. Until the end of his virile days, the victim displayed sexual potency only when and if his partner wore a riding habit.

Besides such fixations on the first sexual impression and a mild general disdain for women, I have noticed no other harmful effects on boys. However, the depreciating tendency toward women is by no means a matter of small importance. Men haunted by this kind of attitude toward the opposite sex are often incapable of love and attachment ("All women are bad") and are often unfit for marital relations. But fortunately, such is only rarely the case. The men I know have, in spite of early sex experiences, preserved their faith in "ideal womanhood," and ultimately have found their mates.

From one point of view at least these early experiences offer an undeniable advantage. The boy's way to the other sex is cleared of shyness, of feelings both of superiority and inferiority. Men with boyhood sex experiences display a psychologically unimpeded potency. The impotent male usually has an entirely different past. He has masturbated too long and his mind has become fixated on sexual fantasies which cannot find their equivalents in reality; or he has been chaste for so long that he is unable to approach a female.

I have already pointed out elsewhere that repression is not so strong among the boys as among the girls of our time. Nevertheless, we find male neurotics who have completely "forgotten" their childhood experiences and whose memory barely extends to the age of ten. Of the earlier period they have retained only a few trivial reminiscences. There is usually a relation between the degree of an individual's amnesia and the severity of his neurosis.

There is one thing of which we are certain: the fewer gaps there are in an individual's memory, the easier it is for him to overcome neurotic tendencies. Many people remember only those pleasurable moments of their childhood which are void of accompanying pangs of conscience. They create for themselves the image of a "pure" childhood and spend their time mourning for the lost innocence, just as humanity as a whole mourns the loss of Paradise.

Looked at realistically, man appears as having exiled himself from the Eden of uninhibited lust to a life of self-restrictions and renunciation, while childhood remains in his memory and fills him with longing for it. The "look backward," the regression, is a real danger to the neurotic. Mental health implies a break with the past. The neurotic clings to his bygone childhood. The early years of his life exert on him a much stronger influence than is the case with normal people.

This book deals with sick individuals who have not been able to detach themselves from their past and whose conscious and unconscious fantasies continue their pilgrimage to the emotional shrine of their childhood.

Chapter Two

MECHANISMS OF REGRESSION

Chapter Two

MECHANISMS OF REGRESSION

1. Intra-uterine and Intrascrotal Fantasies

If one has worked for many years with neurotics, one finds among them men with a rosy, baby-like complexion, men who are beardless or have only slight indications of a mustache. Their infantile behavior and childish mannerisms are conspicuous. One sees also women who never develop into mature wives or mothers and who appear to be children themselves. They wear a wedding ring. They give birth to children and raise them, yet they are often assumed to be siblings of their own progeny. They possess an eternal youth, psychic and organic, and unconsciously emphasize youthful traits through their apparel and conduct. One could easily conclude that there must be an organic basis for this infantilism. The men may have an unusually small penis, cryptorchidism, and infantile structure of the larynx; the women may have an infantile uterus, weak menstrual flow or scarcely any flow.

The constitutional factor has something to do with the disposition to these conditions. But two observations lead me to believe that the constitutional factor is of secondary importance. First of all, I have observed psychic infantilism in fully-developed males, and in perfect females who gave birth to half-a-dozen children; secondly, one can observe a change in this infantilism after prolonged analytic treatment. The "eternal boys" turn into men, their beards start growing again, and the child-women develop into full-fledged women. Who can determine how psychic and organic factors overlap or supplement each other? We have seen cases in which psychic infantilism developed first and the organic symptoms appeared later. Men became boys again; they lost their hair, their testicles became smaller. Women lost their menstruation and their facial expression became child-like. Sexual glands alone cannot be responsible for this sexual regression. Otherwise one would see such manifestations in castrated women. Just the opposite occurs in these women. They age quickly. Likewise, the facial expressions of eunuchs —as a rule—become those of old men, and not those of children.

We do not wish to overestimate the implications of psychic forces. However, I have observed almost daily that physicians tend to underestimate the influence of psychic manifestations. They often fail to realize that the patient's wish and will power may have an enormous influence here. Those who *want* to be young, those who *feel* young, can release—consciously or unconsciously—within their organisms forces of rejuvenation. But, as mentioned before, the organic concomitants are not always present. Some clear-cut cases of sexual infantilism are purely psychogenic in nature.

I use the term "psychosexual infantilism," which Eulenburg used to connote sexual retardation. Magnus Hirschfeld and Ernst Burchard extend the meaning of sexual infantilism and place the emphasis on a disbalance between sexual drives and psychic resistances.

I do not emphasize the incongruity between desire and inhibition as a prerequisite for differentiating "sexual infantilism" from other disorders. The same incongruity can be observed in the lust murderer and in the sadist. One can take my view as confirming Freud's concept of the "polymorphous perversion" of the child; the sexual compulsions would then represent a relapse into the infantile. This formulation is undoubtedly correct; it can, however, be applied in all cases and, as a result, all paraphilias would be considered expressions of "sexual infantilism."

Under the term "sexual infantilism" I understand an expression of sexual life in its clearly infantile forms. Whereas other authors, when speaking of perversions, put the emphasis on the "psychopathic personalities" and associate them with imbeciles, epileptics, "degenerates," and organically infantile disorders, my cases show that paraphilias are forms of psychosexual infantilism which might or might not have any connection with an organic condition.

Such neuroses manifest themselves in two forms: (a) as an inhibition in the development—the neurotic has remained a child; (b) as a regression as Freud uses the term—the neurotic has returned to childhood.

If we divide the libidinal life of the child into periods, which will be of use to us for our investigation, we find the following stages *in men:*

(1) The embryonic existence until birth.
(2) The period of sucking (first year of life).
(3) The period of the first impressions prior to entering school (2-6).
(4) The period of the first school years (6-10).
(5) Pre-puberty (10-14).
(6) Puberty and adolescence (14-18).
(7) The awakening of manhood (18-24).
(8) Adulthood.
(9) The climacteric period of the male (varies, mostly 50-60).
(10) Involution and senility.

In women one notices the onset of femininity (7) around sixteen—and sometimes even earlier. Adulthood (8) then ensues, and the female climacteric period (9) with its psychic manifestations occurs, usually in the middle and late forties, to be followed by involution and senility (10).

There is a classic form of psychogenic infantilism in which retardation occurs on a definite level, usually in the post-pubertal period. There is another classic form in which regression, rather than retardation, is the basic manifestation, and the individual may go all the way back to his embryonic stage. There is a tendency to regress in daydreams long before actual regression begins.

The disposition to infantilism may stem from either physical or psychic causes. The illness can be cured by psychological means if it is psychogenic and by opotherapy or operation if it is of organic origin. It should be emphasized that etiology and treatment are actually to one degree or another complicated. There are rather clear-cut cases in which classic characteristics give a simple basis upon which the physician can direct his efforts. But there are mild forms and transitional forms of infantilism that are disguised by a great variety of neurotic symptoms. Thus, most physicians and neurologists, even sex researchers, may not be able to discover the psychosexual infantilism that lurks behind some of the symptoms they observe.

Before giving a detailed description of the various forms, I want to emphasize that all neurotics show infantile characteristics.

Lovers, too, show many infantile patterns, no matter how mature their inter-relationship as such may be. The lover returns to childhood temporarily; the neurotic tries to cling to it eternally. To each other, during the play of courtship and affinity, a pair of lovers speak the language of children, sometimes exclusively. The coddling of lovers and their blind adoration and preponderance of affectivity are other typical infantile trends. Infantile mechanisms are apparent in various phases of petting, and the use of names taken from elemental or primitive nature, from birds and beasts and flowers. The lower the ebb of the psychic component of love, the more easily it leads to regression into the infantile. When the psychic component is strong, the childish manifestations of erotic life are pushed into the background.

An almost universal manifestation of regression is apparent in senility. Old people become as children. This is also the time when their long-displaced infantile paraphilias may reappear. Their pathological love for children is like the blossoming of long-dormant buds.

Embryonic soul cells are present in every human being. As Antheim referred the origin of neoplasms to the reactivation of embryonic cells, so can we describe the reappearance of some paraphilias in senility to the reactivation of dormant infantile tendencies. Whether the inhibitions and reactivation are of organic or psychic nature, I cannot say. But the phenomenon does exist and is worthy of thorough psychological investigation.

Infantile forms of masturbation also are often practiced by senile people. The masturbatory activity is concealed from consciousness and is rationalized. An elderly woman may suffer from *pruritis vulvae* and thus may have a quite convenient excuse for scratching. Many elderly men disguise masturbation by excessive attention to the anus, scratching it, introducing a finger, or by frequent irrigation.

Time and again in our work we have seen the meaning of the infantile in the formation of paraphilias. In certain disturbances of the sexual function it is simply impossible to eliminate the infantile tendencies. The neurosis is actually a demand that the infantile desires be eternally fulfilled, and paraphilia is a means of satisfying this demand. The demands of the child (which are to be found behind all psychosexual diseases) present the real and difficult problem in therapy.

All human beings have at one time or another cherished the wish for eternal childhood. In all of us there is a longing for the lost paradise of childhood. Everybody fears the accumulation of years that means the approach of old age. Yet there is a "normal" sexuality for each age. The sexuality of the twenties differs from that of the thirties, and that of the thirties differs from that of the forties. People protest against these manifestations of advancing years. The paraphilias, like the climacteric, are struggles against aging.

This fear of old age is a disease of our day. How many men and women today fight desperately against old age! They employ all kinds of cosmetics, dye their greying hair, massage their wrinkles, carry on a pretense of youth which often is so obvious that its absurdity is clear to all except the stricken individual.

In other times, in the world of the classical Greeks and Romans, for example, old age was accepted with high respect. The "old man" was regarded as a man of wisdom, but today he is a "doddering old fool." The "old woman" of understanding has become an even more ridiculed figure. Expressions such as "He talks like an old woman" are increasingly common. And the sexual implications of such ridicule are most clear in the many variations of the "old maid" story. People become ridiculous when they do not fulfill their sexual functions. The impotent man regards his condition as tragic, but to other people it is a source of entertainment, in itself a joke and an inspiration for gossip, ridicule, and jokes.

The potent man and the sensuous woman are always surrounded by an atmosphere of glory, even though their affairs are openly denounced as being opposed to good morals. Behind moralistic condemnation there is much envy. I have known many women who admitted that they had always been envious of coquettes. It is also the coquette who leads the way in fashions of women's dress.

The fear of old age can appear in childhood and become the psychic dominant force around which other neurotic symptoms develop.

Case No. 11: A twenty-seven-year-old woman suffers from sleeplessness and various other neurotic symptoms. She declares that since the age of seven she has been suffering from the fear of aging. As a child, she would awaken in the middle of the night, count the hours, and say to herself, "Now you have aged one more hour. You'll soon become an old maid." This fear spoiled her whole life. She did not enjoy youth, for she considered herself to be growing old. She was always a few years ahead of people who were chronologically her own age. She did not play with other children because she thought their gamboling was "childish." As she grew up, she ignored the attentions of young men her own age because she thought of them as "too young." She sought mature men, and they were always too young or too old. She was engaged in an interminable battle with time.

It is in the neurotic's relationship to time that we find a clue to sexual infantilism. The neurotic acts as if time were not passing. Some even have the feeling that time remains at a standstill and that their age actually remains unchanged. When feelings of passage of time and increase of age strike them, they are unhappy. They try to act as though time had overlooked them or as though they were immune to time.

Only a colossal impairment of the sense of reality can create such a fiction and permit it to persist. As Freud noted so accurately, such people use an infantile lust currency which is not acceptable to the environment. In psychosexual infantilism the individual constructs his own world in which the lust currency has universal significance. With all his senses and all his power he must turn from reality. All neurotics have such a tendency, but the sexual infantile type, in trying to retain the world of his childhood as the years pass, gives an ever-increasing dominance to his fantasy over the demands of his real life.

Such people are always dreamers. They sleep long and deep and they like to have additional sleep or naps during the day. They are inactive people who dream of action. Even during their school years they have difficulty in making progress. They cannot fit into any profession. They want to be independent so that they can keep their dream world. They exploit their relatives and friends to such an extent that as soon as they find someone, whether it be father, mother, aunt, godfather, or friend, who is willing to provide for them, they lose their ability to work and become utterly dependent. In their dreamy stages they may be exhibition-istic, touch children on dark staircases, loudly voice vulgar words (psychic exhibitionism), suddenly quit jobs. In these dreamy states there is a senseless, childish attitude which sometimes even leads to the commission of impulsive acts.

Their handwriting is infantile, their grammar shows childish errors, they like to resort to baby talk. They have the motility of children (skipping walk). They are depend-ent like children, without logic, are fond only of those peo-ple who gratify their demands, and hate all people who deny their wishes. They lament and complain and seek pity. They are frequently impotent and manifest many infantile sexual symptoms. They are confused, unable to concentrate on work, and are interested only in themselves. They give all kinds of neurotic reasons for avoiding work which they are obligated to do. They may have writer's cramp, astasia and abasia, neuroses of the digestive tract, an occupational neu-rosis—it seems they can always devise a symptom when work threatens to deprive them of their peculiar infantile pleas-ures.

It is impossible to describe all types of this illness. I want to limit myself to certain manifestations. I have already stressed that infantilism can appear in two forms, fixation and regression. Regression, which is the more frequent form, can go back to a certain stage of childhood. It can go back as far as fetal existence. I do not agree with Ferenczi that it is caused by pleasurable memories of the womb. I believe that it is caused by fantasies and identification with a certain role. Behind womb fantasies there is a tremendous wish to start life anew.

I was quite taken by surprise when I analyzed the first spermatozoon dreams. The patients were overwhelmed with the thought of becoming a sperm and a new person. But one may regress further, and the psychogenic origin of the disorder then becomes clear. I do not think that this regression involves mneme (Semon) and that it looks back to old engrams of a primordial existence.

There are people who regress to certain periods of human history. They become Romans or Greeks or Old Germans. They cultivate the thought that they have previously lived and that they know their historic existence. Sometimes they become spiritualists and search for the spirit who has given them their superior knowledge. Sometimes they become primitive or criminal. And criminality itself is a regression to an infantile stage of mankind. Sometimes they become animals or imitate Adam, the first man. All these people believe in the transmigration of the soul and in a former existence.

These attitudes are revealed in their dreams, and render their waking, everyday life a sort of dream state. The prerequisite of such an illness is the annulment of time, and this can be accomplished only in dreams or fantasy images.

The dream life and sleep are at the center of sexual infantilism. Some extreme cases are "asleep" or "almost asleep" for many years—and only here and there during that long period have they actually awakened for a few hours. Milder cases commonly sleep ten to twelve hours a day; otherwise they "wouldn't feel well." All pathological sleep conditions indicate regression to an infantile stage. Freud speaks of the retrospective tendency of the dream—that is, its return to the infantile.

One can point to the semi-scientific, semi-artistic description of Fritz Wittels, who speaks of the "child-woman." He refers to the woman who remains a child in many respects. The infantile woman is a product of retarded and one-sided development. Her health is delicate and she looks upon the world with the amazed eyes of a child. She is fearful—like a little girl who goes through a forest which to her is peopled with ghosts. And she is fearless—like a somnambulist walking across a rooftop. She has lots of spunk, but also extremely bad manners. Ibsen gives a marvellous portrayal of this type in his play *The Doll's House,* in which a young wife plays with dolls and makes childish demands.

How do organic factors, such as disturbances of internal secretion, influence psychic manifestations? I have seen patients suffering from infantilism suddenly become old after treatment brought an "awakening." Their entire personality changed. Their handwriting acquired adult characteristics. Signs of manhood, such as growth of beard and mustache, appeared. These facts lead me to the assumption that psychic factors definitely influence the internal secretion. The famous experiments of Pavlov teach much about the importance of the psyche as an influence on the endocrine system. The wish, "I want to be a child," and the complying inactivity of the sexual glands are, apparently, closely related to each other.

I do not take it upon myself to give final answers to the questions of interaction between psyche and soma in psychosexual infantilism. But on the basis of my experience I will attempt to describe a few relevant cases.

Some neurotics have peculiar fantasies of lying inside the father's body. Such people often dream about "sperm existence." Usually they are physicians or medically trained individuals who possess precise information about sperms. The first such case described by me was that of a doctor, which appeared in *Conditions of Nervous Anxiety*.[1] This finding was later verified by Marcinowski and Herberd.

The person who has intra-uterine fantasies is of a different type. He is of a dreamy nature and complains of the strangeness of life and of frequent spells of dizziness. He submits to daydreams which are almost like the sleeping states mentioned above, except that his eyes remain open. He has peculiar tendencies. He likes small rooms and dislikes large rooms. He likes to spend time in tiny bathrooms. He cuddles up in his blankets, pulls them over his ears, and folds his body into the shape of an embryo. His dreams are concerned with birth and existence within the womb.

The intra-uterine fantasy is often of such a form that contact is made with the father. Most of these neurotics shake their heads when their attention is drawn to their womb fantasies. They consider them absurd. Others admit that they have frequently harbored such thoughts. One patient told me that he particularly cherishes the fantasy of being in the womb of a female giant, for there he can move around to his heart's desire. In this intra-uterine world he has a swing and all the facilities which any child could want for play. In addition, he enjoys the seclusion, the feeling of being inseparably united with his mother and of being protected from the inclemencies of the outer world.

On the other hand, the intra-uterine fantasy may express itself in a phobic sense. We find cases of sexual infantilism in which we see fears of narrow places, fears of being enclosed, fears of being buried alive. In the following analyses we will become better acquainted with such intra-uterine fantasies. For the present I merely want to relate several dreams which permit a diagnosis of the womb fantasy.

[1] New York: Liveright Publishing Corporation, 1950.

(1) I am going to the country to purchase flour. I am sitting with the farmer in a dark room. Through a small window I can see the light green of a meadow which is covered with sunshine. Suddenly I ride in an open wagon and sit with my back toward the blowing snow.

(2) It is winter. I live in a lonely house. I have just returned home and I look upward in order to see the curtains on the window. I notice that they are torn. I decided to tell mother that she should mend them. At the entrance to the door I think to myself: "To live here in this wilderness surrounded by fields and trees is a fascinating picture and leaves its impact on the development of the child." In front of the main gate, boys throw snowballs. One just passes by me. I am not clear whether this is a threat. I pass two adjacent gates and arrive at the third which is somewhat covered with snow. As I contemplate whether I will be able to open it, a boy arrives all ready to serve and he opens the gate. I realize that he has nothing bad in mind against me. I arrive at a barren garden. Hardly any grass. A hare approaches me. I encounter Mr. Kitzler,[1] an acquaintance, who asks me, "Have you already seen this animal?" I give him a negative answer. Suddenly I notice a young pig sleeping peacefully under a bush. It must have gotten lost.

(3) Several people are visiting us. Some of them come from the lavatory and therefore I have to wait as I also have to use the toilet. Finally, the lavatory is vacant and I go into it. I hook the door so no one else can enter. Father is standing in the doorway and his fly is half-opened. I let down my trousers. Despite heavy feces and urine I sit on the floor with closed legs. Next to me I set my little pocket mirror and comb in order to enjoy look- ing at myself and combing my hair. (This patient often grooms his hair.) *Urine pushes out, but I don't let it go. A drop appears on the surface. Emission.* (The patient also has a strong urethral erotism.)

(4) I find myself in the house of my business partner in the forest. From the apartment one has a view of a beautiful cot-

---

[1] The dream was dreamt in German. "Kitzler" is the German word for the clitoris. (Editor's note.)

tage. I walk through an alley in which there are booths with pencils. As I am about to buy a pencil, a bald-headed man passes.

Let us examine these four dreams. The first, in itself, would hardly suggest mother's womb fantasy. But the analysis of his other dreams and his condition enables us to make such an interpretation. The dark room is the uterus. The window is a symbol of the vagina. The picture changes, that is, the womb becomes a wagon. The snow symbolizes the sperm which splashed against his body. Incidentally, I once treated a homosexually-inclined patient whose only wish was to be splashed by a man. His analysis revealed the peculiar fantasy that he was in his mother's womb before his father had put him there.

In the second dream we see the womb as a desolate house. This picture, which has its "impact on the development of the child," is clear. The throwing of the snowballs symbolizes the splashing with sperms. He meets youngsters and a hare (phallic symbols). The introduction of Mr. Kitzler (clitoris) is amusing. A man of this name exists in reality, but he is utilized in the dream for the purpose of symbolization. The patient himself is the pig.

The third dream shows us the womb fantasy of a urine sexualist. The womb is represented by the toilet.

The fourth dream shows pencils as phallic symbols. The bald-headed man is a symbol of the penis.

In all four dreams we deal with retrospective fantasies about fetal existence. Much more peculiar and bizarre are the spermatozoon dreams. Silberer, in his treatise *Spermatozoenträume* (Spermatozoon Dreams), writes:

Case No. 12: "Recently, I had an adventure as dream interpreter which merits special mention, not only because of the rarity of such cases as the one involved, but also because of a rare meeting which made me guess at first glance what usually would have required much skillful analysis.

"On January 6, 1912 (the date, as we shall see later, is not without meaning), Dr. W. Stekel made to me the surprising announcement that he had succeeded in revealing in the dream of a patient a plain intrascrotal fantasy. Fantasies in which the dreamer puts himself back into his mother's womb are known. These fantasies are not only interesting because they represent the closest sexual approach to the woman and to the mother, but also because they approach thoughts which are close to the fetal existence. As for the intrascrotal fantasies, they are different from womb fantasies, although both can be considered as excessive expressions of the desire for regression, as a retreat from life and as a death fantasy.

"The dream which Dr. Stekel told me about was distinguished by *a sort of stream where numerous small people, men and and women, glided*. Finally, the dreamer *saw himself among these people*. The whole thing was viewed as picturesque.

"Dr. Stekel arrived at the thought that the small people in the stream could be regarded as sperms in the seed stream, and the analysis confirms this hypothesis. As the dreamer puts himself in the sperms of the seed stream, he puts himself in the father's body. He has an intrascrotal fantasy. While I was talking to Dr. Stekel about a similar dream, he called my attention to the similarity which exists between his interpretation and the belief of some primitive tribes about the creation of the seed. Both assumptions consider spermatic fluid as inhabited by small figures which later develop in the womb. It seems that in these dreams are expressed a trend of thought which corresponds to the mentality of a primitive period of humanity.

"To come back to the sperm dreams, the two which Dr. Stekel discussed with me had in common the motives of dirt or stickiness (consistency of the spermatic fluid).

"The day following the talk with Dr. Stekel, a lady, whom I shall call Miss Agatha, told me a dream. I have analyzed many of her dreams and am quite familiar with her symbolic language and with her conflicts. She dreamed, on January 6, 1912, as follows:

"I was on a train or I was standing on a snowfield on half-melted snow. Surrounding me was a winter landscape. A narrow, snake-

*like path of ice leads into a foreign land, the name of which I
knew in the dream, but which I am now unable to recall. I stand
next to the path and observe how people with skis run down the
hard ice. I think this must be a new sport. Actually there is a small,
elongated boat in which there is a man. The whole view is like
a picture, and the men are drawn very thin and narrow. At the
place where I stand there is a turn. Two one-year volunteers
come down this path by foot. At a curve they step away from the
boat which rushes downward. I descend from the train. As the
boat passes, I just see a soldier in a light grey coat. I would very
much like to go on the path which leads into the foreign land,
but for certain reasons I can't do it. I find myself in a railway car—
it seems as if I had been on the train before and had just alighted
in order to look on. The railroad leads in the same direction as the
ice path. I stand outside, near the open window, and watch when
we arrive. The boats can be seen speeding down the path. The
train arrives at night at a dark depot. I am uneasy and tense
because I am not certain if this is the right depot. I can't figure
out the name of this place. It seems important that I know.*

"As Miss Agatha gave me this oral description of the dream, I
was taken aback. This picturesque view: does it not resemble a
vivid sperm dream? Does it not prove the observation which I
made yesterday? The thin, meagre figures which slide into a
tempting 'foreign land.' Are they not beautiful sperms? The
melting snow, white and of semi-fluid consistency. Melting snow
is also sticky and is a fitting substitute for human seminal fluid.
And Agatha herself was on the snow and had the intention of
gliding into the 'foreign country.' Does this not indicate a fantasy of being in the father's body? I decided not to risk being
led astray by this amazing coincidence and uniformity, which
might make me prejudiced. Listening to the continuation of the
dream I withdrew my assumption, however.

"There was an 'empty boat' which Agatha sent down. It became immediately clear to me that we were dealing with a complaint about sterility. Agatha intended to sail in such a boat
into a foreign land, and she was sad because she could not do it.
That brought us back again to the sperm idea. We lacked only
proof that the content of the 'boat' was an 'undeveloped person.'

The bodies in the other boats were very thin and elongated. One could easily recognize them as sperms. I was sure that in some scientific magazine Agatha had seen pictures of sperms, but she could not recall any such incident.

"While we were talking through this dream, Agatha presented the following supplementary material: *The ice path leads from the upper right side to the lower left side, sometimes in snake coils in the foreign land. The name of the strange land was poetic and somewhat Japanese. Agatha expected to recall it again. She was surprised that people could ski on hard ice. The path led into the distance; the train paralleled it. It was as though they were going toward Trieste. The foreign land was covered by darkness. It was unclear how the riders came. As Agatha led the boat—it was actually a baby's bath tub—through the train window, she was sad that it was empty.*

"The new material cast light on hitherto obscure parts of the dream. Agatha had gone to Trieste with a man through whom she became pregnant. The trip to Trieste points toward sexual relations as well as to pregnancy. The direction of the path, from right to left, and the downward course of travel show that Agatha regrets her association with the man. (Stekel has clarified the symbolization of 'right' and 'left'—'left' is the wrong.) Resulting from the sexual relationship were pregnancy, abortion, and an operation from which the young woman emerged sterile, an ovary and both tubes having been removed. I kept this interpretation to myself. The empty boat—a baby's bath tub—which Agatha sent down could not contain a child, for Agatha is sterile.

"In order to clarify this point further, I asked the patient to tell me more details about the boat or tub in the dream. What were the utilities of a tub in a household? Well, it could be used to bathe little children, to wash clothing, to bake bread. Something white and foamy of the consistency of melting snow is common to all of the processes that take place in the tub—that is, to all processes which Agatha mentioned. Melting snow and sperm.

"I asked Agatha what the boat and the tub represented. She replied that the elongated boats were penises and the tub was a female utensil. Now it occurs to me that the tub or uterus not only carries water and a child (cf. also 'tubes'), but it also has something to do with dough. In response to my questioning, Agatha related how bread was made from dough. As bread is made from dough, so is a child shaped and developed in the mother. Agatha remarked that there is a comparison to be made between a child and a loaf of bread. The loaf is elongated like a child and one carries it like a child. She used to carry newly-baked bread in her arm as though it were a child.

"I asked Agatha why she was sad as she sent the empty tub down the slope in the dream. Who should have been in it? I hoped that she would somehow explain that a child should have been in it, for this would open the way for me to explain that at the base of her sadness was a knowledge of her sterility. Agatha replied, '*I* should have been in it.' Then she added, 'Maybe I should have put somebody in my place in it.' After a few moments hesitation, she continued, 'I must tell you that I thought about it last night. What a pity that I don't have a child from Paul. I would have liked a child so much. It would have been a wonderful child. I even thought that in case Paul should change his mind, and have a child from another woman, he would owe it to me.'

"Then Agatha suddenly said, 'Have I not mentioned before that those thin people appeared as if they were about to melt as soon as one touched them?' Under the impact of this development, I could not deny that the elongated people were sperms. Agatha informed me that she thought the human form appeared as a vision immediately after the fertilization of the seed. The ice path is snakelike, and the snake, as Agatha asserted, is a symbol of the penis and of life. In the dream, she thought that riding down the path was a new sport. In reality, it was something new on the road to Trieste. The so-called rhythmic riding, the impression that from time to time a rider glides down the path into the beautiful, dark, foreign land, seems to point to the rhythmic movements of sexual intercourse.

"Who are the one-year volunteers in the dream? This apparently points to Paul, who does not want any children, shies away in the dream (steps out of the train) when the riders (sperms) approach (coitus interruptus), and wears a coat (condom).

"The soldier in the grey coat has another very significant meaning. He reminds Agatha not only of Paul but of a Mr. F. whom she used to call 'Mr. Death.' The soldier in the grey coat is death standing but one step from Agatha's path. She had looked death in the eyes at the time of the operation which followed her adventure in Trieste. Agatha later reported that the soldier in grey had placed himself opposite her in the dream. During the operation she had lost one ovary. The disappearance of one soldier meant that the one who took the role of a death menace also assumed this role in the course of her disease.

"What is the duty of death in this dream? Here we find the deepest thought of the dream. Agatha wants to start life anew. This theme was already familiar to me from my previous analytic work with her. In the present dream she utilizes three main symbols in order to depict this wish. She wants to look for a foreign land; she calls death to push her from the life path; and finally, she imagines that she was never produced at all and avoids being produced in order to get to be a sperm on the ice path of the seed stream which flows into the dark land of her mother's womb.

"Then Agatha recalled the name of the foreign country; it was 'Chiuka.' This word does not belong to any language with which she was familiar. It reminds the patient of a fairytale name that had a similar sound. This is really a reminder of childhood days and the mother's lap. Agatha recalls that soft, melting snow covered the scene described in the fairytale and that the land from which children came was swampy and that storks pulled the infants from the morass.

"The sadness or disappointment of Agatha as she discovers that she does not have a penis but instead a female sex organ (the tub) is determined not by the emptiness of the boat but by her wish to be a man.

"Agatha had decided against her 'better judgment' to relate the dream. The resistance indicates the factual existence of the broken hopes which our analysis has already shown.

"As the puzzle of the dream was solved, Agatha remarked

that there must be several previous dreams which one could solve with the same key. The symbols of the sperms seemed to her to be close to her feelings. By accident, I had not yet analyzed one dream which she had submitted three days earlier. I now began to read it.

"In reporting the entire dream, I shall emphasize those scenes which made a particular impression on me. I still have to remark that Agatha intended to go to her parents in Frankfurt in order to participate in the engagement celebration of her brother Gustav, but she dropped this plan.

"The dream: *On the street-corner sits my brother Gustav and his fiancée, Dora. I beg for money from passersby. I go toward my brother and say, 'Give me some money. I forgot my pocketbook.' He reaches into his pocket and takes out a handful of brand new silver coins. I admire the beauty of the money and as I want to take a krone, I notice that the silver has changed into ivory and that in the strange plastic there were small, thin figures visible. I am very disappointed and think to myself: 'Ah! I don't even want to have them! and I run away without saying a word.*

"The 'small, thin figures' which suddenly appeared on the money represented sperms. The drawing of the coins from the trousers of brother (who was prominent sexually in Agatha's childhood) also speaks for this meaning."

From the analysis of other dreams and the dreams reported by Marcinowski, I have seen many wonderful examples of this regressive fantasy. All of these dreamers want to turn life back and resume a fetal or pre-fetal existence. This regression sometimes involves many generations and thousands of years. Such cases are rare, but the intra-uterine fantasy is one which is found frequently.

2. THE ETERNAL INFANT

The eternal infant is a dependent person. He dreads being alone. His psychic infantilism is manifested in many of his physical habits. His abnormal attitude toward food—either he has great desire or is disgusted by particular foods—has a sexual basis. His oral zone substitutes for the genital zone. He gets childish pleasure from boat rides, swinging, and traveling. On an outing, he is like a child going to a picnic. In dreams he sees himself on a high wagon, a tower, or an elevated porch, looking down. He lives with giants in his dream-life and is carried by them. Such a person has feelings of inferiority, a fact emphasized by Janet and Adler particularly in relation to organ inferiority.

But neurotics would not cling to their weakness and pettiness if they did not get secret gratification from such "inferiority." They are pleased to retain the fiction that they are the "little ones" among the adults. Because of guilt connected with their criminal fantasies they also long to retain the purity of childhood, and they are careful to forget that their childhood was actually filled with criminal wishes. They want to push their own responsibilities onto the shoulders of adults. Like a child in the arms of a nurse, they wish to be protected.

To the above description I want to add that each of these eternal infants has a specific sexual picture. Most of them are impotent, frigid, or have no normal sexual relations at all. The males lose their erection when they contact women, or they have *ejaculatio praecox*. The females become frigid or limp, as though they were paralyzed. (That we are not dealing with organic influences in these cases is proved by the success of analytic treatment.) Some eternal infants resume masturbating after having given up for years. They are overly attentive to the mouth zone; often they prefer kissing to intercourse. They suck the breasts and are—as a rule—passive sexual partners. Sometimes they favor cunnilingus or fellatio. They show keen interest in urination and defecation, an interest that often leads to the development of polyuria and all kinds of stomach disorders. To reconstruct a fictional childhood, they "create" many neurotic symptoms and may even go so far as to reintroduce enuresis and defecation in bed.

Childish crying and spitefulness are common to these people. The real world is removed as the infantile ego, "His Majesty the Child," through anxiety and compulsion symptoms, seeks to vie for the attention of the environment. The day is passed in daydreams, idleness, or childish games.

These people glory in filth and dirt. They find excuses for not washing, or they prefer to have another person give them a bath. They play with dirt, stay on the toilet a long time, bite nails, devour the nasal mucus like children, and enjoy many unpleasant mannerisms which they hide from the people they know, but which come out in analysis. General practitioners have little idea of the strange world inhabited by the psychosexual infantilist.

Case No. 13: Mr. G., a husky man of twenty-eight, dressed in a juvenile suit, appears at my office one day with his mother, who leads him by his arm, draws a chair toward him, and helps him become comfortably seated. The woman then says, "Drink, my child, so that you can talk." The "child" pulls a milk bottle with a rubber nipple from his pocket and gulps some milk. Then he takes a roll from his pocket and hands it to his mother. The woman breaks off a piece of the bread for him and pushes it into his mouth.

"Excuse us," the mother apologizes. "But you see, doctor, every fifteen minutes my son must have a little milk and a bit of bread, otherwise he will collapse. Until a few days ago he had to go out by himself because my husband considered him a malingerer and threatened to chase him away from home. He did go out by himself, without his milk and bread, and he collapsed on the street. He was brought home dangerously ill! Help me, doctor!"

Through his peculiar behavior, G. was manifesting symptoms of his psychosexual infantilism. He had been in this helpless condition for three months. Previously, he had been in sound health, held a good position, was a model man. The mother was especially concerned about this "boy's" illness because she had another son who is severely neurotic and who tormented the household, refused to work and constantly demanded money. Until his infantilism broke out, G. had been her consolation. But now, without any apparent reason, he had changed.

Formerly, he had had satisfactory contact with women. Now he was shy, had wild erotic fantasies, and had resumed masturbation. Sometimes he would masturbate several times a day. He was a daydreamer; he could not work or even dress himself.

His daily program went something like this: when he awakened in the morning he remained in bed daydreaming. He did nothing at all unless given an order to do something. He would stay in bed all day if his mother did not urge him to get up. Then she had to dress and wash him. She treated him as a small child, giving in to his whims. She served breakfast to him in bed. When he arose from bed he followed his mother around the house like a shadow. He was afraid to be alone. The mother had to take him with her whenever she left the house, otherwise he would have a severe "attack" and be a completely helpless "baby." He mumbled nonsensical phrases, laughed without provocation. His symptoms were frightening to the parents, for they thought he had lost his mind.

His disease started when he noticed that the hateful brother, who was a brat and an "ogre," as his mother called him, was really loved by the mother. The brothers had not spoken to each other for years. Both had strong mother fixations. The father had little influence on the family. The mother was a pretty woman with lustrous eyes. The older brother hated her and would not allow her to come near him. "Don't touch me," he would shout; "I am disgusted with you!"

The younger brother, our patient, adored his mother and brought her every penny he earned. But when he was seized with the feeling that his mother loved the older brother and that this was why she let his brother stay at home to loaf and dominate the household with his sickness, he said to himself: "You are not rewarded for your decency and manliness, so you'll get sick and lazy like your brother." This thought flashed through his mind just once. But soon afterward, his illness "struck," and continuously worsened, so that now his mother even had to accompany him to the toilet, hold him on the seat, and wipe him.

Surprisingly, the analysis ended with a complete success. In most cases of this type, it is necessary to remove the patient from his home environment before he can be cured. But this patient remained at home and soon his manhood was restored and he was again active in his profession.

He had regressed to the suckling stage. He became an infant, completely dependent on the mother. The worry and pity which the mother had expended on the brother was now shifted toward him. This had an excellent effect on the older brother, who suddenly used his exceptional talents to get and maintain a good job. The older brother now had the chance to prove that he was stronger than his hated sibling. The brothers persisted in their refusal to speak to each other and the atmosphere in the house was tense.

When, during analysis, our patient began to improve, his first love interest was directed toward the family's maid. As stated before, maids frequently symbolize someone in the family. The mother approved his play with the maid and even advised him to have an affair with the girl. By all means, her son must become a man! "It is better than getting a venereal disease outside of the house." This was her rationalization. She really wanted to know when and with whom he had sexual relations. She needed the stimulations (deeply rooted in her own incestuous tendencies) which her son supplied when he reported his sexual affairs.

A regression to childhood is often connected with a hatred for work which interferes with daydreaming. The disease often first evidences itself when a person who is dissatisfied with one job sets out to seek another. Simultaneously, the regressing individual becomes a burden upon his family.

Case No. 14: Mr. J.B., a sturdy physical specimen of thirty, cannot leave the house by himself. He is brought to my office by his mother. He is suffering from such feelings of weakness that he cannot walk without crutches and even then he falls if his mother does not support him. This weakness contrasts tremendously with his robust and powerfully-muscled body. His secondary characteristics, penis, scrotum, and pubic hair, are well-developed. There is not a single feminine trait on his body. Physically a strong man, he has been bed-ridden for six months. In his helpless condition his mother has waited on him. He is engaged to a girl who seems to be a fine mate for him, but because of his "weakness" he cannot marry her. He pleads with me to help him, to restore him to normality. He must not lose this wonderful girl whose patience is at a breaking point. Only recently she said, "Joseph, you are not a man. You are a child!"

Before he had met this girl, he had formed good and close contacts with other girls. He had been engaged several times, but before the final step he had usually found fault with his fiancée. None of the girls was quite "right" for him. Now he had found the perfect mate—but his disease turned him into a helpless weakling.

His misfortunes began in the following way: one day, while at work in a store, he decided that the job was not the right one for him. He found another job. Then he yearned for the position he had left. He became preoccupied with the thought that he must return to his old job.

Our patient longed for his mother's love. He wanted to return to the infant stage and to be at his mother's bosom, which he had enjoyed during his first three years. His mother's breast was the "old job" for which he longed.[1] He was so disturbed

---

[1] The German poet, Christian Morgenstern, expresses this sentiment in a beautiful poem entitled *Zum Muttertag* ("To Mother's Day"). We quote here the German original alongside an English free translation.

Zum Muttertag	*To Mother's Day*
Im Mutterschoss,	In Mother's lap,
im Mutterschoss	in Mother's lap
zu ruh'n,	to rest,
nach all der Hast	after all the rush
im Mutterschoss—	in Mother's lap—
o selig Los,	O, blissful lot
das kaum ein Herz umfasst!	your heart has ever known!
Im Mutterschoss—	In Mother's lap—
nach so viel Last und Hast.	after all the fret and rush.

by his desire for the former job that he lost his new job. Now he was without work and had an opportunity to long for his first job night and day.

A change had also taken place in his sex life. As his life had unfolded from childhood, there had been two forces pulling him in opposite directions: one toward infancy and his mother, and a counter-force seeking recovery and liberation. All neurotics seek cure and liberation from their neurosis. (Otherwise we would be dealing not with a neurosis, but with a psychosis.) But they seek their cure in an ambiguous, neurotic way. Our infantile neurotics run away from home, emigrate to other lands, seek a new environment in which they hope to forget the old one. They do not realize that true detachment from infantilism is possible only from within and no amount of geographic change can solve their problem. Our patient also tried to liberate himself from the trap of infantilism—in his neurotic way. He went to prostitutes, and he displayed good potency with them. He fell in love with many girls, played with the thought of marriage but always found a way out. Then he became engaged to a girl of whom he was very fond, and as the wedding day approached, he became displeased with his job. Reason: he needed a larger salary if he were to support his fine wife properly. He actually provided an obstacle to the approaching marriage. Neurotics have great skill in fooling themselves and their environment.

Both his fiancée and his mother were sure that his income was sufficient. The girl was surprised by his sudden concern about finances. They had known all along that she expected him to have only moderate means of supporting her, and she was keen about helping if more income were needed. But he insisted that he must make more money. He tried a new job,

---

Im Gottesschoss
im Gottesschoss
zu ruh'n,
Nach so viel Streit
im Gottesschoss—
o Trost, so gross,
dass alles Schöpfungsleid
ein Seufzer bloss
vor deiner Ewigkeit.

In God's lap,
in God's lap
to rest,
after all the strife
in God's lap—
Oh, solace sweet,
that all creation's ache
is but a sigh
before Eternity!

—*The Editor.*

promised more than he produced, and finally lost his energy and the job.

Now he wanted to speculate. His bride-to-be had saved some money. Why not buy a store? His oral fantasies caused him to decide on the purchase of a dairy products store. But he did not tend to the business. He became sick. He had to stay in bed. His mother had to take care of him. He had to live on milk. He could eat nothing solid, for this would give him an upset stomach.

For several months his impotence had been complete. With every prostitute, he failed. Then he knew he could not marry, and he told his mother of his impotence. The mother, in turn, told the girl, who thought that behind this illness was a resistance to the marriage. Accordingly, the young lady severed relations with the patient. This permitted him to lament and wail about the disloyalty of women. He was the noble fellow who wanted marriage! He was stricken by a terrible illness and his sweetheart deserted him! He became weak as a fly. He was helpless. He was an infant. His mother brought him a bottle when he had to urinate. She placed a rubber sheet under him so that he would not soil the bedding. She bathed him. She was quite devoted. Perhaps she was pleased to have her only baby again.

There was a second reason for his illness. The mother was an attractive woman who looked younger than her years. She was occasionally visited by a man who—apparently—supported her. The son did not know any of the details of the relationship, but he thought the man wanted to marry his mother. He was jealous. In his first job he often worked late at night and consequently could not check on his mother's evenings. On the second job he had the advantage of being able to come home for lunch, and at irregular hours which would not be known in advance. Therefore, the mother would always have to reckon with the possibility that her son might come home unexpectedly. His engagement was a form of punishment for the mother.

When he became sick, he tied his mother so completely to himself as to make sure that there would be no disloyalty on her part. He became so excited when her gentleman friend called that his mother's suitor had to leave the house and refrain from visiting again. The mother remained silent in order to hide her secret fondness for the man, whom she still hoped to see, even if she had to arrange meetings outside of her home. But the son kept her busy all the time. She could not leave him under any pretext or he would become terribly ill and his life would be in danger. He could digest nothing but milk, so that he lost weight and became emaciated.

His dreams are interesting:

(1) I am sitting on a bench in the Prater.[1] *Suddenly my mother sits next to me, opens her blouse and says, "If you are thirsty, you can drink."*

(2) I dream that my whole body is tightly bound in diapers. My mother opens the diapers and washes my entire body.

(3) I am lying next to a strange woman in bed. She hands me her breast. I drink with great gratification, and think to myself, "If only no stranger would come! I would be very ashamed."

Mysophilia accompanies the return to childhood. The patient, who had always been clean and had hated dirt, now began to neglect himself. He did not want to wash and refused to have his shirts laundered. However, he would let his mother bathe him and dress him neatly. He was pleased when he urinated in his clothes. He enjoyed the odor of the urine and also of his feces, with which he liked to play.

He also resumed games and hobbies of his childhood. He began to carve figures from wood. He would play with these toys which he himself had made. He liked to cut out pictures with a pair of scissors. He particularly liked to cut out figures of soldiers and once he succeeded in walking to a nearby store where he purchased a cut-out book.

He was interested in water and fire. He could sail and dip his toys in water by the hour. He loved to watch the water drip from the toys. He loved to stare for long periods into a fire and to toss bits of wood and paper into it.

He sulked and used baby talk. He sobbed and lamented like a small child. He maintained that his sexual desires, when he was alone in bed, ended in enuresis rather than emission.

I have presented but a small part of his seemingly countless

[1] Natural park in Vienna.

symptoms. Yet within two months after beginning of the treatment he was back at work in the store. Gradually his infantilism was dispersed. As he became interested in work, his interest in a sexual partner revived. He became fond of the housemaid, quarreled with his mother about this girl and then rented an apartment of his own and brought the maid into it to live with him. A little later he arranged with his employer to be transferred to Berlin and he moved to that city and married the maid, who was hated by his mother. His only solution was revenge on his mother. He could not part from her on good terms. But he had turned his back on all infantile symptoms and led the life of a grown man.

Case No. 15: Mr. G.L., thirty-two, was a healthy man until two years ago, highly talented, and busy in a wonderful position; but now he has come to my office, a totally broken and extremely anxious individual. Because of his anxiety about food, he can consume only liquids and cereals. He cannot tolerate being alone. Several times he has fallen on the street and remained there helplessly until his mother brought him home in a wagon. He can leave his apartment only when his mother accompanies him, and then he can walk only a few blocks. His mother gives him careful and continuous attention. Our first impression is that he has regressed to an infantile level.

He used to love to have coffee in the morning, but now he eagerly awaits the milk which his mother brings to his bed. Since he can eat nothing solid, he has his mother put some bread crumbs in the milk. In the morning when his mother goes shopping, an aunt watches over the "poor infant." He holds a clock in his hand while mother is away and becomes impatient when he thinks it is time that she should be home. Mother rushes about the necessary shopping as fast as she can, for she is earnestly striving to please her dear boy. She must return quickly to prepare her son's cereal. The aunt could never do it properly! Only the mother knows the correct process of preparing his food. If the cereal is the least bit too thick, the son will suffer from terrible cramps. The dreadful possibility of flatulent attacks also lurks in the background. He is also anxious about defecation.

His meager diet does not permit daily feces, so he has mother give him frequent enemas to aid "nature."

He occupies his mother's attention all day long, and thus gets a peculiar revenge on his father, who died three years ago. His father used to take most of the mother's time, depriving the "boy" of his share. Now the patient makes up for lost time. He exceeds the complaints and demands his father made.

As my experience with cases of episodic psychosexual infantilism grew, I became fascinated by the observation that most of these patients develop their symptoms after the father dies. I do not say that this death is an essential in a set formula which causes such conditions, but I do think the patient often reasons as follows: "If I can't actually replace father, I want at least to regain the active love which mother gave to me in my infancy."

Our present patient became engaged while his father was alive. This love affair seemed to be a revenge on his mother for her partiality toward his father. Then the father died suddenly. Immediately, the patient was tormented by the thought, "What will mother do?" He became nervous, irritable, and indifferent toward his fiancée. She too withdrew, and so the engagement was broken by mutual agreement. Meanwhile he became sick and could not stand the girl's lack of concern for his serious illness—that is, his regression to infantilism.

He became shy, impotent, indifferent to all women. He took to thumb-sucking. He acquired an insatiable taste for sweets as only his mother could bake them. He had "rheumatic pains" so that his mother could massage and tickle him. He scrutinized his stools and put them in a bowl by his bed so that mother could see them. He liked to pull the blankets over his head and emit gas. He would sit on the toilet seat so long that his mother would become frightened and knock at the door. Sometimes he would "take sick" in the toilet and his mother would have to come to his aid and help him back to bed.

He began to get enjoyment from coprolalia. He was happy

when he used "dirty" words in the presence of his mother or even when he was alone.

His dreams involved situations of suckling. Sometimes, however, his regret about the breaking of his engagement broke through in his dreams.

Analysis brought rapid improvement. Soon he was able to ride by himself to my office, and a little later he made the trip by himself on foot. Within two months he was in love with a beautiful girl. Then he married her, made a complete physical recovery and was able to free himself from his mother.

The mother was cooperative throughout. She carefully followed my instructions never to give in to her son's infantile wishes and to be independent in her own life. She showed no resistance to his engagement and marriage. In after years, when her son had become a father, she found in her grandchildren a happy substitute for her own "baby." But, essentially, she was one of those fortunate people who come to realize that it is never too late to live for oneself.

The following cases are regular paraphilias rather than episodic returns to infancy. The strongest libido is tied to a particular infantile scene which is repeated over and over in the neurotic's life.

Case No. 16: Mr. W. comes into a brothel and asks a prostitute to tie him tightly in the bed sheets. After this wish has been granted he remains quiet for a short while; then he requests manual, usually anal, stimulation. In this paraphilia, he is repeating the situation of a baby in diapers. His strongest passion is aroused when he is totally in the hands of a woman. He wants to be tied by a woman. He sometimes symbolizes this procedure by binding his legs and arms with ropes or neckties. For a while he undertook hydrotherapeutic treatments which, as a rule, also induced ejaculation. But whatever he does, he seeks to repeat a scene in which he is completely in the power of his mother.

Case No. 17: A twenty-eight-year-old physician consults me by mail because he is unable to work. He is strong and masculine. Sometimes he visits prostitutes, but often his sexual gratification is on a more infantile level, such as playing with his feces and urine and binding himself with ropes. This patient has read some of my books and he utilizes some of the information he has found in them to describe his condition:

"I am trying to be a man. But there are always relapses in which I become a child. I believe that childhood impressions are strongly alive in me. Previously, in my practice as a physician, I did not observe such things. Your book, *Conditions of Nervous Anxiety,* opened my eyes. A veil had hampered my vision. Now I have observed my patients and myself and have found much material which agrees with your writings. To my great sorrow, I cannot come to your city to visit you. Therefore, I must ask you to give me your advice in writing.

"My father was nervous and my mother was passionate. As a child, I slept in my parents' bedroom. I often listened and watched in the darkness as they performed intercourse, including some perversions. Even as a child of five, I hated Father as a rival and sought Mother with the burning desire of an adult lover. My mother sensed this from my intense kisses. She used to push me away. I especially sought to kiss her breast and was furious when she revealed her breasts and then cruelly pushed me from them. Mother had nursed me for a long time, and when she weaned me I became ill for many weeks. I maintained a fantasy of being at her breasts. Even today I precede intercourse with a prolonged period of nipple-sucking which eventually induces an erection.

"When I was three, a brother was born. I hated him as a competitor. I often wanted to choke him. He died when he was only a few years old, and I got the fixed idea that Father had choked him to death. This gave me a good reason to hate Father. Then I did not know that I was projecting my own criminal thoughts onto Father. Now I know that I had an ambivalent feeling toward my father. I hated him and I loved him at the same time. I played both father and mother in my fantasies. Sometimes I was Father's wife; sometimes I was Mother's husband.

"I believe that my hatred for Father was at least partly a protection against my own homosexual desires. I was shy and withdrawn in his presence, and I was happy when he left me alone.

"I also hated Mother because she did not place her body at my disposal. The trauma of the forced weaning is probably the source of this hatred. In some dreams *I am torn from the breasts of mother or another woman and I kill the one who drags me away.*

"Otherwise my childhood was rather placid. I dreamed along happily and quietly, sucked my fingers, played with my genitals. Throughout my life I needed constant erotic stimulation. Even today I have this need.

"My love vacillated between Mother and Father. Sometimes I was interested in boys and preferred Father, sometimes I was interested in girls and craved Mother. All of my life the pendulum has been swinging between male and female. Sometimes I think it would have been best if I could have engaged in both homosexual and heterosexual activity.

"During the first year of grammar school I was an obedient student. Then I began to steal from my schoolmates and from my parents. The objects I stole had no particular appeal to me; it was just that I had an irresistible passion for stealing. I had many criminal thoughts. I wanted to set fire to the school and was quite serious in my intentions of going through with this plan. I thought of ways of poisoning or shooting Father because he was too strict. But my father was really a kind-hearted man who thought a certain amount of discipline should be observed. But when he scolded me or struck me I became indignant and thought of killing him. I heard that the Talmud contained the following statement: 'He who hits his son educates him to sin.' This seemed to apply to me.

"My parents often had arguments. Many of them were about my father's strictness with me. Mother took my part, and inwardly I supported her. Father would insist that his way should be followed if my laziness and stubbornness were to be corrected. Nevertheless, I liked to aggravate Mother until she cried. My mother did not realize that I wanted to be loved and petted as in my infancy.

"My daydreaming tendency interfered with my schoolwork. If I was punished for a poor record in school, I became filled with thoughts of rape, hatred, and revenge.

"Early, I began to masturbate. This substituted for my loss of contact with Mother. With schoolmates I had masturbatory and homosexual play. Until I was twenty-two, I masturbated frequently, sometimes several times a day. It did not seem harmful. My potency was excellent. I can verify your opinion that masturbation is harmless.

"Work which prevented me from daydreaming was resisted. Studies were also avoided for the same reason. I did like to study when it was not a question of duty but a matter of free choice.

"Though I loved my parents, I often wanted to run away from home. I wanted to be alone, unrestrained, able to escape from masturbation and homosexuality, which seemed criminal acts. I often thought of suicide, but I was too cowardly and too fond of life to destroy myself.

"I wanted to remain youthful eternally! To be a child forever!

"My criminal thoughts must have caused my anxiety. I had many anxiety dreams in which I was raped or killed. I always ran after something unobtainable or was pursued by a man (Father?). I was basically cheerful, but lamented and played sick because I wanted to be pampered.

"I have observed in my practice that all patients become children to a certain degree. In my illnesses I also felt like a child.

"Even now I have a series of infantilisms which I cannot abandon. I still masturbate occasionally, and I like to soil myself with feces and urine. I go to hotels, urinate and defecate in the bed, and in the morning I complain of having had an attack which prevented me from getting up and, with this excuse, I pay for the inconvenience I have caused. To be on a sheet with my urine and feces is my greatest pleasure. I put the sheet through my legs, tie myself tightly, and become like a diapered baby. When sitting in a rocking chair, the motion brings desires and orgasm, pleasures connected with my childhood chair.

"At sixteen, I visited a prostitute for the first time. It was a pleasurable experience. I thought I had become a man. Unfortunately, I was still an infant. Although, as protection against my homosexuality, I have daily contact with women, I submit at least once a month to my deeper infantile drives and enact the disgusting but, to me, pleasurable scene in which I become a diapered baby in a hotel room. I knew more than a dozen women who were eager to join me in sexual play and I tried to divert myself from abnormality by having intercourse with them.

"In my practice, my nervousness usually increased when I examined men. My nervous shaking was a homosexual agitation which disturbed my emotional equilibrium. Your books helped me to get over this symptom.

"I sought treatment in many quarters. I could not be hypnotized. All treatment was a failure.

"As my nervousness increased, sadism became rampant in my fantasies. My fantasies contained unbelievable cruelty. I became arrogant and cocky when in the presence of others. I enjoyed telling people things which I knew they would regard as unpleasant. My desire to destroy was boundless. I bit wood, broke plates, bit women during intercourse. My desire to commit lust-murder became so strong that I chose the infantilism of masturbation as a means of preventing the crime. I punched myself and bit my nails and skin. I became furious whenever a patient called me, particularly if it was at night. Day and night I am half-asleep, daydreaming.

"Baths, cold or warm, excite me sexually. I am reliving the bathing period of infancy. When I wear a tight bathing suit in a bath, I have an instantaneous orgasm. I try to avoid bathing, for whenever I take a bath I masturbate. During my more infantile crises, I bathe daily. In a hot bath, I must be careful not to fall asleep.

"I have many intra-uterine fantasies. I am in a narrow, red room and, in the distance, I see a small window through which a neighbor pushes his tremendous penis. Again, I am suspended in a globe and magically carried about three feet above the ground and I can swim delightfully and with the ease of a fish. Sometimes I push myself through a narrow shaft and when I am threatened by rising waters I grasp a hood which is overhead. Through your writings, I have been able to understand these fantasies.

"Sometimes I feel like a female and want to wear women's clothing. I have little beard growth, and my pelvis is formed like a woman's. I used to think I might be a hermaphrodite, but my excellent potency convinced me otherwise. However, I would like to be a woman in order to enjoy the sensation they have during intercourse.

"I have strong anal eroticism of infantile character. As a child I often inserted a pencil and other penis symbols into my anus. Even today, when I stimulate the mucous membrane, or have women stimulate it, I get a stronger sensation. Anilingus renders the pleasure so intense that it becomes painful.

"For the past two years I have been married, and I have a healthy baby. But marriage and fatherhood have not cured me. For the first three months of marriage I seemed quite manly; then I relapsed—during a bath. I want to be psychoanalyzed, but I cannot leave my practice and must try self-analysis. There has been some improvement in my condition. My visits to a hotel where I play the role of an infant now occur but once in three or four months, for example. But I am still an infant."

In response to this colleague's letter, I wrote that in my opinion his infantile periods were substitutes for homosexual excitation. Whereupon I received a characteristic reply: "You have expressed something to which I have given thought for a long time. I find among my old dreams one which verifies your opinion: '*I am in a room with Mr. X. He opens his trousers and shows me his penis with the request that I give him special treatment. I notice that the penis is erect, but I say that this is not my specialty. At the same time I shrink more and more until I can just reach to his knees. He looks at me disdainfully and leaves the room.*'

"X. is one of my favorite patients, a quiet man with whom I have an intimate friendship. In the dream he wants homosexual treatment. But I shrink—that is, become a small child."

Let us summarize our findings about eternal infants:

(1) All of these patients have a tendency to daydream and to sleep excessively.

(2) They dislike work and become anxious in any routine work-setting.

(3) A relationship with the father is important in deter-

mining the psychosexual infantilism in males. Death of the father is frequently the precipitating factor.

(4) They are—as a rule—constantly or temporarily impotent.

(5) They energetically struggle against their repressed homosexuality whenever it seeks an overt outlet.

(6) Repressed criminal tendencies are manifested together with other features of infantilism.

(7) Through the re-educational processes of psychoanalysis the disease is curable.

3. ON THE LEVEL OF A LITTLE BOY

Physicians seldom recognize cases of infantilism for the reason that the patients conceal the infantile habits—partly because of embarrassment, partly because they do not want their secret enjoyment taken away from them. Only in the course of analysis do the infantilistic phenomena come to the surface. In the following case we have a good illustration of the peculiarities of psychosexual infantilism.

Case No. 18: Mr. L., who looks much younger than his fifty-four years, complains about persistent erections which occur only during the night. In the daytime he has no sexual sensations or desires. But at night when he goes to bed he gets such strong erections that his groin and back hurt. He suffers both from insomnia and hypersomnia. His sleeplessness is based on his fear of sleep, for when he goes to sleep he has dreams followed by emission.

Ever since the age of eighteen he has had emissions from one to three times a night. When he arises in the morning, he is so exhausted that he is totally incapable of working. For this reason, he has had to forsake his career as an attorney and live on a modest fortune.

His back pains are so severe that he sometimes thinks he is going to lose his mind. He has been to many doctors and has taken much medication. Nothing has helped. Some of the physicians told him that his satyriasis may stem from a spinal disease. He has no history of syphilis and he complains only of vague nervous symptoms. From time to time he gets a swelling in his left knee. During this swelling, erections and emissions are more frequent. With his increased erotism there is an increased general irritability. Coitus, which appeared to offer the only therapy for his satyriasis, is not possible, for, despite his powerful erection, he is impotent.

When he attempts intercourse with a prostitute, he either has no erection at all or a premature emission. In his younger days, doctors recommended forced intercourse as a means of overcoming his sexual difficulty. He would spend the night with a prostitute, experience several premature ejaculations and perhaps one normal intercourse, but when he returned home and fell asleep, he still had his nightly emissions. Therefore, he abandoned this form of "therapy." His few attempts with decent girls were also unsuccessful. For this reason he did not marry.

He blamed his condition on masturbation. He masturbated from the age of fourteen to eighteen about twice or three times a week. He was introduced to masturbatory acts by other boys with whom he engaged in this activity. He had never, however, been inclined to homosexual acts.

His sexual life story is told in the following words: "I have slept with mother as a child. . . . Otherwise I have no recollections. It is such a long time." After hearing this, I asked him the nature of his emission dreams. He told me that they were lively, wildly erotic, with beautiful women, usually imaginary figures. Earlier he had dreamed of having relations with his mother. But in recent years, especially since the death of his mother, he dreamed of unknown beautiful ladies. He wanted to know if his condition was "mental or physical." I could not give him an answer.

If this book has convinced general practitioners that they should not be content with the material obtained during the first days of treatment, it will serve a fine purpose. I can say without hesitation that the most important things are not reported in the first sessions.

On the following day the patient told me he had a bad night filled with constant erections and a tormenting dream:

I give my father an order. He leaves the house, falls on the staircase and is carried into the room. The doctor comes and says to me: 'Your father has a concussion of the brain and is going to die soon.'

It was after the death of his father that the knee-swelling first appeared. Previously, he had had no trouble with his knee. Then his potency improved so that he could have intercourse with prostitutes three or four times in an evening. Also, after his father's death, he became lonesome and sad. The mother had died several years earlier. Her death had not seemed to touch him deeply. He had frequently quarrelled and fought with her. The relationship between mother and father had always been excellent.

As a rule, he presents the same picture just before the onset of his knee-swelling. He becomes sad, speaks only in monosyllables, feels bad, gets restless, loses his appetite—and his knee shows marked edema. Simultaneously he thinks of his father's fall and death.

The knee condition is an angioneurotic edema of the joint (Quincke). He must remember the swollen head of his injured father. The inflammatory condition of his knee is like a memento; it constantly reminds him not to forget his father. There was a period of one year during which his knee did not swell every week. This happened after hydrotherapy, but also during that time he was a successful social figure. He was in a stimulating circle of friends with whom he regularly dined and drank. These friends "talked him out" of his suffering. Apparently by expressing his homosexuality in small, disguised quantities he derived sufficient erotic stimulation to forego the somatization. After a year of this pain-free life, the erections and emissions from which he had suffered since his sixteenth year returned.

One of his more important revelations was that he had dreamed repeatedly of watching other people having intercourse.

During such dreams he usually became highly stimulated. He also frequently had fantasies of similar type, and he began to wish that he, too, could be observed during the sexual act. But in the dreams he was always a passive observer. He also dreamed that he had an *ejaculatio praecox* and that the girl said, "Much too early! It happened much too early!"

As the observation dream is the most common for him, I ask if he listened during his parents' sex play and intercourse. He verified that he had done so many times. When he was about ten this experience was very exciting.

This gives us a connection between his dreams, fantasies, and infantile experiences. He looks for a third person when he is with a prostitute; he is a voyeur and erotic listener. He retains his fantasies and relives the scenes of the past. That is why he sleeps so long and is lost in dreams during the day. That is why he cannot endure reality.

Another dream: *I met a man who was taking a dog for a walk. I played with the dog for a long time. Then I asked the man: "Is your father still alive?" "Yes," he answered, "he is well and is almost seventy-eight years old."*

In this dream he cried and thought how sad it was that his own father was not alive. Without interpreting the dream, I want to mention that the patient said spontaneously, "The man with that dog is you, doctor."

I noticed that this was the beginning of transference and a release of latent homosexual forces which were operating in his neurosis. He showed me his knee, which was very swollen. The psychogenic nature of the condition could be seen in the history which shows that until several years ago it was localized in the right knee and that since then it has occurred in the left knee. Before the acute edemas developed, he suffered from severe attacks of diarrhoea and rhinorrhea, a fact which agrees with Féré's observation that hydrops and nervous diarrhoeas may appear in combination.

His acute neurosis set in at the age of twenty-nine when he was walking on the street. He felt an intense pain in the sacral region and had to bend forward. He thought at that moment that he had just become impotent and was stricken with a consumptive disease of the spine. On the same day he developed a writer's cramp, a complaint which has never left him. A successful attorney thus was transformed into an invalid.

The precipitating cause seems to have been an affair with a reckless woman of the underworld. He liked her better than any other woman he had known. He was at first more potent with her than with any other woman. His impotence and his acute neurosis set in as a matter of "self-defense." He loved this reckless woman and feared that he might have to marry her. He had to destroy this possibility. And so he became totally impotent and negligent in his professional work. His income dwindled so far that he had to live on the funds left to him by his father.

He came to one session in a particularly bad mood. He reported that he had had an emission dream in which *he was very affectionate with a thin, blonde lady with whom he eventually had intercourse.* This lady was in keeping with his ideal, the origin of which he did not know. He complained of his desire to sleep constantly and to spend the days in fantasies. Asked what he was thinking about, he replied that he constantly thinks about the past. He blames himself for all the deaths and accidents in his family and among his friends. If he had only supported his sister she would be alive yet. He always strikes the theme of what he should have and should not have done. He is an unlucky fellow, an evil raven, he brings misfortune to all who meet him. This is why he has withdrawn from all his friendships.

He has a deep yearning for return to his childhood. When he was little, he was frequently sick and everybody was kind to him. Mother pampered him. The desire to re-experience these days permits him to ignore the passage of time. He thinks of the future with fear and disgust, but he also fights against the ghosts of the past. He regrets that he lacks the courage to commit suicide.

On the night following this session he has another emission dream, which he cannot remember at the subsequent session. But its contents, which probably involve the riddle of his neurosis, are betrayed by the words with which he introduces himself: "How come I feel so disgusted when men touch me or pass close to me in the trolley car? When the trolley is packed I am revolted. I always say to myself, 'Phew! How disgusting!' The conductor arouses in me feelings of nausea when I pay him my fare."

Here he is depreciating men in order to protect himself against them. He is expressing a homosexual tendency which often appears in such defensive disguises.

He indulges in a number of infantile pleasures. He frequently draws the blanket over his head so that he can preserve the smell of his flatus and reproduce the situation of resting in his mother's womb.

Among other infantile traits displayed by the patient are dawdling and playing with small things. He can occupy himself with a new knife for a month, take it into his hand and compare it with the old one. He plays with his watch and his handkerchief and utters nonsensical words. He is like one who is in an uninterrupted dream state.

In his night dreams, he returns to childhood and denies that he is an elderly man. Such people usually go as far back as the mother's womb in their dreams and fantasies. Our patient does not know that many of his fantasies concern life in the womb. He sees a car and thinks, "I would like to be inside of it and draw all the curtains. Then, in the darkness, I crawl into a corner and let myself be carried and I will sleep there many, many months." Or he sees a railroad car and has the same kind of fantasy. He would like to be locked inside a suitcase and be carried on a long trip. He wished he could be locked in the toilet for months. He would live in the narrow room and eat there. In contrast to such fantasies, he has in reality a fear of narrow rooms and a need for large rooms and windows.

This desire for freedom includes also his environment. He likes to be surrounded by people of liberal opinions, with broad views upon life. Even his clothes must be loose and airy; he cannot stand tightly-fitting clothes.

Our patient's infantilism is also seen in other traits. He buys a new tie and views it for hours in the mirror. When people are around, he plucks at the tie and keeps adjusting it until someone comments that it is pretty. Like a child, he is proud of his clothing. He looks at his new shoes and pushes his feet forward, until someone notices that he has "nice, new shoes." He throws keys into the air and catches them. He throws his cane far ahead of him as he is hiking.

His guilt feeling originates in childish criminal thoughts. He crosses a bridge. In front of him is a boy. Fast as lightning comes the thought: "Throw this boy into the water!" Then, like all people who think their criminal impulses will break through, he suffers from the fear of insanity.

He devaluates reality. All work is "dirty." Of what good is work? It is disgusting. Only sleep is real life to him. He never falls asleep without thinking, "If only this silly life were over! If it would only end!"

He is an eternal student. He wants to learn something new. He begins a study of languages, of botany, of many subjects. He wants new knowledge. Then he loses patience and abandons one study only to begin another. As long as he is studying he is a child, a pupil.

Suddenly, in analysis, he recalls that at the age of eight he had suffered from erections whenever he had stooped to play with his dog. This recollection of the eighth year represents an important progress. Even more important is his knowledge that he is improving daily. He recalls that before falling asleep he has been playing "horsy," a game in which he is a small child who rides a hobby horse or puts another child on the horse. As he goes to sleep, a voice says, "But this child has a temperature." Such fantasies are recollections of the childhood days when his mother surrounded him with boundless love.

He touches on a similar theme when he suffers from sleeplessness after he has had intercourse. Such insomnia is common to all people who have unsatisfactory intercourse. When his knee swells he is also sleepless. On other occasions he sleeps so long and so deeply that he cannot recall his dreams.

With prostitutes he can have an ejaculation but, with rare exceptions (and then only after three or four ejaculations), he cannot have an orgasm. Even when he does achieve an orgasm in contact with a woman, it is not as strong as the orgasms he achieves when he is dreaming that he is sucking a woman's breasts.

His orgasm is associated with infantile gratification. He is a suckling. He has never sought this form of pleasure with real women. His devaluation of reality extends to the women with whom he has relations. He is indifferent to reality, including these women. His guilt feelings bother him continuously. Recently he saw a movie in which a father shot his son. This disturbed him, for it was a picture of his own crime, only shown in reverse. He, too, is a murderer. He has killed his father.

He keeps thinking a great deal about his childhood. His mother was indeed most kind and affectionate toward him in early childhood, but then, during his tenth year, her disposition changed—she became nasty and moody. She quarrelled all the time. That is why the patient has longed for his early childhood. His first ten years were happy, while the subsequent years brought unhappiness and dissatisfaction.

In analysis he remembered that formerly he had but one fantasy during masturbation: he was watching his parents having sexual intercourse. "I must have an abnormal sexual constitution," he said. "I always imagine the female organ. When in a cafe, I close my eyes and see a vagina. Tonight I also had such a dream. . . . I think that someone is being born and I am present. . . ."

The birth he sees in his dreams is his own. He also has many birth fantasies. At night he often awakens breathless because he has dreamt that he has to push through a narrow chimney. Birth and death preoccupy him constantly in many variations. As a child, he had a vivid interest in the origin of children. He asked his parents many questions about many things, but he never dared ask the important question, "Where do children come from?"

The masturbatory fantasy of watching the parents in intercourse must have inhibited his potency and caused his general fear of women. He said to himself as a youngster, "You will never get married. You won't have to have a wife to torment you the way mother tormented father." Later, after intercourse, he was always stricken with guilt-feelings. "My God! What have I done!

This is terrible!" He always took the oath that he had done this "terrible thing" for the last time. He recalled that his mother, when she saw the spots on his bedsheets, would talk about contagious diseases. When he was fourteen, his mother said that one could be ruined for life by infectious diseases.

The patient learned that people who are afflicted with infantilism on an endocrine basis lose their pubic hair. Our patient also found his pubic hair to be "disturbing," and he frequently shaved it to support his fiction of being a child. He hated people who behaved like adults. He depreciated all accomplishments of grownups. According to him, life should be a play.

At the same time he had an abnormal sense of superiority. In his fantasies, he was a famed commander-in-chief, a great poet, an outstanding inventor.

Once he permitted himself to imagine that he was going to get married. In the fantasy he saw himself crying bitterly just before the wedding. He was saying farewell to his childhood and was ready to become a man and a father. In reality, by avoiding women and by his impotence he defended himself against any such possibility. His visits to prostitutes, of course, entailed no danger of marriage. And he could always say to himself, "You have time. You have lots of time."

However, he wasted time whenever he could. For example, if he gave a suit to the cleaner and was told that he could call for it in three days, he would let three months pass before he would call for it. Meanwhile he would say, "I have time."

His criminal thoughts always broke through when he was surprised or disturbed. If he was awakened, he would say, "I wish you were dead!" He said the same thing when his father used to awaken him and give him unpleasant orders. He hated work, for it prevented him from daydreaming. He was afraid of every kind of work and always postponed it as long as possible.

He always dreamed while walking on the street. In these fantasies he disrobed all the women he passed and violated them. He always looked first at their legs and then disrobed them from the feet upward. Children first see the legs of grownups.

He thought that people did not pay much attention to him

and he was easily insulted. People were doing him an injustice. He was right; the others were wrong.

He brought another dream: *I am at home and hear mother say, 'Something happened to him.' Then she was affectionate with me.*

After he told of the above dream, he made a statement which showed a relationship between his impotence and his mother fixation. "I was sixteen when I heard Mother say to Father, 'It seems to me you can't do it any more. You are impotent.' " When with prostitutes he repeated this one scene. He was the impotent husband-father.

Such patients try to break the chains that hold them to the family. He, too, vainly sought liberation. He was ill-humored at home, frequently locked himself in his room or went away for long periods of time. The air in his home seemed foul. He wanted to go away, far away, to America, and he spoke many times about this plan. But he never had the energy to go through with this scheme. In such cases he would feel sorry for his father, who seemed kind to him even though he actually was a tyrant. The father warned him against the company of carefree young people and even went so far as to forbid him to attend a dance. His hate toward his father often broke through in the form of death wishes. He then fantasied taking his father's place. But the mother actually died before his father. Then he wanted to replace her, to be his father's wife. Now, as he approached the homosexual tendencies, his recollections failed him completely.

He came to another session with the report of a particularly horrible night. In the evening he had attended a lecture and had fought in vain against falling asleep during the lecture. He was stricken by terrific pains in the groin so that he could hardly walk home. In analysis, the pains proved to be a punishment for his hostile thoughts against father. He associated: "Father was ruptured."

He found that when his regrets about his father's death were at their height, he usually hastened to a prostitute. After intercourse he usually became depressed and—as stated before—took an oath that he had visited a prostitute for the last time.

He brought a dream which was quite different from any he had yet reported:

Two armored horsemen appear and want to attack each other with spears. I tell them to forget it and to make up. The reason for their fight is a girl, a love affair. My mother sits next to them and so I say, 'Look at what a kind woman that is and make up.' Whereupon one horseman kissed the girl. He opened the visor. Both men put aside their spears and made up. Then one horseman married the girl and the dream was over.

In this dream, two forces are in conflict. The patient is being drawn toward women and is afraid of them. The reference to the mother should end the battle. He would get married if he could find a mother image. The dream has a prospective tendency. It is as though he wanted to terminate the internal conflict and proclaim the possibility of a cure. On the other hand, the experienced dream interpreter notices that the girl is a symbol for the mother and that the father is a rival in the struggle for the mother. The dream advocates peace and reconciliation with the father.

This patient shows unusual reactions after the various baths. After a steambath he becomes just as sleepless and worn out as after intercourse. The massage which usually follows the bath excites him greatly and confuses him for several days. This reaction is typical of the unconscious homosexuality. The patient gets similar reactions in all baths where men walk around in the nude in large numbers. Also the lukewarm bath has an unpleasant power of making him sleepy and sad and tearful. These latter reactions are concerned with recollections of the baths his mother gave him in early childhood.

Erotism in baths is important in the lives of many people. It is associated with infantile impressions. I know men who are potent only when they have intercourse in a bathtub. Every infantile influence can act as a stimulus or an inhibition, sometimes both in the same individual. Certain hydropathic cures are influenced by infantile associations. The happiness associated with bathing has infantile roots. Pain attacks our patient in two waves. First he has the pain in the groin combined with a terrible pain in the back. Then comes the pain and swelling in the knee every thirteen-and-a-half days exactly, a female period in Fliers' sense. Occasionally, both attacks come at the same time, and that, of course, is his worst physical circumstance. He then is so incapacitated that he cannot leave the house.

Interesting explanations about the psychogenesis of this disease are contained in the next statements of the patient. He relates that his father suffered from severe arthritis and had to walk with care. The father also complained of pains in the groin (he had a hernia) and the son did not want to believe it. Now he experiences the pains on his own body. He has had them for twenty-four years, that is, ever since his father died.

The pains and somatizations of his self-reproaches represent punishment and serve as recollections.

I have described similar cases in *Conditions of Nervous Anxiety*. None of them is characterized by such a long duration of reproaches. With the outbreak of the World War, the patient's condition became worse. This can be explained by the influence upon his latent sadism.

Only the layman is surprised by the fact that our patient enjoyed total peace from all pains and complaints two months after a nose operation. Neurotics, who suffer from a pathological sense of guilt, regard the operation as a sort of test by God. They are in His power, and He determines whether they should live or die. Thus one can often see great improvements, sometimes also serious aggravations, after major operations. An acute attack of appendicitis and an operation can be considered as God's punishment and the successful medical outcome can be God's blessing. Most of these patients admit that they have prayed and made an oath prior to the operation. One can, therefore, observe interesting character changes after operations. I have described in *Conditions of Nervous Anxiety* how anesthesia in women, and also in men, can become a trauma through the revival of dormant rape fantasies.

The patient complains of a pain in the anus which, to him, is an erogenous zone. During one whole night he suffered from diarrhoea. As a child he suffered from constipation and received many enemas from his mother. Now he suffers from tenesmus. His father, too, had this discomfort. His father would have flatulent attacks lasting all night and the smells and sounds were perceived by the patient with resentment.

The nose of the patient had never been normal. It had either seemed too dry or too plugged. And while going into the subject of his spinal and back pains and his nasal trouble, he suddenly remembered that as a child he had suffered from swollen knees and he recreated the scene of a physician measuring his knee to see how much it was swollen.

At this point, for the first time he became aware of the infantile root of his knee trouble. Without any intervention by me, his thoughts shifted directly to a favorite fantasy of how one could gain money without working. Work is his greatest enemy. In one fantasy he is given a prize of not less than half a million dollars. Then he goes to his office and discharges the manager. He tells all his colleagues of his fortune which makes it possible for him to do whatever he wants, namely, to daydream!

He then reports how excited he recently got in a restaurant. He saw a man, for whom, some time ago, a collection was made, playing cards. The patient became extremely excited and made a scene in the restaurant. He is still agitated while discussing it with me. I assume that there is a deeper connection with his case.

"Do you play cards?" I ask.

"Not I, but my brother."

"You have a brother? You never told me about him."

"Because I am glad if I don't have to think about that cur."

"Why do you refer to him as a cur?"

"Because he is a scoundrel. He always comes to me for money. Then he sits in cafes and loses everything I have given to him."

"Why do you give him the money if you know all that?"

"I can't help it. I believe him time and again and always fall for his stories. I am ashamed to refuse him. I also am afraid that he will do something to himself if I don't give him the money. I can't take that responsibility."

We know that the patient plays with death thoughts. He always fears that he is responsible for the death of other people.

The other day he gave an orange to a child, and immediately he thought that the child could choke on the orange, or that it could slip on an orange peel and break its neck, and he would be responsible for its death. He wishes death to everyone. His brother is no exception either; he is, so to speak, at the mercy of the patient.

But our patient also loves his brother. His brother has, on the whole, determined his life. He is married and seems to have a gay time with women. But the patient must be careful of all women. His condition is worsened after a visit to a prostitute. The physicians who always encouraged him to see women are blamed. They caused his ruin.

Suddenly, he said, "Have I told you that I have had a prostate massage? It was painful. The physician, however, thought it was important as he said my disease stems from an enlargement of this gland." His associations then drift to the penetration of the anus—anal sexuality.

He remembers a dream which was disturbing: *I was with several naked men in a bath.* He has nothing to add. We notice how the homosexual tendencies (pain in the anus) become stronger. He tells of his chronic depressions. We always find this type of depression in people who are dissatisfied with their own sex. We find it in men who want to be women and in women who want to be men. They mourn the gap between their physical appearance and their sexual desires.

His thoughts continually return to his brother, but he tries to force them into different directions. During such association he is anxious.

While under analysis such patients create realities which make the retrospective tendency of analysis impossible. Conflicts are produced or strengthened in order to divert consciousness to the present or future. Our patient finds immediate difficulties in reality, which gives him an opportunity to get so excited that he is able to emphasize that treatment in such times is of no use. He complains of his misfortune and his relatives. "Everything was going so smoothly," he will say, and then his nephew had to come to visit him.

Nevertheless, his picture becomes increasingly clear. The en•

vious person overpowered by his superiority complex comes to the foreground. He is so unusual as a person that he always brings misfortune to others. Wherever he steps no grass can grow. Whoever contacts him will soon perish. If he wishes something bad on someone, the wish will be fulfilled. He isolates himself from all people with his secret belief in the omnipotence of thoughts. As he wishes everybody something bad, he takes upon himself everything bad.

Now we understand why he went to confession after his father died, and why he blamed himself for the death. He asked for strict punishment to repent for this crime. He frequently tells himself that he is a murderer. His suicide thoughts are a reaction to his universal hatred of fortunate people, of lovers, of people who enjoy doing their work. He is envious of such people and he scoffs at them at the same time.

He confesses that once he wished to marry an elderly lady. She was a niece on his mother's side—a mother image—but his impotence was an insurmountable obstacle. He expects the treatment to make him potent. He is "fed up" with the life of a lonesome bachelor and would like to become a real man. . . .

This idea of marriage is one of his attempts to emancipate himself from his disease. His whole life consists of such decisions, which are never carried out. He feels that he will never recover as he lacks the will power. If he undergoes any treatment, and notices an improvement, he is afraid of getting well. An inner voice tells him, "You are not worthy of recovery."

Now, he sees that all people will starve to death because of the war, and that is just what they deserve. All people are dumbbells, all are silly. All must perish.

At the next session, he tells of terrible pains in his back and groin during the preceding night. The pains were so intense that a physician was called and the patient was given an injection. The doctor was a young, pleasant man from the neighborhood. The injection served as a symbolic substitute for a homosexual act, a fact revealed by the patient's next association: "I can never lie on my stomach. It makes me feel insecure, as if somebody would approach me and press from the back."

By learning to hearken to the language in which hypochondriacs relate their complaints one can frequently find the sexual symbolisms. Our patient, in referring to his backache, said, "The pains go from the back of my spine to the mind, as if a hellish fire were burning. Have you ever heard of such a thing? As if a candle (penis) were burning in the back of the spine and the flame then goes to the back of the head (displacement from below upward). There is also a pain in the anus as if something hard (old feces or something of the kind) were accumulated there...."

These complaints disguise homosexual fantasies with an emphasis on the anus as an erogenous zone. The patient himself stresses that homosexuality is "the most unpleasant thing that exists." If he only thinks about it, it makes him vomit. We are familiar with this negative affect-charged reaction and recognize in it a repressed libido. We ask if he has conducted any homosexual games with friends during his childhood. First he does not want to know about it, then he recalls scenes in which his brother participated. Once his brother put up a tent and completely undressed inside it. He does not want to recall anything else that might have happened in the tent. He wants to leave the topic, begins to yawn, looks at some of my pictures and thinks it is rather late and he has to go to the office.

However, at this point, we can comprehend why he had to masturbate after intercourse. It was because his repressed homosexuality was not gratified.

The death of the father fixated the disease. The patient's permanent daydreaming and sleeping enables him to regress. His disinclination for work renders him a semi-invalid. He suffers from satyriasis (constant erection) and yet is impotent with women.

I regret that I could not continue with his analysis. It has been my experience that, in these cases, patients usually interrupt when their latent homosexuality tends to become manifest. Our patient one day declared that the lack of money prevented him from continuing the treatment. He added that he had benefited a great deal from my work. I told him that I would continue the treatment without a fee, but he indignantly refused, stating that he would not take my precious time away for nothing.

In reality, he does not want to know the truth. He does not

want to get well. He is happy in his misfortune. He wants to remain a *child* and to play childish games and luxuriate in his morbid dream world. He goes to bed, groans and complains, "If only everything would end! I wish I would not awaken again! I only wish I could sleep eternally! That would be my ideal!"

A few days later he is back in my office. "I had such a terrible pain that I again had to summon a doctor and had an injection administered." My treatment was unpleasant for him, really unpleasant. So would I please ask quickly whatever I had to ask?

"You are mistaken," I reply. "The treatment does not depend on my questions. I simply wait until you yourself tell me everything."

"It is very unpleasant. I feel I am before a judge."

"You are telling me now that you are withholding important facts, and that this is the reason you want to get away. I don't insist in any way that you tell me."

"What sense does it make? I want to get well. I know that I have to tell you everything. Ask me!"

"No, I leave it to your judgment to tell me whatever occurs to you. You know, however, that you should tell me everything that you recall. If you don't find the courage, then we may as well give up the treatment."

"No. I don't want to give up. I feel considerably better despite the pains. My head is freer. I don't have the constant need for sleep. Please ask...."

I do not reply.

He resumes: "Now, if you don't want to ask, I'll talk. I told you about my listening to my parents during their intercourse, at which time I masturbated. I heard everything, everything they said. When Mother expressed pleasure, I was excited. I wished to be Mother or Father. Oh, there are so many ugly and unpleasant things, I can hardly tell you everything. However, I know now that those impressions from childhood have made me sick and that I must always think of them."

After a while he continues: "I also thought about my homosexuality, and I must unfortunately admit that I am in no way relieved of it. Father was not at all ashamed in front of us. I always compared his penis to mine, and I was unhappy that I was weaker than he. From that time I retained the habit of inspecting the size of the penises of all men. My first view of a man is always toward his fly. I also have other homosexual fantasies. But they are not as prolonged as the heterosexual ones. I call them 'flash thoughts.' They go through my head and vanish fast as lightning. Then I always see a large penis before my eyes. I do not want to think of homosexual acts. They come and go like lightning. Is that homosexuality?

"This treatment is unpleasant. Here I must talk about things that I do not want to see."

"People get sick from 'not wanting to see,' " I tell him. "Whoever wants to get well must see everything openly and consciously. He can thus overcome his bad thoughts and his neurotic inclinations more easily. The repressed always comes back."

"I begin to comprehend," he interposes. "I didn't want to know about those things and yet I had to think about them constantly. It is late. I have kept you too late.... I feel much better. I am not as sleepy as I used to get, and I begin to be more aware of my daydreams. I know now that my mother played a great role in my disease. I saw her many times in the nude. She dressed and undressed without hesitation. She did not realize that I was swallowing her with eager eyes. The first time I saw her in the nude she wore white stockings, and I even made one prostitute put on white stockings. I also know that the first few times I tried to have intercourse I thought about mother. I used to fail in intercourse because of these thoughts. After these attempts I would have a bad feeling, and I would say to myself, 'What have you done? Such a sin! Such a sin!'

"Now, I still want to tell you about playing with my brother. It was not as harmless as I first described. We used to get undressed, my brother and other boys, and creep under the tent which was built between two beds. There one had to look into the anus of the other and smell it. We used to tickle each other with a thin feather. Nothing else happened."

I know that he is still withholding material, but I do not press him. He then continues:

"Yesterday I got into the trolley car. Behind me was a man who touched me by mistake. I got angry and could have knocked

him down. I said repeatedly, 'Such an unpleasant chap!' However, it was a good-looking young man in uniform. I thought
that I wanted to protect myself through rage and disgust against
my homosexual drives. When he touched me, I felt a certain
heat going through my body.... I want to say everything and
feel freer now than ever before. I want to try to start a new life
after the treatment. I also do better at work. Yesterday I could
already write for an hour or so without disturbance. No cramps!
I said to myself, 'You lazy dog! You just don't want to write!'
And see! Suddenly it worked without difficulty. Then I fell back
into daydreams and the cramp returned. What should I do?"

"Your next duty is to try to catch your daydreams."

At his next visit he brought a strange dream: *I am at Dr. S.'s.
He shows me a lot of pictures in the room. They are pictures of
girls who are all at my disposal. The doctor gives me daily the
address of a different girl and says, 'You are going to have
them all.'*

Associations: Dr. S. is a physician whom he visited a year ago.
This doctor maintained that he had an "inflammation in the
spinal cord." He promised that after a few injections into his
spinal cord all the complaints would disappear.

The injection into the spinal cord becomes the symbol of a
homosexual act, and the physician represents me. The dream
shows us how Don Juanism can originate from repressed homosexuality. In the dream, I give him addresses of girls. For several
days, the urge has been rising in him to run to girls. He waits for
my permission. I have advised him against sexual experiments
during the treatment. Now, through transference and the discussion of past experiences, his homosexuality is aroused and he
is looking for outlets.

He emphasizes that he always gets aroused sexually prior to
the swelling of his knee. This shows that he has his feminine
periods in which he gets pains in the groin and in the back and
masculine periods in which his knee swells. The swollen knee
substitutes for an erection. The knee is his erogenous zone. Bare
knees have always stimulated him sexually, and he always had
the desire to be as strong as the Tyrolian peasants whose dress
permits them to show their bare knees.

Now he has a "strong knee" and can show it. Therefore, he always mentions that despite his swollen knee he can undertake mountain climbing.

He interrupts the analysis again. He cannot go on without paying. He feels wonderful. He is engaged to his niece and wishes to be married in a short while. The swellings of the knee are no longer painful.

A few years later I see him on the street. He introduces me to his wife, and whispers, "Don't tell her about my nonsense." Then, in a loud voice, "Fanny! This is the kind physician who massaged my inflamed knee until it was cured."

4. TANTRUMS

Expression of intense jealousy through tantrums is common among children. In his spiteful reaction to a denied wish a child will drop to the floor, stomp and kick, wrench his hair, break his toys. He may assault and curse the adults around him.

The child who has such outbursts may ordinarily display a quiet, sweet disposition. If, however, he is frustrated in his demands for attention, he may have recourse to dramatics, in which he discharges his uncontrolled rage. In some cases strange sadistic fantasies, barred from consciousness, lead to tantrums which may even terminate in epileptiform seizures.

I have known people whose habit of "throwing" fits continued far into adulthood. Most of these individuals used fits, from their earliest days, to secure a dominant position in the household or to exact vengeance on their environment.

In some of these cases, I have found that fits were clear-cut neurotic reactions to a denied wish or to the impracticability of a fixed idea. More often than not the reaction was provoked by unrequited love.

Here is an illustrative example:

Case No. 19: Mr. Z.O., age twenty-three, seeks relief from the "vice of masturbation." He began to masturbate at the age of twenty-one, and all his efforts to stop have been in vain. He knew of no outside influence or seduction, but one night he felt an irresistible urge, and he spontaneously found relief in self-gratification. Thereafter, he was regretful and so disgusted with himself that he resolved that never again would he give in. One week later, however, the urge again proved stronger than his will power.

The patient's sexual reminiscences revealed that in his early youth he had heard much about sex, and the disgusting, "filthy" words and thoughts were so impressive that he vowed never to associate with women.

His father apprenticed him in a carpenter's shop. But the boy finally succeeded in following his strong artistic inclination, took up music, and despite his late start in training, became an excellent violinist.

At the age of fifteen, while he was still working in the shop, he woke once in the dark of night from a vehemently erotic dream. He cannot recollect the details, but he remembers that he had been kissing nude women. On that night he had the first of the spontaneous emissions which were to recur until his masturbation habit began.

When he was sixteen, the housemaid, a girl of twenty, teased him about stains on his bed sheets and tried to seduce him. She brought licentious books and pamphlets to him as a means of arousing his desire, but he stubbornly refused to have intercourse. Soon thereafter he devoted all of his time to music.

Many people who claim to be asexual are "so busy," or deliberately take on so much work, that there is no time left for sex. In such cases the latent sexuality may erupt suddenly.

Later on, when our patient developed the habit of self-gratification, he did it with the image of that pretty housemaid in mind, recapturing in his fancy all the opportunities he had missed in reality. This arrangement is in conformity with his general shyness, his feeling of inferiority, and his lack of self-assertiveness. He is short, self-conscious, and of the opinion that no girl could ever love him. He rates his musical abilities low and wonders how he has ever been able to pass his examinations. This attitude, typical for an individual who indulges in autoerotism, also contributed to his isolationism. Not only is he without friends, but he also generally avoids public gatherings. Besides, he keenly feels his lack of education and is in constant fear of social situations where the conversation would reveal his ignorance.

Significantly, the patient's earliest reminiscences already point to his present state of mind. He has forgotten everything up to the age of seven (an indication that he has suppressed his early childhood experiences and among them his infantile self-gratification). The first episode he remembers occurred at seven.

"I have just returned to Vienna from a visit with my grandparents. Father, with his bicycle, meets me at the railroad station. He puts me on board a streetcar and tells the motorman where to let me off. Then I get off by myself and walk up to father's place of business, where I remain outside, for I don't dare go in, until a worker comes out and brings me inside."

The episode reveals shyness and lack of self-reliance. The boy did not jump off the car and run into the building to meet his family, but lingered self-consciously on the sidewalk. To this day, the patient is hesitant about entering a shop.

Of even more significance is his father's immense role in early recollections. In the second reminiscence we hear: "Father rides his bicycle in the country, and I am allowed to ride along with him—this makes me happy."

He had always adored his kind father. The father was killed in an accident and the boy was deeply grieved. He wished the father were alive to acclaim his success as an artist.

The patient's third recollection: "I look at the moon and see figures of saints playing musical instruments. I can distinguish one haloed figure playing the cello."

The foreshadowing of the future career is apparent in this memory, but the libido-symbolic significance of this recollection, as well as of the other two, will be unclear until further analysis furnishes a clue. (It should be kept in mind, however, that the patient's present condition may well influence his selection of recollections.)

Speaking freely and without prompting, the patient presents the following material:

The part of the house adjoining his bedroom was the sleeping place for the house help, and one night a manservant was boisterously frolicking with a maid. The sounds that came out of the servants' quarters were the immediate stimulus for the patient's first masturbatory act.

He feels quite certain he will refrain from masturbation in the future. His good common sense has saved him from folly many times. When he was seventeen, another maidservant tried to seduce him. She told him that the boys were all so stupid— they had no idea how willing the girls were. But the patient played dumb. He did not want to have sexual intercourse because he "knew" that it would weaken him physically. Even at present, there is a maid in their house who does not mind being kissed by him and keeps on telling him that she never closes the door to her room for the night. However, he dares not make use of her invitation, although he "knows" that masturbation is harmful. He has it "straight" from a friend that self-gratification causes impotence and he has also read in an encyclopedia that masturbation causes emaciation. A physician advised him to indulge in sexual relations, but the patient just doesn't seem to do it. He knows many girls, but he is not daring enough. He is afraid of failure. He has always avoided defeats.

There is a "mean pride" in his character. Failure makes him miserable. Once father threw a book at him, and though mother was very sick at the time, the boy ran away from home and stayed several weeks with an uncle.

When I expressed my suspicion that he wants to remain a child, the patient exclaimed, "Yes, that's it, exactly. I know that, for instance, sexual intercourse would at once put an end to my childishness and make a man of me; yet, strange as it may sound to you, I do not want to become a man. I remember that when I was fourteen, and in the last grade of junior high school, I was depressed because the beautiful years of childhood were drawing to an end. I kept saying to myself, 'From now on you're responsible for everything you do. The police may arrest you, and you may be punished by the courts, you are not a child any more.'

I am terribly afraid of getting old. My physical health also worries me. If I cut my finger, the first thought that comes into my mind is blood-poisoning. When I think of sexual intercourse, I visualize all the terrible consequences of it, and I shudder at the idea of a venereal disease."

Such stories of resistance to temptation are indicative of diminished urge. The patient's libido must be fixated on some object of its own; perhaps we are dealing here with repressed homosexuality. But we still have not enough data to go on, and have to wait for the results of further analysis.

At this point the chain of the patient's verbalized meditations, so characteristic of the mentality of a masturbator, stops abruptly. Without any apparent associative connection, he recalls a trip with his uncle to Norway. The trip with his uncle would have been fine if the patient had not been unusually irritable all the time. He quarreled with his uncle over trifles. He felt that the uncle's admiring words about his son implied criticism of the patient. Toward the end of the journey, he separated from his uncle after a clash.

The patient elaborates on his yearning to remain a child forever. He does not undertake anything of importance because his "time has not yet come." He has no faith in his abilities, changes his mind from day to day. Consequently, he drifts along, and is incapable of deciding just what he wants.

This significant symptom points to a hidden, all-absorbing desire, compared to which all other aspirations appear drab and worthless. What is this basic desire?

He forgets his dreams. He has not reported one stereotyped dream. But now he brings his first dream, which, like all first dreams of analysands, we may be sure, will contain basic neurotic data or refer to the patient's relation to the analyst.

I see a lady with a gaping, bleeding throat. I don't know whether it was I who bit her.... Presumably, I am the one who bit her. All of a sudden, it's my uncle. He gets to his feet and asks, "Am I dead, or something?" I begin to run, and the lady is after me, and she ties my hands, but she does such a poor job of it that I easily untie them.... Then I jump down into a coal cellar and say to myself, "I'll put on my magic cap and become invisible." *Then I meet the lady again at the grocer's and we* *discuss musical overtones. And again I run, and the lady and* *another uncle of mine are after me. I jump into a well and say* *to myself, "I'll leave the place unlit". . . and I wake.*

Asked to point out the most consequential element of the dream, the patient refers to *uncle's coming back to life.* The patient's father died only several weeks ago, and on that occasion this uncle said, "It just doesn't seem possible that your father is dead. He was such a healthy man." Then the patient recalls that a few days ago, before he came to consult me, he dreamed that his father had been revived. Again, it was this uncle who, at the time of father's death, said, "Maybe he's only in a trance. The doctor ought to stab his heart to make sure."

The patient's dreams reveal that his relations to his father, which he has depicted as most harmonious, were in fact anything but ideal. It is well to remember that only yesterday the patient related an episode in which his father had thrown a book at him, causing him to flee to this very uncle of last night's dream. The initial part of the dream points to a latent, but potent, trait of cruelty.

The patient says that he regrets having treated his father coldly. At times, when his father was mean to his mother, he even hated the man. He also resented his father's refusal to let him study music in his early years. Nor did he like his father's insistence that he work in this business. Guilt feelings about these old resentments oppress him now and give him regrets. He fears that his father will one day rise from his ashes and take revenge. The lady with the gaping wound in the throat reminds him of his teacher's wife, a blonde, tall woman. She has always impressed him. Tall, blonde women are his feminine ideal. This is an obvious counter-image of his mother, who has been like a guardian angel to him. But even she has been ill-treated by him, and he regrets that he hasn't yet been able to achieve great things to make her happy.

The metamorphosis into a man points to the bisexual character of the dream. The lady and the uncle belong together, and additional analytic material indicates that they represent his parents, both active in the same business. Mother (the lady with the gaping wound) is also, symbolically, the patient's chastity, which he has defiled. Chastity ties his hands with the injunction, "You must not masturbate." But the commandment's binding force is not strong enough, and he throws off the shackles of chastity and of parental prohibitions. The bipolarity of the patient's paraphilia is determined by the two opposite tendencies: to preserve the childhood attachment and to gain the freedom of manhood.

The riddle of the patient's neurosis and his masturbation reveries are enclosed in the mystery of his dream. As much as we would like to know more about the sadist's initial vision, the dream itself precludes any further revelation; the patient dons a magic cap to become invisible; he jumps into a well and leaves it unlit so as to be unseen. The well is, symbolically, the patient's soul. He does not wish any light to be cast upon his soul, and he jealously guards his secrets.

The next day he remembers the dream's ending.

He lay hidden in the well and peeped cautiously to see whether any one was there. Reassured, he climbed up the well on the run, and woke.

A beautiful image: Well—sleep, climbing up—waking (cf. Silberer's "threshold symbolism"). More important, however, is the functional meaning of the dream—*to hide and to escape.*

Quite in keeping with the dream, the patient asks whether a trip abroad would be beneficial at this juncture. His mother is of the opinion that the treatment may confuse him even more. He has another dream in which *Father was not really dead.* He is at a loss as to the meaning of these persistent dreams.

Abruptly, he begins to talk of love. He wonders why he has never been earnestly in love. He has met girls who made him think, "Here! I could go for this one." But nothing ever came of it. "I feel a beginning of love," he says; "I adore the girl from a distance. Then I cut the feeling short. Why?" Reminded of his remarks about his flight from decisions and fear of failure, he goes on, "That's right. I have the feeling of bodily and mental inferiority. Many girls give me the 'come on,' though. Only recently I was asked by a girl, a fellow student, why I was always in a hurry, and she said that we could walk home together. I am handicapped by my peculiar pride." He agrees with my general suggestion that pride may cover up weakness. "Of course," he says, "I have said many times to myself that it was not really pride, that it was an attempt to hide my cowardice, that I was afraid of love."

Asked to be more specific about his fear, he says, "I want to go on being a child. I read somewhere that early sexual intercourse causes premature aging and death. People who spend their forces early do not live long. Well, this won't happen to me, I have full control over myself. Even if our housemaid came into my bed, I still could resist her. Although otherwise it would just suit me fine not to have to be active about 'making' a woman. In my thoughts, I always visualize the girl coming to me and telling me, 'Here I am. You can have me.' But I won't make use of our housemaid's advances, because I presume she is a virgin. If she were that first maid, the one who tried to seduce me, it would be different. I'd have no scruples at all."

Asked whether he was completely sure that he wouldn't have sexual relations with her despite his vow to remain chaste, he replies, "That's true, I want to stay chaste as long as I can. I want to prove to myself that I have the will power.... And I am sure I will stop masturbating, too. On the morning after having indulged in it, I feel so miserable. I have an unspeakable disgust and such a hatred that I could kill myself...."

It can be seen clearly that he is engaged in a struggle to ward off sexuality which, to him, is "beastly." At my suggestion that he may be afraid to overstep the normal limits, he admits being very passionate. It is, according to him, this rapacious cupidity which makes him so hesitant. He knows that as long as he hasn't given in he is still in perfect control of himself.

Without transition, he then begins to speak of modern theories of harmony. The harmony of the past is boring, whereas the modern harmony, though at first maltreating sensory nerves with cacophonies, makes us jubilantly accept the emergent consonance.

The patient dreamed:

I am sitting at a very long table, which looks like those dinner tables used for wedding parties. A tall dark man pushes me off my seat. (The tall dark man wore black and his face was pale.)

The dark man in this dream is Death. The patient hears an inner voice constantly admonishing, "Don't fool with women, or you'll die."

The patient talks of his avarice, and relates many episodes which reveal his extraordinary miserliness. I draw his attention to another form of his parsimoniousness, namely, regarding his semen, and he tells me that ejaculation makes him very unhappy and that for this reason he always tries to stop "in the middle" of the masturbatory act. With each loss of semen he calculates the number of weeks or months his life has been shortened.

We can understand his avarice and his fear of death. He is accumulating his strength in order to attain his life's goals and to triumph over his rivals. His desire to remain a child fits into this picture. As a man he would be under obligation to account for some of his achievements; as a child he is under no such obligation. And by which yardstick does he measure the extent of his strength? Obviously, by the great achievements of his father, a very energetic self-made man who had risen high from humble beginnings.[1]

It has been noted that sons of famous men, even those endowed with talents of their own, usually achieve comparatively little. They are hamstrung by the compulsive duty to achieve success and the simultaneous feeling of inability to live up to expectations. Their feeling of inadequacy is not based on organic inferiority, but the latter may be exploited to serve as an excuse for their failure. The origin of these feelings may be traced back to the stage of differentiation from their father, or from any other idealized object. They feel that they "will never surpass him." This feeling of inferiority born from a comparison and a hopeless competition is nurtured by their subsequent belief that the cause of all that lies in their moral deficiency. ("I can achieve nothing because wicked men achieve nothing.")

[1] In the patient's description of his avarice there is an overtone of complaint against his father who had contributed nothing toward the boy's musical studies. He owes everything to his uncle. For his mother, however, he has only praise.

"Do you know what I dreamed on the night I had my first emission?" asks the patient. And he continues, "I dreamed *I had sexual intercourse with my aunt.*"

This aunt is the younger sister of his mother, whom she strikingly resembles. The dream implies incestuous tendencies and the possibility of rivalry with father in the sexual domain. The patient's first dream contained allusions to mother and to certain concealments.

In his incestuous dream he has an emission. There is reason to believe that incestuous fantasies also accompany his masturbatory act. His repugnance to this activity and his negative attitude toward women in general begin to make sense. I remind him that two days earlier he told of an escape into the safety of his room to avoid the temptation of the spirited eyes of a lady visitor. I ask him to tell me more about those eyes.

After a pause, he says, "She had dark, ardent, sparkling eyes."

I ask if he knows any one else with such eyes. He again pauses, and then, haltingly, "My mother has such eyes."

Again the patient speaks of his avarice. He ruefully relates incidents illustrating his shabbiness. Only recently, when he learned that his father had willed great sums to charitable institutions, he could not refrain from thinking, "I must forego so many things, while father's money goes to strangers."

His reluctance to earn money on his own is, obviously, an expression of his wish to go on living on the fortune of his father. Money is identified with love. He does not want to lose any of his parents' love for him. To him, to fall in love would mean to give up his older love.

He displays in every detail the egoism and the self-centeredness that are characteristics of the autoerotist. He is never bored with himself, and he prefers to be by himself. He abhors groups and flees to his room whenever there are numerous guests in the house. His shyness makes him hesitate before entering a crowded place, and he is always preoccupied with ideas of what people will think about him. But behind this outward timidity lurks a devouring ambition to achieve grandiose successes.

When the patient speaks of his father, he wonders why he did not shed tears at his father's death. He interprets his subsequent, exaggerated grief as a sort of "making up" for the previous indifference. It makes him think that he is wicked, and that this wickedness of his is the source of his inferiority feeling.

Following the report of a long dream, many elements of which hint at preoccupations with homosexual ideas and houses of ill-repute, he says:

"There is something I forgot to tell you. ... The housemaid, the one who enlightened me at the age of fourteen and tried to seduce me, told me that my father was very indecent and left no girl alone, that he frequented the red-light district and squandered his fortune on prostitutes. I was so shaken by her story that I had a fit of temper and—for the first time, ran away from home and fled to my uncle."

The effect of the housemaid's story was quite different from the one she had probably intended. The boy was so disgusted with his father, and the sexual behavior of men in general, that he vowed to be different from other men. We see in that traumatic experience one of the causes of the patient's stubborn defense of his chastity.

The growing child's differentiation from his parents is an important process in the child's development. We often observe excessively prudish daughters of prostitutes; and as often we note adepts of free love among daughters of highly moralistic mothers. Differentiation from the parents is often of greater significance for the psychogenesis of neuroses than identification with them or the perpetuation of their ideals.

Haltingly, the patient relates the details of the original seduction scene, and he confirms our suspicion that much more had occurred than he at first cared to admit. It all happened on an evening when the maid, slightly indisposed, was in bed. The boy entered her room (which proves that he was not entirely passive in this experience), and the girl told him to quit being so shy and to sit down on the bed near her. He obeyed; whereupon she took the initiative in arousing him sexually. He enjoyed the manipulation, but presumably failed to understand what was going on. He does not remember whether or not the scene ended with an emission.

We see that he had not stumbled spontaneously upon masturbation. His masturbatory activity proved to be patterned on the
seduction scene. That is why his accompanying fantasy usually
revolved around that girl.

The patient plaintively confesses an irrepressible urge to tell
lies. This symptom is frequently found among those who masturbate compulsively. They have to lie in most cases, for they
have something to conceal, and the tendency is coupled with
an equally frenetic longing to be absolutely truthful.

He also complains that he may feel enthusiastic about things
one day and be unmoved by the same things the next day. His
musical conceptions are characterized by polyphony, and his very
thoughts are bipolar. For this reason, also, he has the tendency
to terminate all his compositions with an unsolved, dissonant
chord. Within him there is a waiting, a tension, a conflict, which
includes even his attitude toward religion.

He devotes several sessions to talks concerning his ambition
and his many ways of bolstering his self-respect. He associates
preferably with simple and humble people whom he is able to
impress. Even at school he made friends with the dullest and
poorest boys. On the other hand, he was obsessed with stage
fright whenever he was to face an audience and possible criticism.

The fog shrouding his childhood years slowly dissipates. He
remembers now that at the age of seven he interrogated the
cook about how children came into the world.

"And then there was another funny thing," he says. "As a
child, I dared not say hello to a girl. I was afraid of what people
would think of me."

He must have had a suspicion that there were illicit doings
between boys and girls, and avoided being suspected. He never
greeted girls on the street, and came to be known as a "stuck-up."

We have no insight yet into the source of his fear of sex and
sin. A series of recollections contains allusions to his preoccupations with God, father, various father substitutes, fear of punishment, and love's dire consequences—such as babies, venereal diseases, cerebrospinal meningitis, idiocy, and the like.

A dream: *Dr. Stekel says, "What's new?" and I say, "Nothing." Then he makes a move to read my book and I quickly close it.* This resistance dream scarcely needs interpretation. The patient has nothing to tell me, and he refuses to let me read in the book of his mind.

Another dream: *The silly things one dreams of. I am going for a walk with a teacher and pay very little attention to what he has to say. Then it is my cousin who is there, and he changes into my girl cousin. We walk through a flight of rooms, until we come into one, in the middle of which there is a music rack wrapped in black. My music master has turned into an old lady, and asks a little boy, "What is this?" And I say to myself, "The boy isn't as dumb as you think he is, he knows more than you can ever ask him." Again we walk through a series of rooms to where Germany ends and the war zone begins.*

Interpretation: He pays little attention to what I say. He transforms me into an "old lady." He is the little boy cousin who turns into a girl cousin (bisexuality). I am questioning him, and he refuses to answer, but he knows a great deal more than I can ask. The rooms represent his brain. I pursue him through all of its chambers, but he hides his deepest conflicts from me. I cannot pass into the zone where the war is raging. Analysis, with him, has poor prospects, indeed!

And a third dream, indicative of his resistance: *I lean on a crutch and hobble as I leave the house of my grandmother, and go down a long, long highway.*

I have already described elsewhere the crutch as a symbol of neurosis (cf. *Zentralblatt für Psychoanalyse*, Vol. IV). The patient wants to keep his ailment, for it is his succor and protection. He is willing to hobble through life with it. From other signs I notice that he considers stopping treatment. He talks often of his lack of consistency. He starts many things, but never finishes any.

The patient recalls, rather abruptly, a summer trip to Norway with his father. When the two reached Prague, the boy was already so depressed that he could not enjoy the sights, and only wished the trip would end soon. His father met a friend in Prague, and devoted all his time to that man. The patient was jealous. He had been expecting that the trip would bring him closer to his father, that his father would mind him more than he did at home, and would help him overcome even his emotional problems. Instead, the trip was a severe disappointment.

We are now in a position to interpret the patient's first recollection. The boy came home from the country, and his father waited for him at the railroad station. But the boy had to go home all by himself. The reminiscence is a remonstration: Father left him alone and went his own way. He had expected his father to take him home on his bicycle, to ask him about his trip. He had expected his father to wait for him in front of the house. It was anger and spite that kept the boy from entering the house.

This recollection contrasts sharply with another about a bicycle trip with father, and a joyful communion in pleasure.

His love for his father, the exaggerated expectations connected with it, and the vehemence of his disappointment over the rejection, makes one wonder about the nature of the boy's expectations and of his attachment to his father.

His feeling of guilt toward his father presses forward with ever-growing intensity. All his dreams speak of unrequited debts and of payments due. At one session he abruptly recalls that upon his father's death he solemnly vowed to give up masturbation.

This vow, his resistance to feminine enticements, and other manifestations point to a desire to sacrifice for his father all his sexual needs, as a form of self-imposed punishment and penance.

Other sources of sex impairment become discernible. He is increasingly restless and obsessed by the idea that he has to find that seventeen-year-old girl whose temptations he once withstood. He thinks day and night of the girl—an indication of a stronger, hidden urge behind the manifest one. Two dreams furnish us some clues.

First dream: *My sister putters with her watch, and I tell her, "You'll ruin your watch, and that will be the end of it."*

Second dream: *We are in the South, at the Adriatic Sea. My sister and I are supposed to go for a swim. Sister is nude when she steps into the sea which is as shallow as a bath tub.*

His thoughts are preoccupied with his sister, who is seventeen. In the first dream he sees her puttering with her watch (vagina) and is afraid she may ruin it. In the course of the session the patient adds to the remembered dream a detail, namely, that his sister uses a wrong winding key (phallus). Behind the patient's fear lest his sister lose her virginity to "the wrong man" lies his desire to possess her himself. The second dream is a reproduction of an infantile bathroom scene and an expression of the patient's wish to see his sister in the nude, as in bygone times.

Thus we come to the conclusion that the housemaid he wants to locate is only a substitute for his sister; she is a member of the household, and of the same age. Similarly, his aunt, in another dream, substituted for his mother and probably also for his sister (aunt—mother's sister).

He admits that he was always jealous of sister's relations with "all sorts of brats," and we are gradually able to understand his own peculiar attitude toward girls: they all assume the qualities of his sister (although, in his opinion, none is as pretty as she).

Consciously, the patient does not involve his sister in his fancies; but it is a fact that she, too, sleeps in the adjoining room. It is safe, therefore, to assume that his fight against incestuous cravings partly determines his struggle against masturbation.

May I repeat here what was said elsewhere, namely, that I regard hatred as a basic force in man's psychic structure. The neurotic's incestuous wishes, too, are often compensatory modifications designed to control an underlying hatred. Our patient must have hated his sister before he began to love her; he must have seen in her a rival and wished death to her.

In connection with this, a dream of his is very significant:

I see a wetnurse and my sister, who is still a tiny baby. The wetnurse says, "The child has diarrhoea, she is not long for this world." I then go off to wash my feet because I have to appear before the draft board.

The meaning of the dream is: his little sister has a severe gastric disturbance, and her life is in danger. This corresponds with reality. As an infant, his sister developed a severe diarrhoea. At the time, he wished she would die. His appearance before the board in the dream represents God's judgment. He wants to appear before His Tribunal cleansed of sin.

There are many other indications that his childhood hatred of his sister plays a part in his guilt feelings and his subsequent neurotic tribulations.

In the course of his further elaborations, he reveals a new facet of his behavior regarding his sister.

He exercises a severe control over his sister's comings and goings and is extremely strict about her relations with boys. He believes he acts in the name of his father, and he easily imposes his will, because everyone in the house is afraid of him. He is enraged at the slightest contradiction. By means of these outbursts of temper, during which he is so irrational that he could commit violence, he sustains his dominant position in the house.

"Even father stayed away from me when I had an outburst. He used to say that it was I who had made him so nervous. When I had a fit of temper, he ran off and had someone else handle the matter."

We see now that his guilt feeling, as well as his belated, exaggerated grief over his father's death are not entirely unjustified. But the connection between his tantrums and his sexuality are not yet uncovered. We suspect a lack of gratification somewhere along the line, for only frustrated people are prone to develop such violent outbursts of aggression. The very love within them turns into hate.

The patient is a vindictive individual who never forgets an insult or an injustice. Lack of ability to forgive is one unfailing quality we find in cases of sadism.

In one of the patient's dreams we find allusions to his leg fetishism and to that period in his childhood when he slept with his brother. He stops analysis at a point when the homosexual feelings toward his brother and his incestuous daydreams toward his sister press to the surface. "I can't be helped," he says. "I'll never change. I do not want to get well. All your work is in vain. . . ."

Like all neurotics, he is essentially proud of his incurability, of the unshakable solidity of his symptoms. He wants to remain an eternal student and renounces, for the time being, the joys of independent and creative manhood.

A look at this case history as a whole reveals that the patient is dominated by the inverted imperative idea, "Don't grow up," a sort of negative "masculine protest." But is fear of failure, is reluctance to assume tasks and to face life, sufficient to explain the mental makeup of this patient? Is the nature of his sexuality only a mode of manifestation of his neurosis?

Basically, this case reveals to us the tremendous effect of infantile defiance. In his childhood, he had demanded love from every member of the family; he had craved the love of his father, mother, uncle, and siblings. He had not wanted just their spiritual attachment, which he had had in abundance, but he had made of them his sexual objects. The reason why, in his dreams, the members of the family constantly change into one another is that he loves and wants to possess them all.

Retrospectively, we understand his first dream and the subsequent ones. The lady whose throat he had bitten is his sister. He wants to deflower her (displacement from below upward). He repels the idea that someone else might possess her. He wants her to remain a child, pure and innocent. To that purpose, he uses himself as an example. He establishes a magic connection between his and her fate. As long as he keeps his chastity, she will, too; as long as he remains a child, she will remain one, too. His sister then becomes his uncle, and the uncle is transformed into a lady who shackles his hands. The meaning of it is, "I am in all eternity tied up with my sister." He tries in vain to escape the incestuous daydreams; they pursue him and endanger his mental equilibrium. Consequently, he must exercise full command over himself (chastity clause). And how else could he demand that his sister abstain from love if he did not abstain from girls?

The man was clearly about to regress to his infantile ideals. Before we parted I advised him to leave his family and to go abroad.

I met him again many years later. He had followed my advice and settled down as bandleader in a small German town. None of his grandiose plans had been realized. He had not become the great composer, the creator of a revolutionary Disharmonious Symphony. But he had come to terms with reality, and married a rich woman.

Analysis had come to this man just in time. He might not have been able otherwise to outgrow his infantilism; he might have resorted to suicide.

The case furnishes us with many insights into the psychology of regression. It shows us the power of unconscious jealousy. He did not know that he was obsessed by jealousy. Quite the contrary, he boasted of being completely free of it. But it was jealousy and the inability to give up possessions he had early decided were his that determined the course of his life.

His avarice, viewed psychologically, represented stinginess with love. He wanted to give up none of his family's love for him, and, by way of identification, none of the money. Indeed, he valued his sister's kiss more than all the riches in the world.

But what availed him his dominant position in the house and everyone's submission to his will? He ruled by means of fury and hatred, whereas he craved love.

His neurosis embraced all his passions and desires and guilt feelings; it carried both gratification and punishment at once.

As a child he had shared the bathroom with his sister; why should not this, which was now impossible, be made possible again? Why should he not be able to rewind the thread of time and be a child again? If he could only achieve that goal, if he could only gratify his innermost craving, he would begin life anew and strive for the fulfilment of his great historic mission.

5. THE ETERNAL ADOLESCENT

In playgrounds and other public places we sometimes see youthfully dressed men who like to play with children. They are carefully shaved so that their youthful appearance will not be marred by beard stubble. They wear sports clothes or even boyish shirts and trousers. These are the eternal adolescents, and we must not confuse them with the pedophiliacs who do grow older but who, at the same time, retain their infantile ideal.

Parts of a letter sent to me by such an "eternal adolescent" vividly describe his personality:

Case No. 20: "I am forty-one today, and realize that I cannot go on as I have been. Yet it seems impossible to rid myself of the thought that I am a boy. Otherwise I am probably quite normal. I am aware of no other pathological emotions. My parents were healthy. One of my four siblings, a brother, died at the age of fourteen from diphtheria. I was a year younger than this brother. My childhood was normal and I recall no specific events that seem connected with my unfortunate condition. On the basis of your writings, I have investigated myself and found nothing abnormal other than my retention of boyhood.

"I like to wear short trousers and I live in dread of a day when I might have to wear long pants. At the age of seventeen, I was the only one in high school who wore short pants. The other students ridiculed me, and my parents demanded that I submit to the customs of adults.

"When my life-long tendency first became clear, my mother encouraged me to continue it. Once I overheard mother and a neighbor talk of a nineteen-year-old youth who had a sweetheart. My mother indignantly remarked that it was a crime. She pointed to me and said that I was innocent and would remain so for a long time. She would prefer to have me remain a child than to have me become a man who would be spoiled by women. The neighbor lady laughed, and said that if mother examined my laundry she would no doubt learn that I was not so pure.

"Somebody arrived and I could not listen to the conversation any longer. But I knew that mother was my ally. My father, on the other hand, saw something pathological in my behavior and tried to put a quick end to it. One morning my boyish clothing vanished and there was a suit with long pants on my bed. I cried like an infant and at first refused to go to school. Later, I gave in, but I planned to purchase a sport suit as soon as possible. Soon I did get such a suit, and again I felt comfortably dressed.

"At high school I dressed in short trousers and parted my hair in the style of a small boy.

"But serious matters soon threatened my boyhood world. Father died of a heart attack. Mother needed financial help. I had to take up tutoring, and I could not go to my pupils when I was dressed in boyish sportswear.

"This period of economic difficulty with its influence on my boyish destiny also passed. I became an eminent lawyer with no financial problems.

"I love to go evenings in a boyish sailor suit. I shave all the hair on my body. And my face is kept smooth as silk. All my thoughts revolve about my desire to be a boy. All the books and notebooks of my schoolboy days are still in my possession. On evenings and holidays I often have great pleasure in looking through the articles of my school days. I am also a stamp collector. For hours I can play with my stamps, classifying them, re-arranging them, and pasting the newly-acquired ones in their proper places. I have had this hobby in the same form since early boyhood.

"I am a bachelor. When I was thirteen, I fantasied that I sat on the lap of a lady and played with her ear lobes. This was also my first masturbation fantasy. Sometimes the lady touches my organ and manipulates it. All my visits to prostitutes have ended in failure. I have tried to change the fantasy into reality. I sit on the knees of the prostitute and have her reproduce the actions of the object of my fantasy. I get some relief from this practice, but the pleasure from fantasying is far greater.

"When I visit prostitutes I am always boyishly dressed. The prerequisite for any sexual gratification is my sailor suit. From time to time I think that I should do something with a boy. I get interested in boys, yet I have carefully avoided getting too close to them, for I fear that I will forget myself and suffer dire consequences."

After reading this letter, I asked the patient to provide more specific material about his childhood. He sent the following answer: "I have thought about it for a long time, and finally I have discovered that we had a nurse in our home who used to take me on her lap when I was ill. I vaguely recollect a scene in which the nurse manipulated my penis. I recall that I have often dreamed about it."

The patient could not come to Vienna for an analysis. But frequently such people suffer from a fixation to a particular scene, and in the above case it may have been the specific type of pampering the nurse employed when the boy was sick.

Case No. 21: Mrs. R.W., thirty-two, married for ten years, childless, and of tender, infantile type, comes to me because she is completely frigid. In the first session she says that she has masturbated since her eleventh year, and that she always has orgasm in this way. In her masturbation fantasy she sees herself being carried around the room by a tall man who tosses her into the air from time to time. She has no recollection of her early childhood.

Mrs. R.W., like most patients of her type, has repressed the pertinent experiences of her childhood. She reports, however, that she has always wanted to walk around in small girl's clothing and to wear her hair in a girlish braid. She was always very happy when men admired her well-shaped legs. When she was first asked to wear the long dress which was the style for young ladies, she was resentful. When it became fashionable for women to wear short dresses, she was overjoyed. But she exaggerated this privilege so much that her husband reprimanded her. If she is certain that she won't be caught, she wears small girl's clothes around her home and plays with her dolls. Even today she likes to wear her hair in Gretchen style and to read or listen to fairy tales. She takes her nieces to children's plays and enjoys herself more than the children do. She wants to be an adolescent.

She does not feel that there is anything abnormal about her girlish ways. She is merely clinging to the happiest and most beautiful time of her life. She wants to be cured of her sexual frigidity but does not want to have an analysis. She thinks the cure for which she came to me can be gotten through a prescription which I should be able to write.

I am going to present now three cases from Hirschfeld's observation which offer the same clinical picture:

Case No. 22: Mr. H., twenty-four, a salesman, is fairly tall but he looks like a sixteen-year-old. His gestures and facial expressions are in accord with this age level. He has the good cheer of youth, but he becomes despondent and fearful easily. At present, he is oppressed by anxiety that he will have to become a soldier like his brothers—none of whom, incidentally, are on the battlefield. The modulation and pitch of his voice are boylike. The beard growth is slight. He writes of his inclinations: "I like ribbons and bows, and jewelry, but I am especially interested in nicely arranged things, my linen for example, which is always neatly-bundled and tied with gay, green ribbons. I am overjoyed when I open the linen closet door and see this wonderful arrangement.

"I am enthusiastic about flowers and one of my special passions is to kiss them or to drink water from a half-opened rose. My favorite flowers are the snow drops, primroses, violets, and the humble forget-me-not.

"I derive much pleasure from making ties, pillows, sport caps and other small things. I like to do all the designing and sewing by myself, but sport caps give me many difficulties which can be overcome more easily with instruction. However, two of the caps turned out so well that they are among the favorites which I wear. Some of my acquaintances in Berlin like them so well that I have accepted some orders from them. To my brothers in the army I have sent pillows stuffed with down. These pillows which I made by myself brought joy to my brothers."

A specially significant expression by this patient is the following: "It is distasteful to me to be called 'Mister.' It makes me unhappy, and I must be left alone until I can get into a happier mood. It is absolutely impossible for me to feel like a man. I intend to wear a suit with short pants or 'knickerbockers' so as not to give people reason to call me 'Mister.' "

Case No. 23: Mr. M., fifty, is happy only when wearing boyish sailor suits. Then he feels like a boy of twelve. In the evening at home he dons one of the seven sailor suits he has accumulated and sits in front of a mirror looking at himself. He becomes sexually aroused but he does not touch his genital because he is "too young for that." He loves to play school with boys. On Sunday afternoons he may be seen in company with boys, riding the merry-go-round or swinging. He allots money to each boy before they go out for their play. Then they all buy candy together. He goes with boys to swimming pools. He and the boys are complete equals. "Willy and Kurt are my best pals," he says. He has no sexual relations with these boys or with adults. But after spending a delightful afternoon playing with the "other boys," he gets complete sexual relief in the evening when he sits before the mirror and daydreams.

Case No. 24: Mr. R.K., forty, has been thoroughly observed by the author for several months. As a student he was a failure. He was always closely attached to his mother in early childhood, often confined to the sick bed or playing frivolous tricks when he was up and around. He recalls the excitement he obtained in early childhood from restraint or anticipation of restraint for playing tricks. At the age of thirteen he became aware of the sexual nature of this sensation when a teacher slapped his backside. The following night, in a dream, he repeated the situation and had his first emission.

After the first signs of puberty, other signs of development occurred. His voice began to change, a beard began to grow and he became increasingly conscious of sexual sensations. With the arrival of sexual maturity and the consequent direction of sexual wishes and inclinations toward grown females, his wish to remain a child asserted itself as the leading factor in his emotional life and in his total personality.

This patient is a short and stout man of rather strong build. A peculiar shyness and timidity are always apparent in his facial expression. The organic findings do not show any particular deviation from the normal. On the other hand, there are marked wrinkles, which are at least partly the result of mental work, on the lower forehead. The disproportion between cerebral and facial skull, the asymmetrical formation of the face, and the hardly differentiated structure of the unevenly placed ears are marks of degeneration. One nervous manifestation is clearly apparent: an inclination to blush and to become pale, parallel with an increased excitability of the tendon reflexes. Psychic findings in all areas suggest complete childishness and immaturity.

All his interests revolve around the pivot of his childish inner world. His intellectual needs are gratified by children's books, fairy tales, and simple fables. At Christmas he prepares a long list of gifts he would like to receive. He wants toys, toy soldiers, a lariat, "to be taken to the movies once a week," ball-playing equipment, and almost every object that would appeal to a boy. Such is the content of the wishes of this forty-two-year-old man. He himself is not aware of the degree to which his sexual sensations are based upon and interwoven with his infantile life. In his games with boys, his sexuality finds release even without overt sexuality. With this knowledge, one can understand the satisfaction he gets from letting boys correct his writing exercises and reprimand him for his mistakes.

There are many people like Mr. R.K. They don't think of themselves as patients. They rarely go to see a psychiatrist. I have time and again seen these "boys" in public parks, but I have never succeeded in getting such a person to accept analysis. There is an unbelievable stubbornness with which they cling to their fictitious "eternal youth."

Chapter Three

THE MECHANISM OF "TRANSFER"

Chapter Three

THE MECHANISM OF "TRANSFER"

A popular belief that certain psychic forces and morbid dispositions may be transferred from person to person is based on superstition. It is of the same genre as the belief that magic contagion controls love, hatred, fate, life, and death. It is related to the senseless assumption that one can get rid of an infectious disease by transmitting it to another person. There are men who have infected young girls, or even children, with venereal diseases in order to get rid of their own ills. The criminologists list this superstition as one of the motives of sexual crimes.

The alleged power of certain magic potions is supposed to be due to this property of transmissibility. Love potions, magic fluids, various elixirs, and charmed morsels which contain bodily eliminations or secretions, allegedly deliver a person from his disease or of an undesirable passion. The assumption that the superstitious use of menstrual blood, sperm, urine, feces, and all sorts of mucus can be observed only in the poorer social classes is untrue. Many neurotics retrogress to this stage of magic, prelogical beliefs. One of my patients, a college graduate, told me that he once had sprinkled a few drops of his urine on a dish of cheese belonging to his father's housekeeper to attract her love. I have frequently been told by patients, both well-to-do and poor, that they drank the urine of their beloved ones, or made the love object drink some of their urine, in order to assure permanence to the relationship. The interesting point in all these stories is that these procedures were prompted by some obscure instinct rather than by observance of a known tradition or the advice of friends.[1]

The belief that the dead are capable of transmitting to us their fate is also strong among primitives as well as among neurotics. I treated an impotent thirty-two-year-old man whose uncle had been killed on the day my patient was born. This patient was plagued by the apprehension—shared by his entire family—that his uncle's tragic end was also in store for him. At times, though, he believed that he was destined to live to a normal end his uncle's life, which had ended so abruptly.

The ancient Greeks believed in the transfusion of magic powers by way of sexual intercourse. With his semen the Greek pederast was certain to transmit his very soul and all his virtues to the boy of his choice. A large number of present-day parents believe that the wetnurse transmits to the child many of her character traits.

The property of magnets to be charged with electric power which can then be transmitted led Benedict to the assumption of non-perceivable substances inherent in matter

---

[1] Many creative writers have developed stories around the theme of magic transmission. Jacobson's story, *Two Worlds*, is a good example. It is about a sick girl who makes a wreath of flowers interwoven with strands of her own hair and sits in wait on the shore of a river. Soon a boat appears, with merrymaking, chattering picnickers, among whom is a beautiful woman. The sick girl quickly throws the wreath to pass on her sickness to the woman in the boat. The girl gets well all right—through sheer autosuggestion, as the author explains—but her peace of mind is gone. Remorse drives her to suicide. As it happens, she throws herself into the river on the very day when the actually unharmed woman who was the object of her attempted magic again sails down the river, this time in a happily decorated nuptial boat.

which can be displaced through emanation. On the basis of this hypothesis he constructed a whole theory of emanations and built "sideric" pendulums to gauge the authenticity of old paintings.[2]

The term "transfer" is part of the nomenclature used by students of telepathy and is applied also by some radiologists in Germany. It is entirely possible that all these telergic beliefs are based on a general and vague popular intuition; yet I can clearly see another source of origin for these persistent views.

Mental transfer plays an important part in the psychodynamics of unsophisticated people. Surprising though it may be, it is quite obvious that many psychic phenomena are totally unintelligible if we ignore this fact. Freud was first to discover and to describe the phenomenon of transference of the patient's subconscious attachments onto the doctor himself.

Experience teaches us that this transference of love and hatred onto the physician is by no means peculiar to psychoanalysis. To quote Freud's keen remark, "Analysis does not produce transference, it only discloses it."

But before I embark on the subject of transference I should like to adduce a few significant illustrations of transfer.

Case No. 25: A family, consisting of father, mother, and three boys, kept a cat, which served as a sort of emotional clearinghouse for the entire group. The cat was not only everyone's declared pet, but even more important, it was in some ways a house deity, and every member of the family curried her favor. At mealtime the cat sat on the shoulder of one of the members of the family and was given the choicest morsels. Most of the conversation revolved around the pet, her looks and her wants. The cat was an inexhaustible source of stimulation and joy. But for

[2] Concerning transfer phenomena in telepathy see my pamphlet, *The Telepathic Dream,* Alexander Baum, Publisher, Berlin, 1920.

the cat, the group would have been at a loss, because the interpersonal relations in this family were rather strained, and communication was, at best, blocked.

It appeared, however, that the cat had a special symbolic significance to each member of the family. To all three boys it represented the mother; to the mother, one of the boys.

Be that as it may, the cat served as a repository for the longings and emotions of the entire family. The presence of the cat permitted also a discharge of the family's libido and aggression which could not otherwise be released on the persons for whom they were intended. Someone would dump the cat onto the floor, and say, "Scram, you low-grade hussy!" or, "A bum daffy-doodle beast, that's what you are!" and in such fashion, the cat always serving as a lightning rod, emotions of love and hatred were vented by all members of the family.

Highstrung people, in a fit of temper, will throw and break dishes or other convenient objects. What they experience is a lightning-like shift of emotion. Let us suppose that such a man quarrels with his wife. At a certain moment he is seized with such a hatred toward her that he could do bodily harm to her, perhaps even kill her—all hatred is murderous. But instead, he gets hold of a plate and violently throws it onto the floor; the plate breaks into a thousand splinters, and with that the man's anger subsides. All his murderous wishes have been transferred to the plate.

The scapegoat ritual of the ancient Hebrews had a similar significance; the tribe loaded all its accumulated fears and aversions onto the innocent goat, which was then driven into the desert.

We can frequently observe the shift of an incestuous desire onto a non-related member of the household. It was Harnik who called our attention to the fact that the maid-servant often served as a dream-symbol of the mother. But Harnik's statement requires an amplification, inasmuch as a maid may also represent a sister or even a daughter of the dreamer.

Sons often fall in love with maid-servants who represent the mother. I have known many boys whose love for the maid evaporated as soon as she left the house. It had been only her proximity to the boy's mother in the household setting which had caused the infatuation in the first place. And I have observed also older men who have shifted their love for their daughters onto the maid-servants in the house. Any member of the household may serve as a "dumping ground" for emotions which cannot be directly expressed. Here are two typical examples of re-routed desires.

Case No. 26: A forty-five-year-old physician entered into an affair with his daughter's governess. He was fascinated by the fact that the governess, although forty, was still a virgin. He used many ways of sexually stimulating this woman who had been a schoolmate of his wife, but he was careful not to deflower her. He stimulated her manually, performed cunnilingus and even drank her urine—in short, all his gratifications were of a marked infantile nature. And the reason why the otherwise normal man in this particular case reverted to sexual childhood patterns was his unconscious infatuation with his thirteen-year-old daughter. He had transferred his desires from the tabooed object to the governess and performed on her the acts he wished to perform on his daughter.

The justly notorious figure of the "boarder" or "gentleman lodger," the menace of many a female—and male!—member of the household's younger generation, is often only the recipient of emotions felt for an incest object.

Case No. 27: A girl of twenty-three complained of a nagging fear of loss of virginity. Every protruding angle of any seemingly-angular object was regarded as a danger, in some magic fashion, to her hymen. Her gait was characterized by a peculiar, shortened step, as she was constantly afraid of breaking her hymenal membrane if she walked briskly. For the same reason, she was most reluctant to ride in a carriage. It could be said of her that she had spent all her life worrying about her virginity. I discuss her various compulsive ideas on another page of this book; here I shall only mention her fear of the bathtub, because a man might have used the tub before and his sperm could get into her vagina and impregnate her. She saw sofas and toilet bowls as potential carriers of semen. She therefore seated herself lightly on the edge of a sofa or leaned against it, and remained standing while at the toilet.

Pins horrified her, and she was on the lookout for them everywhere. At times, she stood up all night and refused to go to bed for fear that some unseen pin might be lurking between the covers and that it would stab her while she slept. Her anomalous relation to her stepfather proved to be one of the sources of her neurosis. The man had a violent temper and was always lustfully in pursuit of the girl. Whenever she was alone in the house, he hugged and kissed her passionately, and even the presence of his wife and the other children did not always prevent him from pulling her down onto his lap and embracing her. When she lay in bed, he came to her side, fondled her bosom, and pressed his lips against it.

Analysis, at first, brought no results, and I was beginning to attribute this failure to the conditions in her home, when her increased and all too grotesque fussiness about her maidenhood struck me as being an utter sham. I knew from other cases of the existence of the neurotic annulment mechanisms which some of our patients use to negate an unpleasant past experience.

Could it be, I asked myself, that the girl pretended to fear defloration because she had already been robbed of her virginity, that she invalidated a past experience by a contrived fear that it might occur in the future?

Then one day I told her most categorically that she was no virgin and asked her to tell me under what circumstances she had been deflowered. And suddenly the truth came out. She had had sexual intercourse with a man who was lodging in her house. She was engaged to another man at that time, and I learned later that during an altercation between the boarder and the fiancé the former revealed to the young man that the girl had come into his room one night on her own initiative.

But why had not the girl preferred to turn to her fiancé for sexual gratification? Simply because he was not a member of the household, while the boarder's very proximity to the girl's stepfather made him a convenient proxy for the stepfather. The girl really longed for her stepfather, who strongly aroused her; on many nights she craved to go to him, but she transferred her sexual goal and went to the lodger instead.

I have quoted from this case only by way of demonstrating the phenomenon of transfer which takes place within the setting of a household. Let us now consider another case which is quite strange and unusual.

Case No. 28: Mr. T.B., a barrister, aged twenty-five, complained of utter inability to study or to concentrate on anything at all. He had lost all his libido. Only three years ago matters in this respect had been quite different. At that time he first met his fiancée, and a kiss from her was enough to arouse him. But at present he was "down-and-out." His relations with his fiancée —his "eternal bride," as he called her—never came to a head; the couple alternately backed out on one another. And, what was particularly bad, he had to masturbate constantly, as he could find no joy in sexual intercourse. He was unable to ejaculate in normal intercourse. He had been in analysis with Dr. H., but the latter had not been able to uncover the specific "masturbation fantasy" as the patient never told him the content of the reveries which accompanied his masturbatory act.

The patient regarded his father as the only cause of his troubles. The latter had always kept him away from girls, and company in general, even on Sundays. Thus, the patient thought his illness was the sad result of father's admonitions against his keeping company. His father should have known better, because he had been a teacher and an educator by profession. The patient dreamed of "repaying his father in full some day" by committing suicide and leaving a letter in which he would tell that man that he had ruined his own son's life.

However, the patient's history offered no substantiation for all this cant. His father had always been kind to him. When the patient was three years old, his mother died, and the father devoted all his life to his son and did not marry again. The father was now seventy years old, physically and mentally enfeebled after a stroke and living in the country.

The patient lived by himself in a large apartment, the appearance of which he utterly neglected, although he paid much attention to his grooming. He was constantly in financial straits. He had no income, and he seldom worked. He existed by gradually selling the household possessions. He had no sense for economizing and at times recklessly spent what little money he had. It was evident that he wanted to become destitute quickly so that he would have to go to live with his father in the country.

First, I investigated his relationship with his fiancée. It turned out that it was virtually no relationship. The girl had long since told him that she was through with him. The engagement had been without genuine intentions on his part and the girl had soon realized this and broken completely with him.

All his emotions were fixated on his father. His history revealed the astonishing fact that he had slept with his father until he was sixteen. He did not remember any playful intimacies, but he did recall that his legs were often held between the father's.

The patient had been very jealous of every cook and governess who worked for the family. Once, when he was eight years old, he woke in the dark of night and, upon noticing that father was not in bed with him, screamed and ran through the rooms "looking for Dad." He was thinking that the man was in the maid-servant's room, when father suddenly returned to the bedroom. Even father's explanation that he was looking for a business letter in the dining room did not quench the boy's suspicion, and he never forgave his father his "faithlessness."

Analysis increasingly evidenced the patient's fixation on his father. He reported the following daydream:

"While I'm lying on my bed some giant creature bends over me and aims for my genitals. I throw him off me, and he falls on his back, his legs raised high in the air. Now I jump on top of him and shove my hand into his anus and pull forth a ring, which I intend to give to my fiancée so that I may be saved."

This reverie shows that he is fixated to his father, particularly to his father's anus. If he had been freed from this tie, he would have married. The ring symbolizes his "betrothal" to father. It is in his father's anus, just as the ring of a Venetian doge had been cast into the water, signifying the doge's betrothal with the sea. The patient "knows" that he is father's "eternal bride."

The analysis also revealed that the patient had shifted his love for his father onto the apartment. The toilet was the locale of his most intense pleasures. He often masturbated while sitting on the toilet bowl. The seat derived its affective value from the fact that his father had been using it. The entire apartment became a representation of the father. That is why he had refused the offer of a woman to pay the rent and to keep the entire apartment in order in exchange for the right to share the apartment with him. But he could not desecrate these rooms by having strangers in them. When he brought girls to the apartment, he was never able to perform a complete intercourse because his sexual goal was his father. His efforts to free himself from this bond through dissipation were unsuccessful.

He wanted to live and to sleep with his father for ever. He had first dated the girl who became his fiancée when he suspected father of being too friendly with the last housekeeper, and he had done so only to make him jealous. There was also, of course, his wish to free himself from the father, a wish which could not possibly be fulfilled, because the patient had transferred upon the girl his longing for his father.

In a most remarkable way the patient made his relations with the girl a complete duplicate of his relations with the parent. He made her, through his own behavior, as inaccessible as father, as strongly and as eternally desired; he could bewail his unrequited love, and he could conceive himself as betrothed. The girl gave him a chance of going through all the emotions that were aroused by his father: bliss, hope, jealousy, disillusionment, and so many others.

In the course of time, the patient shifted his father-directed emotions onto the doctors who treated him. The physicians made him angry because they did not fulfill his infantile daydreams of an eternal father-son love relation.

We often encounter goal transfers from homosexual to heterosexual objects. Transference in an analytic setting is such an emotional transfer, but there are many other ways in which such transfers occur, even though they are not always easily discerned. The following case report illustrates this phenomenon.

Case No. 29: A man of thirty-four was plagued by neurotic indecision and doubts. He was in love with a lady who had been having sexual relations with him for several years. He wanted to marry her because of "moral considerations," but he doubted his sexual potency. Most of his sexual acts ended in *ejaculatio praecox.* He was still masturbating, although much less frequently, and his ejaculation seemed normal in this practice. He decided to announce his engagement, but immediately he was beset by all sorts of doubts and reservations. After endless consultations with relatives and friends, he did announce his engagement, only to cancel it the next day. He repeated this on-and-off play several times, and finally he came to consult me. He could not live, he said, without his lady friend but, unfortunately, he was now completely impotent with her.

Analysis revealed that the man had shifted his infatuation with a male friend onto his fiancée. The shift had been made easier through an incidental resemblance of the two persons.

Worthy of note are the transfers to inanimate objects, such as dolls, walking canes, pictures, pieces of furniture, books, entire collections, jewels, clothes, old documents, letters, instruments, or any other objects which have belonged or have been associated with the loved person.

The pillow deserves special mention as a possible receptacle of a displaced emotion, as it is of important symbolic value. There are many infantilists who are in the habit of sucking a corner tip of their pillow just before going to sleep. The tip, to them, is a substitute for the breast of mother or the wetnurse. Other infantilists hug, caress, or stroke their pillow, as though it were an object of love. One of my patients—I shall speak of him in greater detail later—could not fall asleep unless he had the pillow placed between his legs. In his case, the pillow represented the back of a horse which was a central figure in all his daydreams.

In still another case, a thirty-six-year-old impotent male was plagued by strange abdominal pains which he could alleviate only through placing a pillow under his stomach and pressing hard against it. In his sleep, he pushed the pillow upward, and, when he woke, the pillow was always in his arms. The pillow in this unusual case was a sister substitute.

Very often pillows are angrily thrown to the floor. Many a pillow found in the morning on the floor in a torn, crumpled state bears witness of the vehement struggle endured in the dream.

The following is an interesting case of transfer of emotion to an inanimate object.

Case No. 30: A man of forty-two was in the habit of playing with the toys of his childhood years. Annoyed with this ridiculous habit, he decided one day to give all his toys to one of his nephews. Unfortunately, there was one toy from which he could not tear himself loose. This toy was a clown dressed as a girl.

In his childhood, the patient had kept the clown close to him at night, and even as a grown man he still played with it. The clown had a place of honor in his room and was protected by a glass case. On holidays it was seated at the table and a tiny toy plate laden with food was placed before it.

Analysis revealed that the clown was a mother symbol. The patient had transferred all his emotions for his mother onto the toy. Whereas his relation to the mother had been somewhat marred by his jealousy of his siblings, he could undisturbedly display his love and affection for the clown. When he acquired insight regarding the identification, the man lost all his affection for the toy and gave it away.

All these phenomena are transfers. The analytic *transference,* however, the discovery of which constitutes one of

Freud's major contributions, is a specific form of transfer and occurs only in the doctor-patient relationship. It may be observed that patients often resort to other forms of transfer before succumbing to transference. They begin to collect things, fall in love, find a new friend, or become attached to some inanimate object.[1] These patients try to evade any strong transfer, and they use passion to dilute and diffuse it. Male patients with strong homosexual drives, for instance, will not concentrate their attention on one man, no matter how fixated they are on him. On the contrary, they will contrive all sorts of fictitious attachments (transfers) to other men, and without any compelling reason elevate chance acquaintances to the position of intimate friends.

Why the analytic setting is apt to make the physician the recipient of transferred early emotional attachments is an unsolved problem. Female patients often indignantly deny that their emotional involvement is only a transference, and insist it is their great and genuine love. This only proves how successful the transfer is and how well-hidden is its mechanism.

The analytic setting engenders love for the analyst in many ways. First, the patient regards the doctor as the first human being who is able and willing to appreciate his problems. As a French *bon mot* puts it: "To love is to be understood." All men crave being understood. To be understood, however, also means to be exposed physically, as well as spiritually. Hence, the striking Biblical expression for sexual intercourse, "And he knew his wife. . . ."

A second love-engendering factor has its source in man's fear of loneliness. It is closely linked with the desire to be understood. The man who feels himself understood by a fellow-man is not entirely alone. As the poet Storm puts it, "Essentially, love is nothing but fear of loneliness."

---

[1] One of my female patients fell in love with a portrait of the poet, Richard Dehmel, which bore features resembling mine.

A third factor is that every patient is bent on a specific single experience and makes all sense and happiness of life dependent on the reliving of that experience. It is a sort of sexual "must," set in a definite daydream frame. And the patient who has such a "must" says to himself, as it were, "Since the doctor understands me so well, he knows also what I expect of life, of the world, of him." The patient's love then becomes a form of anticipatory fulfillment. What often appears in analysis as stubborn resistance on the part of the patient is the reaction to the analyst's failure to comprehend that the patient is fixed on a specific experience and demands from his analyst its revival.

The phenomenon of transfer helps us to understand many facts about group life. Emotional shifts onto an entire social unit, or onto an object symbolizing this unit, are understandable only in terms of transfer.

Besides being actors, neurotics are also jugglers, engaged in constant play with their emotions and drives. Unlike jugglers, however, they are themselves deceived by their legerdemain.

Psychosexual infantilism bears most clearly the mark of a transfer. Just as the child bestows life upon every inanimate object, so these neurotics, who never cease to be children, bestow life upon the objects about them. Basically, transfer is an emanation of the ego vitality onto the things, large and small, of the surrounding world.

Chapter Four

MONOPOLIZATION OF SENSES

Chapter Four

MONOPOLIZATION OF SENSES

1. General View

Normal sexual life presupposes the integrated function of all sense organs. The man in love enjoys being close to the object of his affection, he relishes the sight of her, he likes the smell of her body, the taste of her lips, the touch of her skin. If and when the love object offends one of his senses, it is safe to assume that he has erred in the choice of his mate.

Women who object to the body odor of their husbands and, at the same time, insist they retain their love, are obviously unaware of the fact that they dislike their marital partners. A man who believes he is in love with a girl, and yet objects to the pitch of her voice, will see the eventual collapse of his affection for her.

Every person, consciously or unconsciously, favors a specific sense. One attaches great importance to the sound of the voice, another lingers on the sight of the object, still another gives priority to the emanation of odor or to the feel and touch implicit in the act of caressing. Within the various forms of psychic infantilism it frequently occurs that one of

163

the senses becomes a determinant force, as though it were harnessing the whole love life to its service.

a. *Visual*

The best known of these monopolistic manifestations is the paraphilia of looking and being looked at (scoptophilia and exhibitionism). The "voyeurs" have perhaps the most harmless and the most common form of infantilism. Practically everyone shows traces of this predeliction, and we can designate it as a paraphilia only when the person renounces the sexual act and achieves complete gratification through the visual act. We have learned from many case histories that these paraphilias can be traced back to childhood. The child is first and foremost a voyeur and tries by all means to obtain the pleasure implicit in looking. Thus he also gratifies his sexual exploratory urge. His parents are his first objects of observation, and if the act of watching is one of his first experiences, a monopoly of the sense of sight may develop.

The adult voyeur acts like a child. He, too, strives to obtain the pleasure of looking. Often his voyeurism goes beyond the sex act back to the acts of urination and defecation. There are so many variations of scoptophilia that I could not possibly describe them all. A few examples will have to do.

One of the favorite forms of voyeurism is peeping through a keyhole or an opening in the wall. It is said that in some Parisian brothels paraphilic clients pay large fees for the opportunity to look through key holes at all kinds of sexual activities. These voyeurs usually masturbate or have orgasm from the excitement of watching the performances.

Case No. 31: A man of fifty-four, socially prominent, consulted me about his practice of approaching a soldier in the red light district and offering to pay for a visit to a prostitute if he could watch the act. Sometimes he would give an additional payment to the soldier he selected. He recalled that in childhood he had often listened to the noises made by his parents during copulation.

A complementary configuration is seen in another case of this type.

Case No. 32: An attorney, aged thirty-four, states that he can have intercourse only when he knows he is being watched. For him the most pleasurable sexual experience occurs when he is in the same room with a male friend and two girls. The two men watch each other copulate. Once the patient asked an especially pretty girl to allow him to have intercourse with her while his male friend watched. She refused. He then tried to hide his friend in the room.

In his play, *Gyges and his Ring,* Hebbel, a nineteenth century dramatist, depicts a similar situation.

Voyeurs, in fantasy, possess a magic ring which gives them invisibility. Or they dream of being transformed into a tiny animal which can see without being seen. The Magic Hood is a recurrent motif in their fantasies. Some voyeurs do not have to see the sexual act or total nudity in order to be gratified. To see a skirt lifted a few inches is sufficiently exciting for some.[1]

Case No. 33: Mr. S.A., fifty-two, a clerk, has the following passion: as soon as it rains he goes into the street and follows the women who lift their skirts to prevent the mud from splashing on them. He knows the corners which will be muddiest and where the ladies will have to expose much of their calves while stepping from the curb and crossing the street. He follows these women and through a hole torn in his pocket he masturbates as he watches them. He has never dared to accost any of these women. When there is no rain he has no sexual stimulation. He has often tried to have intercourse with prostitutes, but he cannot get an erection with them. His entire sexual life revolves

[1] *Editor's note.* Stekel refers here to the floor-length skirts which were in fashion early in this century.

around a setting of rain and the raising of a woman's skirt as she walks over wet and muddy streets.

Every physician dealing with sexual problems encounters cases of this kind. They represent some form of infantilism. The sexual act for all of these people is confined to looking on or being looked at.

b. *Auditory*

Cases manifesting sexual interest in listening to a sex act (without seeing it) are also not infrequent. The creaking of a bed, the utterances of the copulating man and woman, or other sounds coming from the scene of the act, are the only means by which these people, by proxy, as it were, obtain their sexual gratification.

Case No. 34: Mr. W.H., twenty-nine, a salesman, had never been potent with women. Ordinarily, he masturbated with the fantasy that he was hearing a couple having intercourse in an adjacent room. Then he began to convert this fantasy into reality. He visited cheap hotels, rented a thinly-walled room, and listened for sounds from the adjoining rooms. He made sure of getting stimulating neighbors by giving large tips to hotel employees. He listened intently, his stimulation grew in intensity and he tried to time his orgasm with that of the couple in the adjoining room.

This patient recalled that for many years he had overheard his parents' sexual relations and had masturbated while listening. In adulthood he repeated and revived the early experiences which took place in his home. All his attempts to rid himself of the habit were in vain. To listen was all he wanted. Only listening was capable of adequately satisfying him.

c. *Olfactory*

Less frequent are the cases in which the sense of smell reigns supreme. It is known that certain body odors cause erotic stimulation and may be conducive to normal intercourse. However, there are "odor fiends" who chase a definite odor, become inebriated, and reach an orgasm from it. I have known men who relished certain perfumes, others who used scented handkerchiefs, men who masturbated while following heavily perfumed women on the street. Others are attracted by the smell of perspiration, or they crave the smell of a definite zone of the body. The smell of linen, underwear, worn apparel, and the like may also become sexual stimulants.

Case No. 35: Mr. T.N., forty-five, a physician, has had since early childhood a craving for the smell of old bedsheets in which elderly women have slept. As a physician, he has had occasionally an opportunity to put his head under a bedspread while ostensibly engaged in examining the patient. At such moments he has had an emission. He has always been impotent with women. He recalls that at the age of three he liked to crawl into the warm bed of his mother and pull the blanket over his head. The stronger the odor of the bedding, the greater his excitement.

Case No. 36: Mr. C.Y., twenty-four, an office clerk, obtains sexual satisfaction from the smell of urine on garments. He makes a great effort to get hold of such underwear and uses it for autoerotic purposes. He has easy access to the underwear shed by his mother and by two of his aunts. In connection with this he speaks of a smell recollection which he has whenever he sneezes—a phenomenon which I have had occasion to observe elsewhere. He says that the memory of the smell comes to him whenever he sneezes. Some compulsive forms of sneezing are but symbolic representations of the sexual act. This smell haunts him for days, and he is most unhappy when he goes to a prostitute who wears freshly laundered lingerie. In such cases he will ask the girl to put on an unclean and, if possible, a urine-stained nightgown. Then he sniffs at it with excitement until he reaches an orgasm without making any attempt at intercourse.

At times such smell hallucinations coincide with attacks of dizziness, fainting spells, or stretches of intensive daydreaming. Féré offers a characteristic case of this kind:

Case No. 37: An epileptic man, aged thirty-four, has subjective smell sensations during intercourse. Later, in the aura of the epileptic attack, the smells re-emerge. No emotional disturbance has been apparent in his own life from earliest childhood to maturity. Until the age of twenty-eight, he had no illness except measles and scarlet fever. He has been married for one year. Two months ago his wife gave birth to an infant. After resuming sexual relations with his wife, he was suddenly assailed by a foul odor associated with his orgasm. The smell was like that of rancid cheese. He thought this odor came from his wife and not from him. He was immediately stricken with a violent aversion toward physical intimacy. He discontinued sexual activity for almost a month until suddenly one afternoon, while at work in his office, he smelled the same vile odor. This time the smell was detached from erotic stimulation. Formerly the smell was connected with the sex act, but from then on his smell hallucinations recurred every ten to twelve days regardless of whether or not he had sexual relations.

The basic pattern of this manifestation was maintained without variation for some twelve months. Then one evening as he entered the house after a long, tiring walk, the smell assailed him. At the same time his vision blurred, and at almost the same instant he fainted. He bit his tongue and soiled his clothing with his urine. After brief but violent convulsions, he fell into a restless, trancelike sleep which lasted for almost two hours. He awakened only for a short while, addressed a few questions to the people who were gathered about him, and went to sleep again just after he was undressed and placed in bed. Attacks of this kind recurred in from six to eight weeks. The old form of hallucinatory manifestation also persisted.

Since this patient went through his paraphilia during an epileptic attack, we may guess at the presence of criminal tendencies in his personality (probably mobilized by the smell sensation) which he is unable to face consciously. Long observation of similar patients led me to believe that we are dealing here with a case of necrophilia.

d. *Gustatory*

In my practice I have observed that a liking for and an aversion to fetid smells often can be traced back to repressed necrophilic tendencies. The finesse of many a gourmet is impregnated with infantile sexuality. The mystery of certain food idiosyncrasies can be solved analytically.

Case No. 38: Mr. G.F., thirty-seven, an engineer. A woman's kiss leads to orgasm if it is accompanied by the strange taste sensation of pus or blood. Women with bad teeth, especially if they have dentures, give him this sensation. A beautifully shaped mouth full of perfect teeth leaves him cold, while the mere thought of a denture causes sexual excitement.

Case No. 39: Miss B.D., twenty-five, remains frigid. She obtains stimulation only from the kiss of a heavy smoker who has just finished smoking a cigar. Her father had been a heavy smoker. She admits the possibility that his early kisses might have given her this taste sensation, although she has never been aware of any connection between her early experiences with her father and her present condition.

e. *Palpatory*

We come now to the sense of touch. It, too, can monopolize sexual life. The large group of "strokers" belongs to this category. Some men and women reach orgasm through stroking while any other form of caressing fails to arouse them. Such conditions can be traced to definite childhood experiences.

Case No. 40: Mrs. A.S., forty-two, mother of four, is completely frigid during intercourse. She can reach orgasm only when her body, especially her back, is being stroked. The gentler the strokes, the sooner the orgasm. She depicts the pleasure of being stroked with the simile of "cold water running down your spine when you sit in a hot bathtub."

The various scratchers also belong to this group. Even children often scratch themselves, sometimes so hard that they bleed and the wounds become infected. Many chronic childhood eczemas are the result of protracted scratching.

This habit contains both sadistic and autoerotic components (Hug-Hellmuth), and a fixation on it may lead to exclusive skin erotism.

The sensitivity of certain people toward tickling is well known. Some people who display marked skin erotism are likely to be ticklish. In certain cases, however, tickling preceeds the sex act and must not be neglected. Paraphilics get sexual gratification not from the genital contacts, but when their armpits, feet, or other parts of the body are tickled. Most individuals have their specific sensitive skin areas capable of generating sexual stimulation.

Case No. 41: Mr. D.K., thirty-four, traveling salesman. He submits his entire body to tickling by his female partner. The girl starts at the top of his head and descends all the way to his toes, and then he has orgasm.

Massaging can also serve the purpose of sexual pleasure. It is skin erotism which makes certain "magnetic" treatments effective.

Case No. 42: Mr. E.O., fifty-three, father of six children, says that only scratching can give him erotic gratification. He has worked out a system whereby he can indulge in exhibitionism and disguised incestuous wish-fulfillment. On evenings, he stands nude before two of his children, preferably girls, and has them scratch him all over his body while he pretends to be suffering from a severe attack of itching. As a concession, he covers his genitals with his hand, but the rest of his body is entirely exposed, and he makes sure that all of it enjoys the pleasures of tickling and scratching.

All cases of skin and muscle erotism belong in this group (Sadger). But the above illustrations will suffice. All these paraphilias are alike in the revelation of their early childhood setting.

2. Exhibitionism

Exhibitionism, or the lustful baring and displaying of one's own body, is such a common phenomenon that it can hardly be designated as morbid. Only specific circumstances lend the exhibitionist act its pathological character. No man, stripping his clothes in the intimacy of a love tryst, will be called abnormal; it is only when this same man begins to undress in front of perfect strangers on the street or in the lobby of a theater that we look for mental derangement. And yet, this qualification granted, exhibitionism still remains a very widespread paraphilia.

Exhibitionism, generally speaking, is a masculine deviation; there are very few women affected by it. We can think of only two reasons for the unequal distribution of pathological exhibitionism. First, the barriers of feminine modesty in our culture are of greater solidity, and secondly, our mores and fashions give women a far greater margin for legitimate, that is, socially acceptable exhibitionism (plunging necklines, display of legs, etc.).[1]

Impulsive exhibitionistic acts are among the most embarrassing ones socially. Jean Jacques Rousseau confesses the

[1] Of great interest are the reports on the connection between exhibitionism and superstition. Gopcevic describes an old custom of the Albanian women which was prevalent during the initial stages of the war between Albania and Montenegro. The Albanian women preceded their warrior husbands into battle and, raising their skirts, exposed their bodies to the Montenegrins in the superstitious belief that this would assure victory to their side. Only the fact that too many Albanian women were mowed down put an end to the peculiar primitive custom (cf. Steinmetz, Vol. II, p. 173).

On the other hand, the "purification rites" of a Koenigsberg religious sect called "Muecker" contained elements of sheer exhibitionism. These rites required that women expose some of their usually concealed charms to the assembled congregation in order to make them immune to temptations. The "Head Priest" of the sect had ten or twelve naked or half-naked women tend to him while he was taking a bath (cf. Stoll, *loc. cit.*, pp. 392-393; Ivan Bloch, *loc. cit.*, pp. 307-308).

shocking episode in which, following an invincible urge, he exposed his naked backside to a band of washerwomen. His was a rather rare form of exhibitionism. Far more frequent is the exposure of the penis—usually when it is erected. Occurrences of exposure are reported by a great majority of female analysands; they are also frequent in girls' dreams. In the vicinity of schools men can frequently be found waiting for an opportunity either to seek physical contact ("frotteurs," "mashers") or to indulge in exposure. A definite preference for children as viewers characterizes such paraphiliacs.

I am inclined to see the main source of exhibitionism in self-love, in the patient's self-admiration (narcissism), in his belief in the magic power of his beauty. (Cf. my short paper on "The Psychology of Exhibitionism," Zentrabl. f. Psa., Vol. I, p. 494, 1911.)

A neurotic person trusts in the omnipotence not only of his ideas but also of his physique. To quote an earlier statement of mine: "Exhibitionism represents the eruption of an overwhelming self-love and the projection of a triumphant self-evaluation onto others. This overestimation of one's own magic charms may include the whole body, or only parts of it. In the latter case, it may constitute one of the roots of fetishism. . . ."

The most remarkable feature of exhibitionism is its impulsive, drive-like, irrepressible suddenness. Men afflicted with exhibitionism—and it is an affliction—inevitably complain of the invincibility of their impulse, of which they are deeply ashamed. In the wake of each act they feel profoundly depressed and remorseful.

Many of them complain of a continuous trance-like state and of an irresistible urge to sleep, and, with tears in their eyes, implore the psychiatrist's help.

We find among exhibitionists many individuals who are mentally deficient (hence, also infantile), a comprehensible phenomenon in view of the fact that the weakness of their inhibitions obviously goes hand-in-hand with a low level of intellectual and emotional functioning. In very old men, the lowering of mental capacities favors the emergence of exhibitionism, often coupled with the appearance of a pedophilia.

Only an analyst has the opportunity to observe the extent and frequency of non-neurotic forms of exhibitionism and its various neurotic disguises, such as morbid bashfulness, fear of blushing and of being looked at, sensitivity to light, and self-consciousness in the procedures of dressing and undressing.

The physical exhibitionism is capable of being transformed into a mental one. It may acquire positive values in the form of outspoken sincerity and courageous frankness, which may prompt a person to confess to foibles and weaknesses ordinarily kept secret. Rousseau furnishes us with a classical example of such mental exhibitionism, based, to be sure, on a physical one.

It should be noted that exhibitionists expose to view those erogenous zones which they seek in others, and that "showing" and "looking" go hand-in-hand. The exhibitionist is also a voyeur, and vice versa. Ordinarily, however, one of the two components is suppressed, and only analysis reveals to us the bipolar character of the urge.

The overevaluation of one's own body may, if maturity and experience fail to curb it, veer into the opposite direction and produce a feeling of inferiority, thus proving once more the bipolarity of all psychic phenomena. In such a case, the exhibitionist will be ashamed of certain parts of his body. He may believe that his ears are ugly, or that his nose is too long, or he will think the pigmentation of his skin is loathsome. The usual strategy of an exhibitionist's self-infatuation is retrenchment. Unable to sustain a steady exaltation of the undivided whole, the mind of the exhibitionist concentrates on single parts. Thus we may observe plain girls boasting about their "most gorgeous" hair, or "best-formed" hands, or "provocative" legs. I shall return to these partial over-evaluations later in this discussion.

The attitude of the adults contributes greatly to the child's formation of a belief in his unique magnificence, and the harm thus wrought by parents, relatives, servants, and friends is incalculable. The child may be subjected to a barrage of praise and admiration. Especially the nude child sometimes elicits the most ecstatic exclamations on the perfection of his form, and many a mother is carried away by her enthusiasm and covers the little body with passionate kisses.

Thus, a connection between nudity and receipt of loving attention is established in the earliest childhood. The child has only to uncover himself to become the recipient of ecstatic expressions of affection. Much later in life, the neurotic adult expects the same from a regression to childhood. It is not surprising, therefore, that exhibitionists prefer to expose themselves to children. From our observations of sex behavior in normal children we know that exhibitionist performances precede all the other forms of sexual games. Children indulge in showing and seeing much earlier than they do in touching and fondling.

The clumsy, silly exhibitionist feats of paraphiliacs make sense only when we see them as regressions, as poignant lapses into old childhood patterns and stages of self-infatuation.

It should be noted that an exhibitionist act very seldom terminates in aggression; whenever the latter occurs, we must look for disturbances on a deeper level. It has been reported from many sides that exhibitionism is widespread among epileptics.

The strikingly infantile nature of exhibitionism induced several psychiatrists (Krafft-Ebing) to relate it to temporary imbecility. We insist, however, on our conclusion that it is not a temporary feeble-mindedness, but a temporary regression to childhood that lies at the bottom of exhibitionism. We have observed states of sexual impotence in many cases of infantilism, and it fits very well with this fact that exhibitionists in their demeanor should be content with childish forms of sexual gratification. While exhibitionists regress, during their act, to the intellectual and ethical level of a child, they may otherwise rise to great intellectual or ethical heights. The existence of men like Rousseau is convincing proof of it.

Case No. 43: A highly respected writer consulted me about recurrent fits of exhibitionism which had almost brought him into conflict with the law. Every two or three months he was obsessed by the desire to stick his buttocks out of the window.[1] He usually performed this act in the dark of the night, and had no erection; after the act, he was always overwhelmed by a feeling of shame and despair. According to him, he performed the act in a trance-like state, and woke only after completion of the act. An elderly lady, living across the street, reported him to the police, but the subsequent investigation yielded no results. The lady was then accused of malicious gossip, and, upon learning the well-known name of the defendant, she readily apologized. The patient asked for a hypnotic cure, refusing to lay open to analysis the deep-seated sources of his ailment. He alleged himself to be subject to trance-like states when his mind was completely detached from reality. It was in such states that he wrote his best books. Unfortunately, it was also in these states that he would suddenly undress. He remembered that his father had often spanked him and that his mother, too, had administered her punishments preferably on the seat of his pants. The patient displayed faintly masochistic traits and a marked homosexual component in the guise of numerous friendships with men on a spiritual, sublimated level.

---

[1] This was also the manner in which Rousseau expressed his exhibitionism. The French author, Courteline, has used it as a comedy device in one of his plays. A widespread vulgar gesture of the sort is usually accompanied by the "invitation" to kiss the backside.

The next case is somewhat similar:

Case No. 44: Mr. I.B., forty-three, a happily married man and the father of four children, complained of a morbid urge to expose his genital organs in front of small children. He loitered in the vicinity of schools, or in darkened hallways and stairways, and imitated the behavior of a man about to urinate. At the approach of a child, he quickly unbuttoned his trousers and mumbled, "Wait a minute, I'll show you something very pretty, such as you've never seen yet." After the act, he would run off, very much disgusted with himself. Having noticed that alcohol made him succumb to his compulsion, he gave up drinking altogether; but he took a drink or two to strengthen his courage once the urge was there. An exhibitionistic urge was always ushered in by a vehement anxiety, by frequent urination, a tickling and pricking in the urethra, by diarrhoea, cold sweat, and congestion, all of which disappeared after the act. During the act, he had no sense of danger or ridicule, and at times he masturbated in front of the children. Only once had he met—in a grove near a summer hotel—a small girl who curiously watched the whole procedure. He invited her to stroke his organ, but when she made a move to do so, he became panicky, woke from his trance, and ran away. Much to the surprise of his wife, he left the hotel and the place in a frantic hurry. The patient was beset by frequent depression and displayed various forms of infantile reactions. His childish behavior when playing games with his children has been commented on by his wife. Unfortunately, his urge drove him to expose his body even to his own children, and for a while he insisted on sharing the bathtub with them. All forms of nudism, sun baths, and other "hygienic" measures connected with nakedness were his pet interests.

Like all infantilists, the patient was an excessive sleeper. He went to bed at nine in the evening and got up the following morning at eight, his head heavy with drowsiness. He also took a nap in the afternoon, whenever the circumstances permitted.

Distressed and fearful of a possible conflict with the authorities, he begged for relief from his illness. Analysis, however, was out of the question, because he lived in a distant town. He wrote frequently to report his dreams, which invariably contained scenes of undressing in front of children. The man apparently was performing in his waking life what he dreamed about at night.

Krafft-Ebing had already noted the connection between daydreams and exhibitionism and spoke of "dimmed" ("twilight") states of mind, but the main fact is that these reveries are of an infantile nature. Exhibitionism besets only those who are oriented retrospectively.[1]

The following report by Liman illustrates the relation between dream, daydream, and exhibitionism.

Case No. 45: Mr. S., high school teacher, was frequently seen as he ran through the Berlin Tiergarten with his genitals exposed. When questioned by scandalized witnesses about his misdemeanor, he explained that he had to do so to relieve his agitation. Only exposure of the genitals could quiet his nervous tension. He often dreamed of running about with his penis exposed. Such a dream usually was followed by an emission, and the patient then had several days of respite. In keeping with these dreams, the man had an overwhelming urge to actually walk about with his penis exposed during his waking hours. During the state of excitement, he was in a trance-like state or groggy as though drunk. He asserted that he never intended to assault women physically.

The important point, however, is that closer analysis usually reveals the dream and the daydream to be reproductions

[1] It seems to me that the myths which express the prohibition against looking backward show cognizance of the inherent danger. Odysseus is given Ino's veil, which carries him safely over the billows of the sea, under the condition that he cast it into the waters and never look back at it. Only then does a man sail safely through life, that is, when his childhood is shielded by this veil at which he never stares again. Lot's wife turned into a pillar of salt when she looked backward; and in this way neurotics too stiffen into the rigidity of infantilism. Many old Hindu funeral rites and sacrifices to the Erinyes and to Hecate contain similar injunctions. Orpheus loses Euridice and Aeneas loses his wife Creusa because of looking backward. We encounter the same idea in many German tales, as in the Melusine story, for example.

of definite childhood episodes. The exhibitionist becomes a
child again and plays his childish game. If he had in childhood exposed himself to adults, he would, as a grown-up
exhibitionist, perform his acts in front of grown-up girls or
women; if his childhood exposures had been part of a game
with playmates, he would be disposed to display his body in
front of children. It is because childhood "exhibitionism"
usually involves only children that most adult exhibitionists
prefer to expose themselves in front of children.

The following case offers us further insight into the psychic
mechanism of the aberration.

Case No. 46: Mr. Z.T., a twenty-four-year-old lawyer, complained of an urge to display his penis in front of little girls
and to induce them to touch it. He was also plagued by a desire
to undress children and to pat the lower parts of their bodies.
He was completely aware of the morbid nature of his urge and
implored me to rid him of it, as his entire future was in peril.
The last time he had indulged his wish, passers-by had inter-
vened and he had barely escaped being arrested and brought to
court.

The patient was a shy, irresolute man, who led a rather soli-
tary life. Between the ages of eleven and eighteen he had been
in the habit of masturbating, but he gave up this practice upon
the advice of his physician, who had pointed out the connection
between his autoerotism and his shyness and fear of blushing.
He had never yet had sexual intercourse, as his ethics and his
desire to remain pure until marriage forbade such indulgence.
He believed in total abstinence and neither drank nor smoked;
he was also a vegetarian. Exhibitionism was his only passion
and, unfortunately, too strong to be curbed. Once a month or so
the urge overpowered him and completely changed his character. He became daring and arrogant, the way he had been in
his boyhood. Lurking in the dark corridors of schools and board-
ing houses, or preferably in the passageways of music schools,
because they had less supervision and were often located in private homes, he got hold of a child, displayed his penis, and

enjoined the child to touch it. At times he stumbled upon children who were willing, but as soon as they assented, he ran, as though waking from a dream.

The patient said that in his dreams he lived through such scenes over and over, but these stereotyped scenes usually ended in emission. On the other hand, he did not remember any other dream ending in such a way. This circumstance proved to us that his libido was fixed on a definite episode.

The stereotyped content of his dreams ran more or less like this: *I am playing with a little girl whom I don't know. She lifts her skirt and shows me her genital. Thereupon I expose mine, and have the girl place her hand around it. As soon as this happens, I ejaculate and awake.*

I shall relate only the high points of his further revelations. He was conceited and firmly believed in the omnipotence of his thoughts. Infatuated with his own self, he often contemplated his naked body in the mirror, looked approvingly at the reflection of his penis, and was satisfied that its size and shape compared favorably with those of his friends.

After many sessions, he recalled a scene which, though it was always present in his mind, he had not heretofore considered worthy of telling. He had a sister two years his junior and, for months in succession, he had performed with her the scene which was now the core of his dream.

It was, then, this scene which he tried to relive in his exhibitionist acts. It required a total psychic regression for him to become a boy again and to be looking for a sister-image in the darkened halls of schools and apartment buildings. Impulsive acts nearly always indicate a regression to an infantile stage, and compulsions, according to my investigations, often prove to be observances of parental imperatives preserved from childhood. What these neurotics really want, reality cannot supply; and so they resort to the unreality of their pathological trance-state.

Let me now try to penetrate the psychological mechanism of the exhibitionist compulsion.

Infantilist aberrations are mostly of a compulsive nature and bestir themselves, as we have repeatedly shown, in a sort of twilight, pathologically dreamy state. The course of action is nearly always the same: the subject is overwhelmed by a restlessness, presaging the onrushing impulse; he has the irrepressible drive to escape, to exhaust himself in violent physical action; and his intense excitability plunges him head-on into feuds and embroilments.

Féré, in his *L'instinct sexuel* (Felix Alcan, publisher, Paris, 1899), notes the connection between exhibitionism and epilepsy,[1] a connection noticed by many others (Lasègue, Hotzen, Pribat, Lalanne, Seiffen, Krafft-Ebing, Burgl, Cramer, Charcot-Magnan, Loehr, Naecke, Moll, Bloch, *et al.*). Féré considers the exhibitionist act to be the compulsive *idée obsédante* of a degenerate, on the basis of his observations of this urge in epileptics, senile demented, alcoholics, psychopaths, idiots, and imbeciles. He totally overlooks the fact that the urge may also be observed in persons who show no trace of degeneration. Krafft-Ebing, too, notes the con-

---

[1] The sexual impulses of epileptics take on many forms. The most common is that of persistent erections. Giacchi has discerned spells of satyriasis of epileptic character in an alcoholic patient. Krafft-Ebing had the opportunity of observing a man who insisted on performing intercourse in front of the assembled family, and he also knew another man who attacked adolescent boys. Nearly always these impulses go hand-in-hand with exhibitionism, a fact noted by many observers ever since Lasègue first described it. "It should be kept in mind," he says, "that the exhibitionism of the epileptic is not necessarily accompanied by a suscitation of the genitalia, by the desire to masturbate, or by an attempt at intercourse. It may be of an automatic nature, and have no ultimate goal; it may be provoked by an urge to urinate, by way of compulsive compliance to an hallucinatory order, or by an urge to uncover parts of the body. Questioning the epileptic is usually of little use, as his memory is blacked out. The impulsive acts serve the purpose of sexual gratification, but the choice of objects strangely exceeds the range of ordinary ones. An epileptic may attack an old woman as easily as an immature girl. In many instances, there is a complete disregard for the sex of the object. Of all degenerates, the epileptics display the most marked symptoms of psychic disintegration and the crudest, commonest teratological stigmata. Their sexual desire is often enfeebled or suppressed, their intercourse is slow and incomplete. In some instances, intercourse is made impossible through overexcitement and premature ejaculation. Epileptics tend to withdraw from their fellow men, to be shy and bigoted. They may masturbate unconsciously in their sleep and also often exert a strong homosexual attraction."

nection between exhibitionism and epilepsy, and stresses the dream-like, impulsive nature of the performance. More than that, he reports a case of alternating epileptic and exhibitionist spells. Bloch accepts the distinction between an "exhibitionist act" and "exhibitionism" advanced by Burgl, according to which the former designates a single occurrence of self-exposure, and the latter refers to frequent or habitual exposures. The first may occur in the life of normal individuals, and the second is characteristic of psychopathological or mentally deficient persons (except those who practice exhibitionism out of "moral depravity").

The crux of the matter is that the term "exhibitionism" is not properly used and that it is applied to acts which in our opinion are not aberrations at all. Nearly all men derive greater or lesser pleasure from baring their body, and, within limits, such behavior is part and parcel of the psychophysiology of Eros. Self-exposure becomes a pathological practice, however, when it exceeds all sensible limits and when it is compulsive. The essence of the aberration is its compulsive nature: that is, the subjugation of the patient's will power to the irrepressible urge despite his awareness of the senselessness and antisocial character of the urge. The origin of a compulsive idea is to be seen in the repression of an unacceptable idea and the subsequent displacement of the liberated affect onto another idea which is less embarrassing. This formulation applies generally in contradistinction to Freud's well-known first formulation, which was limited in scope. "All compulsive ideas are transformations of self-accusations which keep re-emerging from their repression and are always concerned with sexual, pleasurable actions performed in infancy."

Clearly, Freud's formula does not embrace compulsive exhibitionist impulses under study in this chapter. It could, at best, be applied to the self-accusation after the act has been performed and be concerned with this last, single act, in

which case the self-accusation should be regarded as a reiteration of an old childhood compunction.

We must, however, look elsewhere for an explanation of
the mechanism of the compulsive drive which, incidentally,
is operative also in kleptomania. The compulsive idea is a
compelling desire to re-live an old experience; it is the chase
after a sensation experienced in the remote past.

We discern the same pressing, hunting quest in severe cases
of systematized fetishism. Time and again, analysis reveals
the obsessive impulse to be a chasing after the infantile past.

The old experience (the "psychic trauma," as it were)
serves as a nucleus of the fantasy which the afflicted craves
to see materialized in real life. The fantasy structure itself
may be forgotten or repressed, or the person may be completely unaware of the connection between the fantasy and
his compulsive urge, since these always aim at the "forbidden." A compulsive act is never an accepted one. Even when
it looks legitimate or harmless, like the *"folie de toucher,"*
for instance, it emerges in analysis as a socially inacceptable
operation. The pathological "palpator" who compulsively
touches everything is obsessed with the unconscious desire
to contact a tabooed sexual object.

The following is a case of exhibitionism, from my own
files, which clearly illumines the mechanism of the compulsive drive involved.

Case No. 47: A photographer and variety artist, aged thirty-
nine, was brought to court for violation of Article 519 of the
Austrian penal code. He was caught in the act of exposing himself to a ten-year-old girl. The defendant escaped conviction
because the only witness of the act, the man who had caused the
arrest, did not appear at the trial. When the defendant was released, he came to my office and implored me to cure him of
his affliction by means of hypnosis.

I wish, at this point, to make it clear that no lasting results
can be achieved through hypnotic treatment of compulsions

of this kind. Deep sleep can only rarely be achieved, and the induced, temporary quiescence of the drive soon disappears. All these neurotics want to be cured quickly if possible by the magic of a hypnotic order, for thus they hope to avoid the pains of telling and learning the truth about themselves. But the cure can only be the end product of a laborious struggle. The patient must have the opportunity of seeing what he has to struggle against so that the repressed and displaced affects may be released. For these reasons I refused to administer hypnosis and I proceeded with analysis.

The family history of the patient furnished no unusual data; his parents were healthy people, and there were among his next of kin neither mentally ill nor otherwise grossly abnormal persons. The patient himself was educated and showed no outward signs of degeneracy. When he was six years old, his mother died, and he came into an orphanage. He was somewhat slow in learning, but he retained well what he had learned. After his father had married a second time, the boy returned home and witnessed the constant quarrel between his father and his stepmother, who were extremely jealous of each other. The boy's life, never joyful, became even less so after he returned home from the orphanage. His relations with father were excellent, but the whims and the severity of his stepmother oppressed him. Strangely enough, she was not prudish in his presence; she washed, bathed, and undressed in front of him without reluctance. The sight of her nude body excited him and gave his sexual desires an early start. At the age of twelve he began to masturbate.[1]

When he was going on thirteen, his stepmother grew ever more intimate with him. In the absence of his father, who trav-

---

[1] Naecke sees the source of exhibitionism in frequent masturbation and the coincidental loss of prudishness toward one's own body. I do not share this view. It is well-known that masturbators are generally bashful and undress most reluctantly in anyone's presence. This does not preclude the possibility that an exhibitionist may indulge in masturbation, and that like all sexual neurotics—in conflict with the prevailing moral code—he seeks a form of gratification that is more subservient to his fantasy than normal intercourse.

eled much in line of duty, she often lay with him in his bed, touched his genitals, and gave him all sorts of sexual information. Then one day the boy and his stepmother performed regular intercourse. The woman lay on the boy and he experienced a vehement orgasm with ejaculation for the first time.

The boy was ashamed of his deed and the thought of his father made him feel miserable; he could not look straight into father's face. But all his good resolutions were in vain. His relations with his stepmother continued for a whole year, and at the close of the relations the boy at times performed the act in normal position, casting off his passive role.

At the age of fourteen, he left the house to become a waiter apprentice. He was not interested in girls. His thoughts were preoccupied with his pretty stepmother, and he lived for the rare occasions when he could go home and have intercourse with her. In the long intervals he masturbated, the vision of stepmother always before him.

His hobby was occultism. He learned magic tricks and became so proficient that he soon began earning a living as a magician. He always had the conviction that he was endowed with supernatural powers and that his abilities exceeded those of any other boy. That his stepmother had come to him seemed to him the fruit of his omnipotent wish. He also believed in the great appeal of his physique; his stepmother had always praised his form.

When he was seventeen he volunteered for military service, and he served seven years in peacetime and three years during the war (World War I—*The Editor*). His promotions, up to the grade of master-sergeant, his many decorations, and his blameless record proved beyond doubt that he was not psychologically "deficient."

As for his sexual life, he gave me the following data: He kept up his masturbation, his only salvation when the exhibitionist urge came upon him. He was interested in mature women and, only by way of exception, in girls. However, he never had the courage to approach either women or girls. (He also alleged that he never had an opportunity to become intimate with women. There was, however, reason to believe that he simply had not been able to free himself from the fixation on his stepmother.)

When the boy was nineteen his father died and his stepmother got married a second time. It was then that he suddenly felt an aversion toward all women. In his hatred toward females he began to imitate the homosexuality of other artists, and, when masturbating, conjured up visions of boys he liked. But he was never actually intimate with any boy.

At the age of twenty his heterosexual desires reawakened, but he cared only for very young girls. A girl approaching eighteen was already too old for his taste. He preferred girls between eight and fourteen, and the sight of their nude little feet, or of their panties, aroused him.

The urge to expose himself in front of such girls came over him when he was at work, and it had such an impact on him that he was not able to resist. In a sort of daze he had to proceed with the gratification of his urge, or else get relief from his obsession by masturbation.

He was so miserable about this that he was ready to do anything to get rid of it; he even earnestly inquired whether castration would be of any help.

I might add here one more detail from this case history. When the patient was nine years old, he went with a group of other children into a forest reservation. One of the older children, a girl of eleven, suggested that they all undress and show each other their genitals. Ever since, the patient's thoughts frequently went back to that childhood scene, although, at the time, he had bashfully run away from the group.

Schrenck-Notzing, in his *Kriminalpsychologische und psychopathologische Studien* (Leipzig, 1902), points out the infantile origin of exhibitionism. He tells of a patient who in his childhood had taken part in games at which the children paraded their uncovered genitalia. But such reminiscences are common in the analyses of nearly all neurotics. As I said before, with children exhibitionism is rather the rule than the exception. Left to their own devices, children will frequently end up inspecting each other's genital organs. And yet not all of them become adult exhibitionists, although some of them may grow up to indulge in the mild, socially acceptable forms of exhibitionism, such as wearing low necklines, adhering to nudist cults, or being addicted to sun baths. In no way can those childhood games be made responsible for the overwhelming urge in the pathological adult, an urge which so often becomes a social menace.

Years ago I pointed out one specific psychological generator of exhibitionism—the belief in the omnipotence of one's own personality and specifically the belief in the irresistible effect of one's own genitalia ("The Psychology of Exhibitionism," *Zentralblatt fuer Psychoanalyse,* I, 1911).

To this, Freud added: "It seems to me very plausible to assume that the unconscious narcissistic component of exhibitionism may also account for the role undressing played in the evil-averting rites of the ancient peoples." [1]

Havelock Ellis and Moll, in their *Handbook of Sexology,* likewise stress the exhibitionist's desire to produce a grandiose impression. Unfortunately, these authors come close to the truth without ever grasping it. They see the exhibitionist's urge to evoke strong responses in the environment, but they do not see the nature of these responses—that is, admiration. And, in the case reported by Garnier concerning a patient who avidly wanted to know what people thought of him, we perceive the same craving for a confirmation of the neurotic's self-admiration. By the way, Garnier brings the verbatim utterance of another patient, who performed his exhibitionist acts in churches. "I watch the reaction of the ladies as they see my penis. I watch for an expression of

[1] Many legends confirm the deep-seated popular understanding for the belief in the irresistibility of one's own seductive features. We may mention only the tale of Phryne and of her appearance before her judges in the bewitching nude. Numerous real-life stories echo this ancient saga. The Frankfurter Zeitung reported some time ago a scene in a courtroom of Venice, Italy. A female defendant suddenly stripped off her clothes in front of the judges to whom she exclaimed, "Look, gentlemen, see how beautiful I am!" (The poor lady got six months for her "Phryne-ism.")

great joy in their faces. I wish they were compelled to admit to themselves, 'How impressive is nature when seen in this form.' " Later I shall have a few words to say about the psychic background of the self-exposure in churches, which is relatively frequent.

Stanley Hall characterizes exhibitionism as an atavistic vestige of the phallic cult, whereas Havelock Ellis and Moll designate exhibitionism as pseudo-atavistic. "Far from experiencing the re-emergence of an old instinct," they say, "the exhibitionist is rather thrown back to a primitive state of mind. The atrophy within him of the higher feelings civilization has developed clears the way for a new growth of correspondingly low drives."

It is my contention, however, that we deal here not with an atavistic, but an infantilistic phenomenon. Obviously, in conformity with the basic biogenetic law the latter recapitulates the former.

The child is always narcissistically oriented and believes in his magic omnipotence. By the same token, the infant is always an exhibitionist and is only gradually curbed by training into due regard for social propriety. On the other hand, the adult exhibitionist, who is under the impact of his urge, reverts to the state of a child, to infantile values; he "grants" other people the favor of his exposure. And because, while the urge lasts, he is again a child himself, he usually prefers the company of children.

In the case of the photographer (Case No. 47), we noted the fact that his stepmother had praised his physical appearance. She had thus reinforced his existing infantile narcissism. Besides, from his early youth he was interested in magic; he was a prestidigitator by trade, and by sleight-of-hand he tricked people into believing that he possessed superior powers. Naturally enough, he also craved to bewitch others with his phallus, his priceless possession, the object of his own love and admiration. He acted like King Kandaules—in Hebbel's play *Gyges and His Ring*—who is not satisfied with the sole possession of the beautiful woman and wants his possession to be seen, admired and envied.

Every exhibitionist wants to be envied for the possession of whatever part of his body with which he is infatuated.

The part exposed in the act is the exhibitionist's chief erogenous zone. If he happens to believe in the magic power of his penis, he will exhibit just that. But other parts of his body may just as well be objects of predilection and exposure, e.g., buttocks.

Rousseau's paranoia was directly related to his latent homosexuality in which the buttocks had erogenous precedence. Rousseau had experienced pleasure when beaten on his backside by his governess. Throughout his life he sought to experience a repetition of this sensation. Rousseau's *Confessions* present also another interesting point—that of exposing one's self to the world "in writing." It is this, the "psychic exhibitionism," which can well be perceived as a source of all literary creativity and histrionic art.[1]

Burgl, who is eminently versed in the subject matter, also notes that indecent contact or rape are only seldom parts of the exhibitionist performance. The most common and harmless form of exhibitionism is exposure in the act of micturition. Having urinated, the exhibitionist suddenly turns round, if and when he senses women or children are in the vicinity. This way he can always plead inadvertence or absentmindedness if he is accused. Of course, the masturbation act which takes place during or after the exposure is also of infantile nature.

In discussing masturbation, I pointed out the paramount significance of the daydreams accompanying the act. The fantasy evoked by the masturbator during the act has its origin in a childhood scene—either actual or imaginary, which he is trying to re-live.

[1] Wilhelm Stekel, *Dichtung und Neurose,* J. F. Bergmann, Wiesbaden.

This explains the trance-like state of the exhibitionist, a state which has been noted by every observer and most accurately described by Krafft-Ebing. The exhibitionist lives his daydream. The struggle between reality and fantasy within his mind ends with the triumph of the compulsion to re-live a thrilling sensation, and, like an actor, the exhibitionist performs for his own enjoyment, and occasionally shifting the roles, the specific scene of his own past.

Exhibitionists, kleptomaniacs, pyromaniacs, mashers, braid-clippers, urolagnists, renifleurs, all and sundry infantilists, driven by their obscure impulses to perform antimoral and antisocial acts, chase infantile sensations. In the grip of the spell they all become awkward, silly-looking children, and when the trance-like state is gone, when they wake up and become aware of the foolishness of their behavior, they are bewildered, horrified, deeply pained.

Let us now return to Case No. 47. The patient, as we know, had been seduced by his stepmother. For two years prior to that experience he had been witnessing the woman's undressing while she shamelessly and temptingly displayed her body to the boy by way of preparing for the future seduction. This whole process of temptation, with its culmination in seduction, fatally determined the patient's life. He became forever fixated to his stepmother. He admitted as much himself when he said that in all the ten years of his military service he never bothered with women because he had the vision of his stepmother in his mind. When she remarried, he was overcome by jealousy and indignation to an extent that he hated all women, and he embarked on his homosexual period. The difference between this patient and other homosexuals lay in the fact that whereas the traumatic experiences and pathologic diversions of the latter belong to the remote childhood and are excluded from consciousness, or, in Freudian terminology, are repressed, his disturbing experiences occurred in puberty. In his reconstruction of the traumatic experience, the boy to whom he felt attracted became the image of his own youth, while he reserved for himself the role of his stepmother; the boy he loved was an image of himself. However, his inhibitions were yet stronger than his urge to recapitulate the experience. Besides, he had the help of masturbation as a safety valve [1] which protected society against an excess of moral offenses, and this case proves once more the correctness of my assumption. Then the patient relates that he began to fight the habit of masturbation and successfully abstained from it for periods of various lengths of time. Remarkably enough, his first exhibitionistic act came in the wake of a two-month period of abstinence. It was followed by a dash toward the safety of his home and a masturbatory act accompanied by the somewhat disguised vision of the stepmother and the seduction scene.

Painfully aware of the morbidity of his homosexual drive, he struggled against it and turned his attention to little girls, recapitulating now the old episode in a new form. He, himself, was now the stepmother, and the little girls personified the patient in his boyhood. (He identified himself with the stepmother and the girls with his infantile self.)

We shall never understand the mind of a neurotic if we fail to penetrate the mysteries of identification and differentiation, if we fail to see that homosexuals, for instance, staging their eternal scene, always switch both their own and their partners' roles.

Now that we have shown the traumatic experience of our patient and its consequences to be the origin of his exhibitionism, and the exhibitionist act itself to be a recapitulation of the traumatic experience, we still have to meet the possible argument that this case is an exceptional one. I most emphatically insist that the case is by no means unique. The more opportunities I had to gain insight into the mind and into the past experiences of neurotics, the more frequently have I uncovered accidents occurring in the course of the patient's upbringing or outright incestuous episodes. Certain acts, performed on children, inadvertently or otherwise, es-

[1] In *Auto-erotism*, Liveright Pub. Corp., New York, 1950, Stekel discusses this mechanism more thoroughly—*The Editor.*

pecially by pathological parents, by drunkards, or by psychopaths, are often graver in their consequences than are hereditary factors. I shall bring a few telling examples later in this
book.

A closer study of case histories will nearly always reveal
certain details which prove the exhibitionist's incestuous experience in the past. As the case just mentioned proves, the
experience is not necessarily a childhood one.

When we read in Merzbach's *Die krankenhaften Erscheinungen des Geschlechtssinnes* (*Pathologic Manifestations of
Sexuality*), Wien & Leipzig, Alfred Hoelder, Verlag, 1909,
p. 339, of a man whose exhibitionist urge became first manifest on the day of his mother's death, our experience justifies
the suspicion that there is a definite relation between the
exhibitionist act and some erotic incident involving the
mother. One of Moll's patients told him that he first felt an
urge to expose himself when, at the age of five, he once
looked at a family portrait. When he grew up and married,
the urge disappeared; but later in life it re-emerged, particularly on those occasions when his wife refused to submit to
him and warded off his attempts with vile, abusive words.

Time and again I have found that infantile aberrations
emerge when the normal form of gratification is either hampered or hurtful. In the case just quoted, the man's humiliation by his spouse caused him to regress to an infantile form
of gratification.

But to produce active exhibitionism requires an irrepressible urge to experience one's fantasy in reality. The obsessive aims of this fantasy are similar to those of kleptomania.[1]

Thus, my previous definition of obsessions as products of

[1] Kleptomania, too, is characterized by a transfer of affect. The klepto-
maniac has the urge to do something forbidden (in the case of women, most
frequently it is a desire to hold something forbidden in their hands). What
the kleptomaniacs do is obviously a substitute action which is even more
"immoral" (Otto Gross).

repression of unacceptable ideas and the subsequent attachment of the freed affect to other, less unpleasant ideas, can
be modified and made applicable to compulsions in the following manner: compulsions are substitutes for other intended actions which are vetoed by the ethical ego. The
affect which is made floating because of the repression of
the unacceptable act becomes attached to a substitute action.
As the latter is only a symbolic substitute for the unconscious
action, it never brings complete gratification, and the urge
persists forever.

Freud's definition of obsessions—quoted above—besides being applicable only to certain cases, fails, through its stress
on the element of self-accusation, to explain the mechanism
of compulsions which are in essence attempts to recapitulate,
in disguised forms, the pleasurable childhood actions.

The afore-mentioned patient is still in love with his stepmother, and all his longing is for a revival of the love scenes
between him and his first seductress.[1] He does not admit to
himself the existence of that love and of that desire, and his
affect is displaced to the impulse of self-exposure in front
of children. In the state of extreme excitement accompanying the act he is able to re-live the scene with his stepmother.

The neurotic's clinging to his first sexual experience confirms Binet's theory concerning the varied forms of psychosexual infantilism.

Many incidental and hitherto incomprehensible traits begin to make sense.

A great many exhibitionists tend to perform their act in
churches or in other hallowed places. (One exhibitionist,
while attending a solemn performance of *Parsifal,* undressed
himself in the back of his box and stepped forward to the

---

[1] The Scandinavian writer, Gejerstamm, depicts, in his novel, *Nils Tuffesson
and his Mother,* the incestuous relation between a young man and his mother
and develops the idea that such relations are of such fixative force as to
make any eventual choice of another sexual object impossible.

railing completely naked, thus exposing himself to the view of the entire audience.)

The following case is very indicative of the psychological origin of this feature.

Case No. 49: Mr. Z.P., aged forty-two, a man of perfect health and without any symptoms of degeneracy, consulted me about his vehement urge to undress and to utter profanities in churches. He had to give up going to church and felt most unhappy about it, since he was a deeply religious man.

His mother was an alcoholic and had to be confined to an institution. Like so many alcoholics, she had many times transgressed the bounds of decency, and as she had many men "friends," the patient witnessed many shocking scenes. Once, when he was twelve years old, he watched through a keyhole his mother's rendezvous with an army officer. She was completely nude, and while the boy stared, his mother had sexual intercourse with the strange man. The impression on his mind was indelible. Again and again through the following years he visualized that scene with feelings of deep depression.

The origin of his exhibitionism then became clear to me. The patient's mother was named Mary, and to the little boy she was like the Virgin Mary. Hence, when his mother was shockingly immoral, the child projected her badness onto the Holy Mother. This was the reason why between his thirteenth and fifteenth years he was compulsively blasphemous of the Virgin Mary. Through a displacement of affect, the vilifications which were intended for his mother were consciously directed against the Mother of Jesus.

During analysis he marvelled most at the fact that, so far as he could remember, he had both loved and hated the depraved woman who had been his mother.

As he had witnessed in his youth a procession of his mother's lovers and had observed many scenes of her adultery, he developed early in his life some sexual aberrations. He had to exert a great deal of will power to keep in check his urge to expose himself, his tendency to drink, his excessive cynicism and moodiness, and other embarrassing character traits. He married and treated his wife well, but without ever being able to feel deeply for her. Later, he became frightened when he realized that he had sexual desires toward his own children. The shock of this knowledge was one of the main factors which caused him to seek treatment.

Analysis revealed that he looked toward his children for the fulfilment of the expectations which originally had been concerned with his mother. His primary emotion during the shocking scenes involving mother and men had been jealousy. He wished he were in the position of the men who possessed his mother. Now, in his renewed desire, he identified himself with his mother and the children with himself as a boy. Only his strongly developed ethical conscience prevented him from actual gratification of his morbid craving.

Psychoanalysis teaches us that the saying, "Like father, like son," is not exactly true. Daughters of dissolute women are often intensely moralistic, and sons of drunkards and playboys may become highly respectable members of the community if and when the force of differentiation from the parents is stronger than that of identification with them. At times, though, a sudden shift may occur, and a re-emergence of identification may bring about a change in character. Specifically, in old age, when, because of organic changes in the brain, many inhibitions are cast off, primary character traits may re-emerge. This is the reason behind the many cases of old-age exhibitionism, which are considered indicative of incipient senile dementia. Old age is susceptible to regressions.

Exhibitionism is much more general than it may seem. Years of analytical practice have given me evidence that there are many people who masturbate in front of a mirror, while they are immersed in reveries, usually of an infantile nature. The masturbatory act as such may at times be omitted, as in cases of a purely psychic autoerotism. Such are, for instance, the neurotics who cover all the surfaces of their rooms with mirrors in order to see themselves from all angles. An exhibitionist component is implicit in all narcissism.

The following case demonstrates clearly that looking at the mirror may be the prelude to an exhibitionist act.

Case No. 50: Miss S.W., a school teacher of thirty-five, complained of hysterical spells which were especially annoying because in such spells she usually stripped all her clothes and ran into the vestibule of the house. She lived in constant fear that a spell might one day overcome her at school and make her perform her antics in front of the "innocent children."

According to the description by her family and the family physician, the spells went like this: She began to scream, "No, no, no! I won't do it." Then she ran to and fro as though someone were chasing her, and she tore her clothes off, all the while using one hand to cover her genital region. As the spells always came on while she was either dressing or undressing, the stripping was rather easily achieved. Once she was naked, she sighed and moaned loudly and she was heard saying most distinctly, "Oh, this is too much! Too much!" She ran into the lobby and onto the street, unless she was forcibly restrained. A brief sleep-like but perturbed trance concluded the spell, and she awakened with no memories of it.

I had occasion to watch one of her spells, and I found no changes in the tendon reflexes during the spell. The corneal and laryngeal reflexes were absent, however, whether she was under a spell or not.

From her history the following data deserve to be mentioned. Her father, normally a very fine and kind man, had been a periodic drinker; while on a spree, he was boisterous, broke things, swore, and shouted threats at his children. The patient does not remember if any indecencies occurred between her and her father. But she does remember that her two brothers had played great parts in her sex life.

She was nine years old when her thirteen-year-old brother once asked her to strip for him. At first, she refused and wanted to run off, but then she agreed to go on with the game, and she let the brother do whatever he pleased. The boy performed a cunnilingus on her and she had a vehement orgasm. From then until her brother left the house a year later, the two children "often played the same game." When she was twelve, another brother, who was fourteen, came into her bed one night, and after a short interlude had intercourse with her. This sexual relationship went on for several months, but stopped when suddenly she had strong feelings of compunction.

She then began to masturbate and tried to imitate all the movements of her brothers during this act. She visualized herself as being in the nude, for this fantasy heightened her excitement.

All attempts to break the masturbation habit were in vain, but her mental state changed markedly. She became over-sensitive, prudish, aloof, so that her girl friends often laughed at her. She decided to become a teacher and was very serious about preparing for her job. She wanted to cultivate her little pupils like so many delicate flowers.

First the marriage of the elder brother, then that of the younger one, caused her to have fits of anger, jealousy, and disappointment. These marriages also precipitated periods of particularly frequent masturbation.

It was after the younger brother's marriage that her hysterical spells began. In these spells she relived the episodes with her brothers, although presumably she never gave them conscious thought.

Analysis brought quick relief. She soon married, and the latest word I had from her was that she had completely overcome her exhibitionist urge.

Another patient of mine told me that she had been abused by her father when she was seven. He had made her stroke his penis. The patient complained of an urge to loiter about public men's rooms, waiting for the men to come out so she could see them fumbling with their flies. Twice she had been "lucky" enough to stumble upon exhibitionists; after witnessing their acts, she had run home and masturbated before a mirror.

Her accusation of her father proved truthful, despite the

fact that neurotic fantasies often seriously distort the factual material. The patients may relate completely imaginary experiences as though they were real. True, the impact of these fancied experiences on the pathogenesis of the neurosis is as strong as if they had been real, and this is particularly the case when the experiences have been fixed in the mind throughout a long period of masturbation.

I was able to establish the truth of the traumatic experiences in most of the case histories to which I have referred in this chapter.

In the case of the last-mentioned patient, the experience was confirmed by her father himself. He came to my office one day, downcast and despondent, and talked of himself as of a criminal deserving the harshest punishment. He had but one excuse—that he was a sick man, and that he had done those things in a state of drunkenness; and he had sincerely hoped that his daughter would forget everything.

In conclusion, I should like to say that exhibitionism is a disease and not a depravity. Once you have got the conviction that exhibitionists suffer greatly from their compulsion, you cannot but sympathize with them. It comes as no surprise that exhibitionism may be one of the features or even the sole symptom of epilepsy, that we find exhibitionists among psychopaths, inebriates, the senile demented, and those persons in the initial stages of general paresis. When a person's inhibitions are on the wane, his infantile self takes over, and he again becomes a narcissist, an exhibitionist, a mysophiliac, and a sadist. We must therefore consider exhibitionism as a compulsion with its own psychogenetic history, to which analysis is always the clue and sometimes the remedy.

3. A CASE OF EXHIBITIONISM COMBINED WITH
A COMPULSION NEUROSIS

It is highly significant that exhibitionism frequently erupts after a period of latency. The regression expressed by exhibitionism is often induced by disillusionments—sometimes unconscious—in love relations.

Exhibitionism may be the only compulsive symptom, or it may combine with others and be buried in the pathological material of a more complicated neurosis. We may also observe the strange phenomenon of physical exhibitionism smothering every manifestation of psychic exposure in cases of extremely bashful and reticent patients. Such neurotics are also otherwise withdrawn, and their most intimate friends have no inkling of the suffering they endure. In other instances, like those of creative poets, one form of exhibitionism may change into another, or both may be present at the same time.

A highly cultivated Hungarian veterinarian, who was analyzed by one of Budapest's leading analysts, so bashfully concealed his exhibitionistic urge that he never said one word about it during his analysis.

The case of the veterinarian is also an interesting study of an *inability to love* and a so-called *manie de perfection*. Persons incapable of love are actually unable to shed their infantile fantasies or are too strongly fixated to a specific early love object. This object may well be a real one—that is, a definite person—or a fantasy image which combines the traits of several real persons. Occasionally, such an image is of a bisexual nature and represents a fusion of many persons of both sexes. It is against these visions that reality fights in vain, because reality nearly always offers only monosexual gratifications.

I have rarely met a more intelligent and brilliant person

than this patient; but he was spending all his energies on his neurotic elaborations and therefore had not fulfilled any of the expectations of those close to him.

Case No. 51: Mr. Otto W., twenty-eight, veterinarian, complained of a tormenting compulsion to do everything in a perfect manner.

For example, when he wrote an ordinary letter, he was tormented by a feeling that he had failed to express all his feelings and thoughts fully. He composed a second and a third version of the letter, and, still dissatisfied, crossed out passages, changed words, edited the text. For this purpose he always carried an eraser in his pocket, or rather one half of an eraser—he kept the second half at home—for he could rub out letters more efficiently with the edge of an eraser that had been cut.

The texture or cleanliness of the writing paper did not matter. The patient had only one concern when corresponding: *the text of the letter had to be perfect.*

He was meticulous about his possessions and collected stamps, butterflies, walking canes, and many other things. He kept the books in his library carefully arranged by subject matter and had great trouble in properly placing books on marginal, overlapping, or related subjects.

Not only had he read Freud, Adler, and Stekel so that he could be a perfect analysand, but he also related his reminiscences with minute and careful chronology.

He remembered that in his second year, his father seated him on his lap and showed him the picture of a man gripping a pistol. The baby repeated the word "pistol," pronouncing it *pipistol* and *pispistol*. Both *pipi* (pee-pee) and *pis pis* may have had a connection with the father's urination, but the patient insisted that he could not connect the words with anything.

He went through a blasphemous period between the ages of three and four and had a recurrence of this in his sixth and seventh years. The depreciating tendency stayed with him in the following years. At about the same time he was greatly impressed when the housemaid let him urinate in the open during a stroll. At the age of five he had a "crush" on a servant girl, and the pain he felt when his mother discharged her remained in his memory.

Here is the first dream he brought to me:

I am going to school where Professor N. is supposed to talk on a current topic, something like commemorating a recently deceased anatomy teacher. I am late, and I slowly open the classroom door. I believe I have erred, as I see two girls playing chess or checkers, but soon Professor N. enters the room and I know that I am in the right place. I regret not being dressed for the occasion, although the suit I am wearing is not bad. Professor N. salutes me, ironically, "Hello, Mister Representative!" and the insult makes me very angry. I refrain, however, from giving him the answer he deserves. Then the professor asks me whether I have lost my eraser, and he pulls out of his pocket one half of an eraser which I recognize as mine.

His associations with some of the dream elements revealed his extreme sensitivity to teasing and condescending remarks (professor's salute). He had always been a brilliant student, and was tragically aware that he had not fulfilled the expectations of his family and friends.

He did not, however, associate the professor with me, and he also had no idea that he had compared analysis with dissection. But his hostile attitude toward me was nonetheless apparent. (By the way, the day before, I had greeted him—he was a veterinarian—as though he were a colleague, that is, a fellow physician.)

Continuing his reminiscences, he told me that upon the birth of his younger brother he had an attack of asthma. He was seven years and three months old at the time, and he remembered clearly that his mother was not able to come to his help.

He related his asthma to constipation, to the stagnation of stool in the flexura sigmoidea.

As far as his relation to his brothers went, he confessed to hatred toward the older one who took away all his girls, but he claimed that he was not jealous of the younger brother.

He was sexually aroused for the first time while climbing a tree. He remembered also that urinating on a gooseberry bush aroused him. The patient soon brought a dream which was concerned with his relations to his father:

I am about to change my occupation, because great financial interests are at stake. On the street, I meet an acquaintance, Mr. S. He is walking with his father, and the two men stop by a music shop and talk. They don't see me, but I can hear their conversation. S. says to his father, 'You're going to give me five hundred kronen, aren't you?' And his father replies, 'I am. That will be better than to let you go bankrupt.'

The patient keenly felt the fact that he was still financially dependent on his father. Simultaneously, he resented his father's inability to make money "quick" during the war. On the other hand, he also had a long-standing grudge against his father who had once lost his money on the stock exchange.

The meticulous bookkeeping showed his father that he was not as irresponsible as he believed his parent thought.

In this connection, the patient's relations to Jews was of great significance. There were Jews in all his dreams. His attitude toward the Jewish race vacillated between appreciation of Jewish realism, drive, and vitality, and outspoken anti-Semitism. He believed that there had been some Jews among his ancestors, and maintained that "some of his best friends" were Jews.

He related the following apparently strange dream:

I am walking on a street paved with wooden blocks, and I feel a strong urge to pick my nose. I eat the pickings, and I suddenly dig out of my nostril a large worm, a triangularly shaped leech. There are two maidservants present, and I put the leech into the hand of one of them, but the creature does not take to the girl. I put it on the lower arm of the second maid, and the leech begins to suck.

Reluctantly, the patient told me that both his father and himself were in the habit of picking their nostrils. The patient still had the urge to eat the mucus of his nose. He felt no disgust whatsoever toward any of his secretions, and he had tasted all of them.

He had gone through a period—a Jewish period, as he called it—of acting like a Nietzschean Renaissance man—a Superman, without moral, ethical, or esthetic inhibitions. At the time, he even tasted the urine of a woman he loved.

But the dream also showed elements of a blood complex. He liked to lick his own blood, and he ate rare or undercooked meats. He was a vampire of sorts, and in the habit of sucking a woman's skin on one spot until blood oozed.

In his associations to the dream, he remembered that the leech had swollen with the intake of blood, and this had reminded him of the erection. The patient had always disliked his small-sized nose, because he believed that women judged the size of a man's penis by the size of his nose. He was dissatisfied with the size of his penis, and he had his doubts about being able to satisfy a woman. He identified the nose in the dream with the genital organ.

The leech was also connected with his preoccupation with money. He was a leech himself, sucking his father; he was a parasite.

Another aspect of the dream was its relation to me and to analysis. He did not like the idea of paying me. He was perfectly able, he believed, to digest his own "filth," and to pull his worms out of his nose, as he put it.

The dream reported by the patient on the following day went like this:

I am at a party. I believe it's a party for children. I meet a girl, Elizabeth; she looks pretty, but her hair is not black; she is fair-haired now, an officer has brought me to her, and now he is watching over our rendezvous so that we shall not be disturbed.

I hear someone say that Colonel L. has written a book, and I see L.'s card on which all his titles and decorations are listed. Then I hear that he has committed suicide.

When the patient was twenty, he met Elizabeth, and although she was only thirteen, he often kissed her passionately in the unlit hall of the house and on the beach. Young children aroused him sexually.

Earlier—at the age of seventeen—he fell in love with a twelve-year-old girl named Helen, fair-haired and strikingly pretty (this explains Elizabeth's change in the dream from black-haired to blonde). He loved Helen for many years, and had intended to take up another course of studies which would have permitted him to be near her. However, in reply to a cordial invitation from her, he had written a rude letter to Helen and her mother, and the two had ignored him ever since. Apparently the patient never reconciled himself to the loss, although he tried to find all sorts of faults with the girl. He alleged that she was an illegitimate child, that her mother was a "kept" woman, and that he had discovered traces of what he thought was hereditary syphilis in the girl. *His own mother had been violently opposed to Helen.*

All these data made the second part of his dream somewhat clearer. He regarded his behavior as suicide. Had he married Helen, he would have achieved the high rank and status of a colonel. As it was, he was spiritually broken, and he tried to forget his anguish through sensual pleasures with other girls.

There was still another meaning to the dream. His brother was actually a colonel in the army, and had received many decorations for valor. The patient wished death to this brother, so that his own share of the inheritance would be larger.

The patient is torn between asceticism and libertinism. In his childhood he had gone through a period of extreme religiousness, which was to recur in adulthood. He studied many mystic doctrines before he became an adept of Spinoza and embarked upon the Superman philosophy of Nietzsche. Lately, his ascetic intervals had grown longer and longer, while he looked for rational, hygienic reasons to explain his abstentions. Thus he advanced his intention to prevent arteriosclerosis as his motivation for not smoking. Sexual intercourse caused him all kinds of belated pains, he asserted.

Like so many intellectuals, he tried to discuss analysis with me rather than to come forth with data, and he generally offered extreme resistance. However, many of his dreams revealed the presence of paraphilic cravings such as a wish for anilingus, intra-uterine fantasies, and a poison complex. He had dabbled intensively in poison chemistry, including experiments with potassium cyanide; apparently he had fantasies about doing away with his brothers.

The following dreams revealed a fixation and another hitherto undisclosed preoccupation.

(1) *Clad only in pajamas, I leave the house and come to some sort of porch. It is midnight, and I am very cold. I am looking through the glassed-in porch, but I cannot get out of it, although I have a key. At length, mother returns home, hears my knocking and yelling, and sets me free. She is sorry for me and loves me dearly.*

(2) *I say to our dog the words "particulier" and "public figure" (private and public figure). To my great surprise, she repeats the words after me. I call for my brother, and we experiment with the dog. She speaks like a parrot, but in a fine nasal voice. We are so happy and yet so afraid she should stop talking before the rest of the family hears her, but the dog goes on talking quite spontaneously. I say to my brother, 'Such a clever bitch deserves a more humane treatment.' But my brother objects with the words: 'She has been contented, happy, and rather grateful until now, she needs no more.'*

The first dream showed the patient's fixation on his mother. He saw himself in Vienna, out in the cold. The glassed-in porch signified that I could see through him. He had the key to his illness; all he lacked was the will to use it. He wanted to go back to mother: her love was all he wanted. He had intended to break off analysis on the previous day. Only his mother's love could save him. I did not love him enough, and he was freezing in my presence. He needed love, not insight.

The second dream requires some explanation. There was indeed a female dog in the house of the patient's father. Liked by every member of the family, the dog was rather spoiled. But to the patient, both in his dreams and in real life, the dog symbolized his mother. The treatment accorded her did not seem good enough to him. He had a feeling that his father had not been fair to his mother. When his father had lost his money on the stock exchange, his mother had had to go into business and help support the family.

The patient explained the French word "particulier" as follows: "Particuliers" were people who did not work. They were like visitors at a factory; that is, they watched others work but did nothing themselves. He did not want to get well because he wanted to remain an onlooker all through his life. He wanted to remain an invalid and thus force his father to leave a greater share of his fortune to him than to the other two sons.

The "public figure" of the dream was indicative of his ambition to fulfil a great historical mission, to be a man of God's choice.

The word "particulier" had also a more important, deeper relation to the patient's intra-uterine fantasy. "Part" is "partus" —parturition—childbirth; "cul"—French for buttock—referred to his anal complex. In his childhood he had thought that babies come out through the rectum. This also gives us a clue as to the origin of his asthma. The night he had the dream, he suffered several attacks of asthma. He denied any connection between the experiences, but he could not deny that at the time of birth of his younger brother he had been plagued by a stretch of severe asthma. Shortly after his brother's birth he had inquired of his mother how children came into the world. It could be assumed that in his asthma attack, the patient reconstructed the act of childbirth.

Other dreams and associations pointed to the patient's fantasies of lust murder and to all sorts of sexual abnormalities with dead or dying persons, and especially with the bodies of people who had just died. Acts of sodomy, too, occurred in his fancies. He had in his room a sort of dummy consisting of the photographed head of a woman and a vagina made of plastic and covered with the skin of tripe bought at the butcher's. He would stand in front of this dummy and masturbate.

He reported the following dream:

I am near the window on the landing of a stairway, then I shift to another window, show my penis to several ladies and young girls who are passing, and I masturbate. I do so only when they look away from me, but I suddenly notice that I have been watched by several people who are yet at a distance, but coming toward me.

In the wake of this dream came a succession of rapid revelations and admissions. It turned out that he was plagued by a strong exhibitionist urge. He performed his acts in front of windows preferably while riding in a railroad train, so that he could be seen by women and girls outside. Of course, he was always on the lookout for an empty car or compartment; and he was also careful to hide his face. Occasionally, he exposed himself and masturbated in public places and in parks, but only when it was safe to do so. If and when he was unable to choose the conditions, he resigned himself to standing in the nude before the curtains of his room and masturbating at the sight of girls passing in the street. According to his account he never exposed himself in front of children, but occasionally he locked himself up in the bathroom and masturbated while looking at children playing outside.

This, then, was the aberration he had not mentioned to his doctor in the first analysis. It was safe to assume that this was not the only paraphilia he was concealing. By his own admission his sexual interest in children was much stronger than he had first acknowledged. Thus he told me of an occasion when, while making use of the momentary absence of a governess, he had raised a three-year-old girl high up in the air and looked at her genitals. He had erections when he played with children.

The patient dreamed: *"I am with mother and Susi G. Susi and I talk of love and the like. I make many allusions and at length get so far that I have only to utter a few more words and the girl and I will become engaged. But I don't want to be engaged. Mother does not like the turn our conversation has taken. She probably fears either an eventual betrothal or the disillusionment of the girl's family if nothing happens. All of a sudden I am in bed, and just getting up. I am wearing my purple pajamas, but only the top. As I get out of bed, mother can see my genitals, while the girl can't."*

This dream pointed to the fact that the patient's exhibitionist acts were repetitions of infantile patterns in which his naked body had been handled by his mother. The dream also revealed that in his fixation to his mother he was not free to love someone else. Susi represented Helen, the girl whom he had wanted to marry at the age of seventeen, but whom he had had to give up because of his mother's objections. It was that emotional obstruction which caused his regression to his mother and to all the infantile traits which were present in such abundance in his make-up.

The patient's dreams, associations, and recollections of certain events (like the sojourn of a eunuch healer in town many years before) indicated the presence of a castration complex, associated with fantasies of chastity.

There were indications of the presence of deeper sources of the complex. There was both a castration fear and a dark desire to castrate someone for a refused pleasure. Analysis of some of the patient's symbolic gestures revealed to me that he associated castration with jealous vengeance on his father.

The patient's way of smoking his cigars was remarkable. He treated every cigar like an object of love. He looked at the cigar with tender eyes from every angle, and when he at last put a match to it, he smoked it very slowly, trying to prolong the pleasure. When he had no cigar, he ate sweets eagerly in an obvious urge to stimulate the erogenous zone of his mouth, while constantly speaking of his fear of an oral carcinoma.

He offered me a cigar every day and was indignant over my refusals to accept his offer. One day he came to a session and told me that the night before he had been in a brothel, and that in his great sexual excitement he had made the prostitute perform a fellatio on him. He was still surprised at what he had done; but to me it was now clear that the innumerable requests and demands and detailed tasks he had been presenting to me throughout analysis had been only substitutes for his one and only real wish—that fellatio be performed on him. This thought, which seemed absurd, was based on a youthful experience. A somewhat older friend, who had introduced him to masturbation, wished to perform a fellatio on him. His inhibitions at the time were so strong that he resisted the temptation. His friend then performed the act on another playmate. The patient must have been regretting his rejection of the offer ever since. In conjunction with his castration complex, fellatio loomed prominently in all his reveries.

I understood now his first dream of the professor showing him one half of an eraser. The professor had shown the patient a castrated penis, the other half of which was in the patient's possession. The patient's hatred for the professor was really hatred for his father. In the course of the first analysis, in Budapest, the patient had played with the idea of killing the analyst. This would have been a patricide.

He was exhibitionistic and masturbated in the bathroom. On the other hand, many of his dreams revealed that the intra-uterine fantasy was paramount in his day dreams and that his asthma was related to both his fantasy and to his childhood conception of birth. His asthma had set in at the age of five, and had persisted until the present time. He still woke up nearly every night, and he had to inhale fumes of stramonium before he could go to sleep again. At our first sessions he had light asthma attacks as soon as he lay down. It seemed clear, therefore, that the fellatio fantasy which began to emerge more strongly in the later sessions was also tied up with his fantasy.

It was at this juncture that he haltingly admitted the following significant fact: The asthma attacks, and especially the inhalations (cigar smoke!), caused him to experience vehement erections.

After a series of dreams revealing his fixation on the unsuccessful romance with the girl Helen, and his subsequent vacillations and tormenting confusion, he told the following incident:

A friend once asked him whether he had ever had sexual relations with Helen. The very question had such an impact on him and had aroused him to such an extent that he had immediately performed an exhibitionistic act. It was the first impulsive exposure of his life.

This case is a clear demonstration of exhibitionism emerging in the wake of erotic frustration. The only phase of reality which might have cured him of all his infantilistic tendencies was his love for Helen. When he lost her, he lost everything, and entrenched himself behind his infantile ramparts. In his fantasy he went on indulging in his eternal urge to expose to Helen's view the beauties of his physique, in order to enchant and bewitch her into accepting him again.

Chapter Five

EXCRETORY SEXUALITY

Chapter Five

EXCRETORY SEXUALITY

1. Uro-Erotism

It is not sufficiently well known that the passage of urine frequently serves the infant as a form of sexual gratification. According to Freud, the development of the genital zone to its dominant role in sexual life occurs in puberty after all other erogenous zones have been relegated to secondary positions. This generally correct view requires one rather important qualification. The genital organs tend to acquire primary significance even in the first years of life. I would go as far as to say that this is the rule and that the strongest sexual stimulations are most pronounced in those parts of the body which are organically predestined to play a prominent part in all future sex life.

To be sure, such stimulations do not at first go hand in hand with outspokenly sexual functions. But they concur with the other functions of the genital organs, and micturition is, of course, one of them. The life of the infant may be conceived as a succession of pleasurable sensations interrupted by short or long intervals of discomfort. The infant derives its pleasure not only from sucking, but also from moving its bowels, passing urine, muscular motility, being bathed, scratching, and from the humid warmth of soiled diapers.

The infant's blissful facial expression during micturition often betrays its pleasure. At a later stage, babies indulge in all sorts of playful handling of the performance. For instance, they try to retard urination to increase the pleasure of the initial pressure of urine against the sphincters.

Older children often admit that they experience a pleasurable prickly sensation at the passage of urine. The occasional final stricture of the bladder muscles brings a slight pleasurable thrill. It is a fact known to few pediatricians that micturition is the given form of infantile emission. It is very often also the culmination of the infantile auto-erotic act: that is, a sort of orgasm.

All these findings are of prime importance, if only because they help us to understand the psychodynamics of bedwetting (enuresis nocturna), and the almost as frequent inability to control the bladder in daytime. The nocturnal enuresis, properly speaking, is only one form of deficient bladder control, and we should justly use the word enuresis as a general term.

Sadger, in his excellent paper on "Urethral Erotism" (*Yearbook of Psychoanalytic Research*, Vol. LI, I. F. Deuticke, Publisher, Vienna and Leipzig), is correct in saying, "It may be safely formulated as a rule that enuresis, beyond the physiologically justified period, makes its appearance whenever a child develops an excessive sensitiveness for the pleasure of urination."

I have been greatly interested in the psychology of enuresis and have made it my duty to study a wealth of material on the subject gathered in a children's clinic. These studies entitle me to confirm fully Sadger's views.

Some enuretics, I might add, show a constitutional predisposition, in the form of a myelodysplastic syndrome (so designated by Fuchs,[1] but vigorously denied by Zappert [2]), such as a more or less hidden spina biffida, flaccid sphincters, underdevelopment of the lower extremities and other malformations. But these cases constitute, according to my data, not more than two per cent of the clinical total.

This numerical proportion prevailed also in the large military hospital in which I headed the neurological ward, but my experience with enuretic soldiers was that the percentage of myelodysplasia was somewhat greater. Most cases of adult enuresis prove to be pronounced forms of psychosexual infantilism and can be understood only in this light. All enuretic children display certain identical traits which I should like to describe first.

Except for constitutionally conditioned enuretics who remain bedwetters throughout life, children usually go through a post-infancy period of latent enuresis. They learn to control their bladder at the end of the first, or sometimes in their second year, and become bed-wetters again after a period of several years, usually at the age of six, for instance, when they start going to school, or even later than that.

No decisive improvement results from such remedial procedures as elevating the position of the child's pelvis, making him void before he goes to bed, rationing his liquid intake, calling on him at night, introducing medications, or punishments, whether in the form of spanking or of letting the child lie in the wet for the rest of the night.

The condition shows a richness of noticeable variations. Bedwetting may disappear for several nights in a row. Sometimes, the children develop a marked neurotic anxiety: they dare not go to sleep for fear of wetting, call repeatedly for mother, ask time and again to be put on the chamber pot and—as a result—make mother fuss about them, handle their genitalia, and the like.

[1] Wiener Klinische Wochenschrift, 1909.
[2] *Ibid*, 1920, No. 22.

It is exactly this neurotic attitude on the part of the children which makes it clear that they are wrestling with some sexual complex; they display the symptomatic pattern of struggling against libidinal drives, those very drives which may eventually mar their future.

Yet even more frequent than neurotic fear of sleep is the opposite trait of many enuretic children: inordinately deep sleep. Mothers of such children have a hard time waking them, and when the children finally do wake up they are so benumbed for a while that they hardly know where they are and what they are supposed to do. Many such sleepers are plagued by nightmares (pavor nocturnus); they scream in their sleep and occasionally jump out of bed. The percentage of somnambulists among enuretics is exceedingly high and serves as another indication of the presence of tabooed desires which find their symbolic gratification in the dream.[1]

The child may seek refuge in the father's or mother's or a sibling's bed. Some parents take into their own bed the child that has wetted, and by thus giving a clearcut reward for the act, make the curative process harder. Very often, enuresis can be corrected through mere elimination of this form of paternal encouragement.

Enuretic children are often generally precocious or have known early sexual stimulation. They often carry over their dreamworld into their daily life, appear "goofy" or retarded, make slow progress at school; but the real trouble with them is that they are absorbed in their sexual reveries.

Nearly always the addiction to masturbation can be established either through mother's observation, or, after the examiner's careful probing, by the child's own admission. In many cases, enuresis emerges with the resumption of masturbation. In fact, in those infrequent cases in which infan-

[1] Cf. my paper on "The Will to Sleep" ("Der Wille Zum Schlaf"), I. F. Bergmann, Wiesbaden, Germany, and Sadger's "Das Nachtwandeln" in *Schriften zur angewandten Seelenkunde,* I. F. Deuticke, Publisher, Vienna, Leipzig.

tile masturbation ends in a temporary non-masturbation period (Freud's "latency period"), enuresis invariably emerges with the resumption of auto-erotism.

In many cases enuresis has been found to serve as a stratagem for the achievement of a definite purpose, such as punishing the parents or keeping them on the run. Soldiers have resorted to enuresis to get out of the army.

The most significant characteristic, however, is that bedwetting affords pleasure. Most enuretics snuggle up in their bedding from the start as though they had resumed their fetal position in mother's womb, and after they have wetted, they enjoy the warm moisture for a while as they did when they were infants. Indeed, bedwetting is a regression to the infantile stage.

Here are first a few cases of enuretic children.

Case No. 52: The boy Fritz could not be "housebroken." He wetted his bed night after night, although he exercised full control over himself during the day. Being the first-born, he had the privilege of sleeping in the bedroom of his parents. Night after night he was plagued by nightmares and kept his parents awake until all hours. After he had wetted, he would not remain in his place but insisted on being taken into mother's bed. Once his demand was obeyed, it was always extremely tiresome to get him out of her bed. True enough, mother herself derived great pleasure from having his tiny warm body snuggled up against her. Even when he occasionally wetted her bed, she was not at all displeased. When the second child—a girl—came, Fritz was treated like a "big boy," but he still continued bed-wetting. He developed the habit of covering himself with blankets, so that he perspired profusely. He was extremely affectionate with mother, and his caresses had a pronounced sexual aura about them. Some night he would wake from his sleep, tell mother that he loved her, and go back to sleep. Apparently, he never masturbated, but his games with his little sister were of a distinctly sexual character.

When he was six, the boy's life underwent a sudden change. His mother separated from her husband, and by court decree the boy was left with his father. The boy later came into the house of a paternal aunt and showed great distress at the loss of his mother, but, on the other hand, his enuresis was completely gone. Only once again did he wet his bed. It was several months later when his mother came to town to see him.

The enuresis in this case obviously served the boy as an excuse for getting into his mother's bed, and the way the bed-wetting has ceased shows how helpful it may be at times to separate a child from a parent when the two are too strongly fixated to one another. Fritz's mother stimulated him sexually to an excessive degree, and the boy showed subsequently many other neurotic symptoms. He could never concentrate on anything and was looked upon as being below average. Only after he came into other surroundings did he take a different course of development. He calmed down considerably, grew rapidly both physically and mentally, displayed above-average scholastic achievements and became one of the best pupils at school.

Case No. 53: Alfred was three-and-a-half years old when he was first brought into my office. He learned to control his bladder completely in his first year. On the other hand, he has never, despite all parental efforts, given up the habit of masturbation acquired in infancy. When he was two-and-a-half years old, a sister was born, and from then on Alfred was relegated to a secondary position in the family. The boy payed great attention to his "rival" and watched with special interest the procedure of diaper changing. Soon he learned to run to mother, at the first cry of his sister, telling her to change the baby; and it was not much later that he himself began to wet his bed. Leaving the boy in the damp bedclothes was no help; he felt perfectly comfortable. Neither did all the other correctives achieve any noteworthy results. I advised the parents to stop paying any attention to the boy's bed-wetting, and above all, to cease punishing him. After a few more weeks the boy's enuresis disappeared.

Alfred had obviously been trying to reconquer his position in the family, and at the same time he made a feeble attempt at regression to the pleasurable stage of infancy.

The following case is somewhat more complicated.

Case No. 54: The patient, a boy of seven, had been bed-wetting for the last several months. He lived in a convent under conditions of strict discipline. Learning and praying kept the boy busy all day long, and even on Sundays there was little relaxation. The patient had all the reason in the world to wish he were back home, even if he were not pining away for his mother as he was. However, to go home was exactly what he could not do. His mother had recently remarried, and the reason why the boy had been put in the convent in the first place was the jealousy the boy displayed toward his stepfather.

A supplementary aggravation of the situation was caused by the influence of one of the overzealous teachers at the convent who, in a dramatic way, was telling the boys horror stories of hell and devil, augmented by an assortment of ghost tales. The patient was always frightened at the approach of evening, and when he went to bed he hid his head fearfully under the blankets. He dreamed of ghosts, and his bedwetting always came in the wake of nightmares in which he was pursued by ghosts or monsters.

At last, the boy was taken out of the convent and put in the care of an aunt. The enuresis subsided immediately and ceased completely after a short treatment, mainly of a general pedagogic nature.

This boy, too, had the strong desire to be a baby again and to have mother all to himself.

In this neurotic disorder, reactions of spite and disillusionment often combine with many others, such as jealousy, protest against adult sexuality, and religious motives, so that enuresis presents an abundant variety of motivations.

Case No. 55: M.B., an overdeveloped grammar school girl of ten, had been bed-wetting for the last two years. As all domestic attempts to cure her of the habit had been of no avail, she was referred to Mrs. H. Helldorf for pedagogico-therapeutic treatment; and a closer questioning revealed the following case history:

As a pupil of elementary school, she had been the pet of the teacher and rated the best pupil of her class. Two years prior to her treatment the girl came late to the class of a very strict teacher who inspired in her a feeling of boundless fear. The teacher also preferred other children to M.B. Quite naturally, the girl wished herself back into the past situation. In her games and daydreams she was the little "tot" in the old elementary, school. She wrote letters with a stylus on a tiny slate-board, played with her old toys, and expressed the desire to eat from a small plate, using an undersized spoon. She had her mother cut her hair short like a small girl's and made her two-year-old sister her playmate.

When her sister was born, M.B. was jealous of her, but then she resigned herself to her fate. She must have preserved, however, a feeling of envy of sister's babyhood, as her bed-wetting set in shortly after the baby girl arrived.

M.B.'s trigger nightmare was a typical birthdream found in many enuretics; *she saw herself rolling down a precipice, at the bottom of which she urinated.*

All the girl really wanted was to be taken out of school and allowed to stay home with mother and indulge in playing with her old toys, an occupation she pursued with such absorption that it made her appear forlorn. The girl was vehemently attached to—and idolized—her twenty-two-year-old brother.

Presumably, she had first masturbated only a few weeks prior to consultation and she professed to remember no particular fantasy accompanying the masturbatory act.

There was the definite impression that the patient had watched or experienced a few sexual practices in the past, but the matter was not further pursued; her insight into the nature of her spiteful attitude toward mother and teacher was enough to produce astonishingly rapid results. She stopped bed-wetting and playing with her childhood toys, and all other regressive symptoms soon disappeared.

This girl, too, admitted that the dampness of the bedclothes was agreeable to her. And, like so many other enuretics, she wrapped herself snugly in her blankets and produced a warm, steamy climate much resembling that of mother's womb.

Emil Gutheil, who at the time was a student at the Vienna Medical School (1922), analyzed, under my guidance, two enuretic children, and the following are his two reports:

Case No. 56: "A case of psychosexually determined enuresis. Franz H., a handsome, vivacious boy of eight, was brought to the clinic of the St. Anna Children's Hospital, with an enuretic condition of four years' duration. Bed-wetting occurred very frequently, intervals never exceeding three consecutive nights. After a single hypnotic treatment, the effectiveness of which did not outlast the patient's own maximum of abstention, Dr. Stekel decided to submit this case to analysis. I was put in charge of the analysis, and one weekly control session with Dr. Stekel was stipulated.

"As children are ordinarily rather uncertain about their past, have little understanding for the sequence and concatenation of events, and moreover, never really overcome their fear and shame of things sexual in the presence of adults, I interpreted the boy's data very cautiously and verified and replenished them through frequent conferences with his father, foster-mother and foster-sister (his foster-mother's daughter).

"Franz was an illegitimate child, and as his mother, a housemaid, had been unable to take care of him, he had been placed in the care of a foster-mother, both father and mother paying joint visits to the baby.

"The boy's mother—she died when he was six—had been an irascible woman (according to her husband); she had been plagued by hyperemesis during her pregnancy with the boy and had a difficult delivery.

"The patient's father was a fireman, plain, yet rigorous and duty-conscious.

"These few background data acquired added significance in the course of the study of the enuresis disorder.

"When Franz was three years old, his parents married officially. The boy was brought home from his foster home and his normal home training seemed secured. He was the only child and enjoyed his home life greatly. Soon, however, his mother gave birth to a girl, and Franz's privileged position was gone.

"While his mother was giving birth to the new baby, he was kept in the house of a neighbor, and when Franz came home he could no longer sleep between father and mother but was put into a bed of his own.

"Soon he was also given the task of tending the baby, a task which he disliked very much.

"Franz's mother soon developed a severe neurosis of which unfortunately we know only through second-hand information. After a period of extreme irritability and violence, she withdrew completely from her housewifely interests, from her husband, and from the boy, and concentrated her time and attention exclusively on the girl.

"When Franz once 'accidentally' dropped his sister to the floor, his mother had a fit of rage and threw the boy out of the apartment. He sat for the rest of the winter day on the stairway, until father came home from work and took him in.

"After another 'accident' with the baby sister the mother threw a kitchen knife at Franz.

"Soon afterward, Franz began to wake at night from a dream that *he had been bitten by a huge, black dog.* As he could not quiet down again, he was usually taken into the parental bed and again came to sleep between father and mother.

"The nightmares were followed a few weeks later by enuresis; the boy became a 'hard sleeper' and could be awakened only with difficulty.

"In his bed-wetting period, Franz developed three types of dreams: 1) *he was extinguishing a flame;* 2) *he was pursued by a dog;* and 3) *he tobogganed down a steep slope.*

"Two of the boy's habits were specifically described by his father. Franz liked to watch the fire in the oven and to throw in matches. This in itself was not surprising at all; yet the boy's absorption and dreamy state while he stared for hours at the fire struck everyone as extremely strange.

"Urination with the boy was a very important job; he called it 'dousing' and showed unmistakable signs of enjoying the act greatly. He was "dousing fires" as his father did.

"Analysis was able to establish the following three regressive factors which were operative in the sense of infantile gratification: spiteful attitude toward the mother, identification with the father, and an excessive increment of anxiety feelings.

"Because of the patient's age, ways other than interpretation and insight had to be applied, and Dr. Stekel suggested a method of turning the boy's fantasy from its fixation on the past toward the reality of the present, of tearing down his idealization of babyhood and bolstering his consciousness of being a big and intelligent boy.

"After a two-week period of systematic pedagogic treatment along these lines, enhanced by the purposeful assistance of the adults who were properly instructed about the boy, the bed-wetting ceased, and after another check period of two weeks, the patient was discharged."

Case No. 57: "The second case of enuresis nocturna referred to me by Dr. Stekel also came from the St. Anna Children's Hospital. The patient, Rudolf W., thirteen, was a healthy-looking boy of average intelligence and scholastic achievement. For the last two years he had been bed-wetting, usually two or three times a week, and nearly always as a result of a terror dream. Extreme depth of sleep and an unusual possessive sense were advanced as the boy's characteristics. He was owner and passionate collector of stamps, coins, and all sorts of antiques. He would frequently get up at night to make sure that the entrance door was well-closed and that all his possessions were intact.

"The patient's father was in good physical condition, but his mother was suffering from severe hysteria.

"The boy's enuresis set in after the divorce of his parents, his mother's remarriage, and the establishment of a new home.

"Even prior to that, conditions at home had been turbulent, and at the time of separation there had been much altercation as to which parent should keep the boy.

"The patient spoke highly of his father, a locksmith by trade, who had only reluctantly given him up. He had met his father a few times after their separation, and the father asked him to come over to see him, but the boy was afraid to come in conflict with his mother. Unlike the stepfather, the patient's father always found time to play with his children.

"The patient had two sisters, and both in his dreams and in his waking hours, he showed the presence of desires to do away with them. At the age of three, he had nearly smothered his sister with pillows, 'to stop her from crying,' and only the arrival of mother saved the girl's life. His stepsister, one year old, was 'eliminated' by the patient in a frequently occurring enuretic dream. Until the arrival of this girl, from the second marriage, mother had excessively pampered the boy.

"The patient had two types of enuretic dreams:

"(1) *There is a war. One man is unaware of it, and the enemies attack him, whereupon he surrenders. A lady rings the church bell, the family gathers, and the man is liberated, but he has to be put to death as a traitor anyway.*

The dream ends in the anxiety and wetting.

"(2) *There is a war. Mother is about to fetch water from the well in the yard. Someone else is present. I shout to Mother not to go because she might be seen by the enemy. Dream ends in erection and wetting.*

"The first dream revealed the patient's reliving of infantile pleasures. He always tried to ignore the 'state of war' which existed between his parents. Mother's attempts to depreciate father have not influenced the boy's attitude. In his dream he creates a situation of legitimate pleasure; he had been attacked by the enemy of his good, conforming self—that is, by his illicit love for his father—and he had to surrender.[1]

"The second dream reveals the boy's jealousy of his stepfather. Mother was fetching water from someone else's well. He tried to hold her back. His bed-wetting was an infantile form of emission which occurred as the result of an incestuous attempt in the dream.

[1] This excellent interpretation of the boy's dream by my assistant deserves further elaboration.

The war raged also in the mind of the boy. The bells rang a loud warning. His hostility toward mother who had broken up the family, a hostility he was not aware of ("one man is unaware of it"), seemed to propel him toward a criminal action (the traitor in the dream). The traitor was his mother who had abandoned father; yet he had also betrayed mother's love when he agreed with father. He was engaged in a struggle against his criminal tendencies and against the infantile desires within himself.

"The nature of these dreams induced us to search for the origins of the patient's enuresis in his psychosexual sphere.

"Such dream elements as church bells (religious determinant) or the recurrent war motive pointed to an underlying conflict between the boy's allegiance to his father and to his mother. The boy's enuresis was a manifestation of his inability to cope with this conflict situation.

"The boy's entire behavior, and specifically his propensity toward collecting and safekeeping of things of the past, were indicative of his deep-seated desire to preserve something of his own bygone days (one of his mother's most definite and explicit data was that the boy's enuresis began when they moved to the new house).

"And lastly, the boy's games (a few boys would dig a hole in the ground and simultaneously urinate into it—our patient had been the initiator of this game), his 'theory' that children were conceived through the male's urination into the woman's vulva, and his identification with father (to my question what he would become when he grew up, he quickly replied: 'A locksmith'), all these factors, while pointing the course of immediate therapy, also served as warning signals for the future of the boy's psychic development and his life 'between his parents.'

"This typical case, where the urine erotism was perpetuated by the child's exposure to faulty sexual information, showed a peculiar deviation of the usual original fixation on one object; the psychogenic origin of the boy's condition was his dual fixation on father and mother. He was the link between the warring parents; in his person the unity of the family was maintained. His perpetual desire for his father to come back home one evening and to stay for good found, in the psychic configuration of wish and guilt, an expression of the boy's compulsive checking of whether the door was well-closed.

"After two months of systematic treatment, which concerned itself with a gradual dispelling of the boy's infantile misconceptions, giving him sexual information, and adjusting his mother's behavior toward his needs, the enuresis began to give way. Bedwetting was first reduced to one occurrence weekly, then to once in three weeks, and then it completely disappeared."

My experience with enuretic children and adults makes me regard bed-wetting as an infantile form of emission. We may assume this in view of the frequent admission by children that micturition had a definite pleas•re value, and on the basis of other pertinent observations.

Infantile urine sexuality persists in some adults, either in its entirety or partially, as I shall have occasion to show later in this discourse. At this moment I want to look into these cases of adult enuresis which represent not the carry-over of an infantile trait, but a regression to an infantile stage, usually as a result of frustrated love relations and a subsequent general withdrawal from adult sexual gratification.

A certain connection between the function of the bladder and sexual excitation can be observed even in "normal" individuals. The condition is rather frequent that a person's sexual stimulation has an immediate effect on his bladder, calling forth an urge to urinate. Unsatisfied people, especially women, are known to void frequently. A neurotic will describe his discharge of urine as being connected with some degree of sexual sensation, such as titillation in the urethra, agreeable after-spasms which radiate into the perineum and thighs, a slight feverish shiver, and at times even an orgasm-like agitation, occasionally accompanied by a slight flow of semen from the unerected penis.

Neurotic distortion and repression often generates bizarre symptoms which, in turn, may give rise to hypochondriacal anxieties. Voiding may then become extremely difficult, or come off in intermittent spurts, or require unusual muscular effort, or be feasible only in progressive stages, interrupted by vehement bladder cramps (pain instead of orgasm). The conversion of pleasure into pain may take place by turning urethral tickling into a burning sensation which may persist far beyond the time of micturition.

A few cases from my own files will demonstrate clearly

the significance of urosexuality in the life of neurotics. We shall see that micturition may take the place of intercourse even with adults. The passage of urine plays a prominent part in infantile sex concepts; many children believe that father urinates into mother's vagina. When later sexual enlightenment is unable to destroy this idea completely and the infantile concept persists in the mind of an individual, micturition will become the prerequisite of orgasm.

Case No. 58: Mrs. G.B., thirty-six, complained of sexual anesthesia in intercourse. She demanded that the man urinate into her vagina. The infusion of the warm urine gave her a rapturous, trance-like orgasm.

Case No. 59: Mr. S. H. thirty-one, scientific worker, complained of being subject to a sexual anomaly. He was homosexual and presumably was never aroused by a woman. From his male partners he demanded the following procedure: They had to spray his abdomen with their urine and then direct the jet toward the patient's thighs. As soon as the urine wetted his penis, he ejaculated.

All cases of urolagnia—the frequency of which I had so sorely underestimated early in my medical career—belong in this chapter.

Neurotics often relate the childhood memory of having either urinated into a playmate's mouth or offered their own mouth as a receptacle for the playmate's urine. Among adults, both the active and passive forms of this kind of gratification is well known to prostitutes with a wide clientele.

There are also cases of urosexuality combined with mictioscopy, when the sight of the partner's voiding is either a prerequisite or the sole content of the act. In a preponderant number of cases the sight and the sound of urination merely evokes erection, whereupon the intercourse can take place; and only in a minority of cases the sight in itself produces orgasm and gratification.

Case No. 60: Mr. G.J., physician, forty-three, could not copulate unless previously aroused by the sight of urination. His earliest sexual recollection went back to his fifth year and a maidservant who was urinating in the characteristic crouching posture.

Sadger reports several cases of this kind, and the following is an abstract from one of his case histories.

Case No. 61: Statement by the patient, a twenty-three-year-old homosexual. "When I was twelve, I locked myself in the bathroom. I made a headstand and tried to urinate into my own mouth. I could not quite make it, but the very attempt brought erection, orgasm, and a sense of seminal discharge, although there was actually no flow. It also gave me the idea of having one of my playmates urinate into my mouth." Other acts performed by the patient were indicative of the transition from urosexuality to retention of urine. The patient continued: "At the ages of fourteen and fifteen, I greatly enjoyed the following game which I played when I was in bed by myself. I tried to urinate a few drops into the palm of my hand with the intention of lapping them up. The attempt usually provoked immediate erection which, in turn, made the performance very difficult; but after many failures I managed at last to accomplish the act. When I was sixteen or seventeen, I used to hold tightly my foreskin and urinate into it, so that my prepuce became as large as a balloon; and the tremendous pressure gave me an orgastic sensation with semen coming forth, as though I had masturbated." The patient recollected that one of his ardent wishes at the age of fifteen was to have his best friend join genitals with him tip to tip, pull their prepuces over them and jointly urinate into the space around the junction.[1]

[1] Sadger notes that "the erotic manifestations of the peripheral urinary tract go beyond the titillation in the erectile columns. They lead to tickling sensations in the urethra, radiating all the way back to the perineum, cause acute pains in the passage and emission-like sensations with or without discharge. States of fear are especially conducive to arousing tickling sensations in the urethra. One of the least known motivations of masochism is a desire to experience again and again the tickling sensation in the urethra induced by fright. Children quite purposefully provoke threats or beatings. The urethral pains, present at times in the earliest childhood, have no organic basis and usually pass as suddenly as they have come on, requiring no

The patient had already begun in his early childhood the partial conversion of his uro-erotism into symbolic acts and sublimated hobbies. From his recollections in the analytic sessions, later corroborated by his mother's statements, it was learned that the patient had already at the age of two an elaborate system of water games.

On the other hand, the patient's urine-impeding erections at the age of fourteen to fifteen had their counterpart in retentional stiffenings of the penis at the age of two. I had occasion to see an early photograph of the patient in which his father had snapped him at such a moment.

This patient of Sadger was also afflicted with psychic disuria, which only confirms my observation that micturition may be obstructed by psychic factors. It is a known fact, for instance, that many men are unable to urinate in the presence of other men (in men's toilets). Physicians often have to leave their office or send the patient into an adjoining room, so that the patient may produce the urine sample needed for a laboratory analysis. Such a disuria may reach the proportions of a serious retention. I have known a patient with a pronounced urosexual condition who had to be catheterized in his early childhood. As a grownup, he had contracted gonorrhea, and the neglected disease had caused him to urinate in intermittent spurts. Quite naturally, upon such complaint, the temporary diagnosis had assumed the presence of a stricture, but a more thorough investigation revealed the condition to be psychogenic. The patient, a man of high intellectual standing, always let his urine drip onto

therapeutic intervention. At a later age, these pains may recur in connection with a bladder irritation caused by pregnancy or gonorrhea and be retained as a hysterical symptom.

The emission-like manifestations with or without secretion also occur in early childhood, and to this category belongs also involuntary urination, occasioned by fright, or even by a cause as slight as a parent's loud scolding. As I have demonstrated elsewhere, the act of micturition may be not only a pleasurable process but also a form of comfort, of palliative solace (like masturbation at a later stage). When denied a wish, some children will not only cry but also consolingly wet their clothes.

his overcoat, and the more stenchy the garment became, the more he liked it. The odor gave him a sensuous pleasure. He also always managed to get a few drops of his urine onto his hands.[1]

In keeping with his condition, a genuine uroneurotic never washes his hands after having "accidentally" wetted his hands with urine.

All these traits make their appearance in early childhood, as can be seen from the following case of a compulsive neurotic, thirty-two, reported by Sadger.

Case No. 62: "When I was a child of three or four," the patient said, "and probably earlier than that, I urinated, even in daytime, so often, that my trousers became imbued with a brownish color. In bed at night the urine often gushed suddenly out of me, and I was always seized with fear that my father, a highstrung man, would punish me for it. But the flow of urine made me feel blissfully happy just the same. In daytime I liked to urinate into my trousers, enjoying the warm flow of the urine down my legs. To have the full benefit of it, I tried whenever possible not to unbutton my trousers. To avoid being caught, I resorted to all sorts of tricks. Nights, I always waited until the sheet dried, and in daytime I let the urine come out in drops, so that my pleasurable business could go on and on until the trousers became discolored with long abuse." According to the patient, he had frequently eavesdropped on and watched the sexual intercourse of his parents, as his father paid little attention to the "kid" sleeping in the same bed. "I remember," the patient said, "that at that time I imagined that father was urinating onto mother. It is possible that in my bed-wetting I was imitating

[1] In my paper on "Compulsions, Their Psychic Origins and Their Treatment," published in *Medizinische Klinik,* 1910, Nos. 5-7, I have described a very illustrative case of urosexual compulsion. The patient, a peddler, had come to my office with the complaint of an inability to urinate. The truth of the matter was that his urination was absolutely normal; yet so strong was his idea that he might not be able to urinate, that it almost drove him to distraction.

Analysis revealed that this man was physically unable to have intercourse with his wife because he liked another woman. The idea, "I cannot urinate" was a substitute for the inexpressible one: "I am impotent."

him." Later in the session, the patient said, "Perhaps my bed-wetting was the result of an earlier experience of having urinated while sitting on mother's or the maid's lap."

Among other manifestations of the patient's uro-erotism, I would like to mention first his tickling sensation in the urethra. When the patient was a boy of eight and in the course of his games had to climb a steep hill, he felt scared and simultaneously experienced a titillation in his penis. At the age of eight or nine he was plagued for a while by a urethral itch so strong that he had to rub his penis even in public.

He recalled that "Mother often thrust her hand between her legs as though she had to keep her urine back, and ran to the toilet. I can still visualize her doing just that. Father, on the other hand, was in the habit of playfully pulling our genitals. It was his way of joking. The older boys did the same to the younger ones. The youngest boy always slept in the parent̶ ̶ ̶ ̶ occasionally Father tickled his penis to amu̶ same to my junior brothers, and, after I was m̶ little boys." All these things presumably had̶ significance and were only a sort of horse-play that ̶ with their family. Other disturbing influences came ̶ maidservants. As they unbuttoned the little boys and pulled fo̶ their penises to make them urinate, they occasionally played with the genitalia, and it is entirely possible that the patient's frequent micturition in childhood was conditioned by these experiences. At times, the maid yanked his penis by way of punishing him for wetting; to stop him from crying, she stroked his organ gently.

The patient resumed: "Nights, I frequently forgot that I was in bed; I had a feeling that I was in the bathroom or on the chamber pot, and in this semiconscious state I not only urinated but at times even moved my bowels right then and there."

He married a girl who was apparently also given to uro-erotism. She often dreamed of having to void urgently and argued with herself, still in the dream, that she ought to be ashamed of doing such things in the presence of her husband; but when she woke, she found that she had let a few drops of urine ooze onto the bedding.

Just as Fritz (Case No. 52) reacted to his mother's presence with enuresis, so did a girl patient of Sadger's. From her history we are now going to quote a few passages. (The enuresis of both Fritz and this girl were infantile reactions to parental sexual stimulations.)

Case No. 63. The connection between the girl's disorder and her father's presence was very pronounced. The family lived in L., but the father stayed in Vienna where he was in analysis. He went home every two weeks. With marked regularity, the girl's enuresis subsided in her father's absence, but as soon as her father returned, or even at the mere announcement that her father was to come sometime during the night, the girl wetted her panties during the daytime, was restless, wept, scratched herself, and, of course, also wetted the bedding when she was put to sleep. ....characteristic was an episode which occurred shortly .... two years old. Once her father had returned .... nexpectedly, and when her mother on the .... came to see the girl in her room, she found .... that moment the girl heard her father's voice, ...ately let go with her urine.

....eek after her second birthday, the girl selected from .... photographs one of herself and one of her father and took them with her to bed. In the morning the two photographs were drenched with urine.

She also reacted with wetting (probably of an additional compensatory nature) whenever father went into a store to shop and left her waiting outside.

In a similar fashion adults may react with uro-erotism to fear of impending danger. I have known male patients who let their urine drip whenever they were afraid that they will be caught in an antimoral act, or whenever they were worried that they would finish what they had started. Other men, afraid of ejaculation, substitute urination for it. One of my patients was wont to masturbate to the point of orgasm, then waited for the penis to become flaccid and void, experiencing a tickling sensation of unusual intensity. Such tick-

ling sensations may take the place of masturbation and or-
gasm in persons who are under a strict masturbation veto.
Galant describes such a case in a fourteen-year-old boy in
"Neurologisches Zentralblatt," No. 16, 1912.

Case No. 64: I have observed a manifestation very similar to
the symptom of female clitoridal crises in one of my male patients.
It was a boy of fourteen, in treatment for reasons of "excessive
masturbation." Within two months I succeeded in curing the boy
of his habit, but after a lengthy period of abstinence he came
back to me with another complaint. Every now and then, after
urinating, he had an orgasm, and was quite worried about this
strange phenomenon. The orgasm was accompanied neither by
erection nor by ejaculation. He was not even unusually sexually
stimulated by this.

I do not remember having read anywhere of another case
of orgasm in a male without erection and ejaculation, and
believe therefore this case to be of interest to workers in
this field. In my opinion such orgasms represent reflex discharges of accumulated libidinal tensions.

The phenomenon is rather well-known and has been described by many sexologists as an infantile form of sexual
gratification. In numerous papers of the Freudian school,
enuresis is regarded as a substitute of emission. I, myself, have
many times and on many occasions interpreted the micturi-
tional orgasm as an infantile form of gratification. On the
other hand, this form of camouflaged masturbation shows us
how illusory all weaning cures of masturbation really are.
The open execution of the habit is only replaced by a hidden one, and the patient goes on indulging himself surreptitiously, having fun without guilt, satisfying both his sexual
and his moral self. The orgasm in question is not a result
of masturbation, but of the pseudo-abstinence.

Let us consider a few other cases of urosexuality.

Case No. 65: Miss A. W., twenty-eight, had periods of involuntary discharges of urine both at night and in daytime. The bed-

wetting occurred in the wake of sexual dreams of various contents; in daytime the discharge followed indefinite reveries, tinged with anxiety and revolving around a feeling of frustration, "inability to obtain something desired," "non-fulfillment," a feeling which is typical of such cases.

Analysis revealed that she relied on her bladder for her masturbatory gratification. She held her urine back as long as possible; when the urge became unbearably strong, she went into the bathroom, and pressed with all the strength she could muster against the bladder to retard the discharge of urine. At that moment she had an orgastic sensation of such vehemence that tears ran down her cheeks. Masturbation through manual manipulations never gave her the tearful thrill of the above procedure.

Case No. 66: Mr. R.B., a college student, masturbated for hours, interrupting the act always before reaching orgasm. At the end of the act, he passed a few drops of urine, and this finally released the desired orgasm. There was no discharge of semen— a clearly infantile form of gratification.

Case No. 67: The patient, a girl of twelve, given to compulsive ideas, had been broken by her parents of the habit of masturbation. She admitted, however, that subsequently she learned to masturbate with the aid of the bladder, and was doing this ten to twelve times daily. She kept her urine back until the pressure grew very strong; then she went to the bathroom and, pressing her hand against the urethral orifice, prevented the urine from escaping. The ensuing bladder cramps gave her a sensuous thrill that grew to orgasm when the warm jet of urine flowed over her hand. She also often provoked her father to becoming angry and spanking her on her buttocks. While she was spanked, she had an orgasm accompanied by an urge to urinate. (Havelock Ellis described a similar case in the "Psychoanalytic Review," 1913.)

Following is a similar case of urosexual infantilism.

Case No. 68: The patient, a writer of thirty-eight, had indulged in his habit of masturbation by means of bladder extension ever since boyhood. His system consisted of holding the urine back until he lost control of the bladder. Wetting his trousers brought a strong orgasm, especially if it occurred in public places such as theaters, museums, railroad cars, parties. He was—unconsciously, he believed—on the lookout for situations inhibitive of urination. Up to the age of thirty-six he knew no sexual intercourse. At that age he married and lived normally with his wife, and his affliction seemed to have gone forever. But it did come back after he became the father of a boy. Marital troubles followed his relapse. He first lost the ability to reach orgasm, then his potency for normal intercourse with his wife. He fell back on his urosexual gratification and lived in constant fear of being apprehended by the police.

Female patients given to such urinary habits often speak of a titillating sensation in the clitoris in connection with micturition. This pleasurable sensation at times hides behind a feeling of pain, or combines with it, and extends to the perineum, or all the way up to the true pelvis (pelvis minor). The following case illustrates this phenomenon clearly.

Case No. 69: A lady of forty-three complained of a serious handicap to her social life: she could never go to parties or public gatherings, because at the moment she left her house she would become greatly excited and urinate all over her thighs. It was no use to change into other underwear and clothes, as the mishap would occur again and again. At the same time she felt a pain in the pubic region and a stiffening of "something or other" in the vulvar region. A urological examination carried out immediately after micturition established that the lady's 1.5 cm. long clitoris did become erected in the process of micturition. The patient admitted that she dawdled long at dressing and undressing —while analysis revealed her propensity toward daydreaming. Her marital life was unsatisfactory, and the comfort of masturbation had been given up by her on the advice of a midwife she knew. Before going to a party, she often imagined all sorts of romantic possibilities. In such moments both micturition and a panicky state would ensue. Analysis revealed that panic usually occurred when in her revery she saw herself in the embrace of a man and being caught by her husband in the act.

Every urologist has female patients complaining of embarrassing acts of "incontinence" which would occur in the most improper situations. When analyzed, these patients turn out to be daydreamers indulging in erotic reveries which have the components of fear in them. In their enuretic performance, orgasm and fright unite in a single discharge.

Case No. 70: Miss G. V., a very robust girl of twenty-four, complained of urinary incontinence in daytime and occasional bed-wetting at night. Although she had been annoying her mother with constant pleas for help, she refused to consult a physician and made it practically impossible even for a lady doctor to examine her thoroughly. A multitude of neurotic symptoms finally induced her to come into my office. Analysis revealed that the girl's enuretic episodes followed a definite arrangement pattern. Whenever she was going visiting with friends, she anticipated the occasion with an intensely romantic revery. On her way to her friends she would develop the fantasy to its critical point, and when she rang the doorbell she imagined that she was about to be raped. She struggled with the man, who always was of superhuman strength, and was about to succumb—her dress had already been torn off her—when at the very last moment the door opened (also in reality) and rescue came in the nick of time. At that crucial juncture the girl went through an orgastic thrill, and urinated.

The mechanism is even clearer in the following case.

Case No. 71: A college boy of twenty-three complained of constant anxiety about being late for his appointments and of always letting drops of urine go at the last minute of his tardiness.

The following episode was one concrete example of his predicament. One day he was supposed to make the four-o'clock train. All day long he was worrying about being too late for the train. However, should anyone have expected him to be overcautious and arrive at the depot an hour too soon, he would be greatly mistaken. As a matter of fact, the later it got, the more "urgent" things had to be taken care of. He had to look for his passport, find his wallet, search for certain books he intended to take along, and so on and on. (An obvious arrangement.) At last he was ready, and his race for time began. First he tried the street car, then changed to a taxi, ran wildly through the station, forced his way through the gate, and jumped onto the train the moment it began pulling out. At that final moment he felt cramps in his bladder, reached orgasm, and shed a few drops of urine into his trousers.

This patient had a strong sister fixation, and his "neurotic arrangement" had the sense of trying to be united with her. It was the symbolic repetition of a childhood scene in which, after playing with his sister at great length, he had tried, at the very last, to urinate into her vulva.

The affective charge and tension of the nocturnal and diurnal enuresis are of paramount importance, because they are our guides in understanding the nature of the disorder.

In closing this chapter, I might add that we shall encounter urosexual manifestations in many of the cases to be quoted later for other purposes. Urosexuality may or may not combine with mother's-womb fantasies. Water and fire play an important part in the dreams of urosexuals and facilitate the diagnosis. Old age is very conducive to regression to this form of infantile gratification. Impotent old men revert frequently to this form of libido, and so do men afflicted with prostatic conditions. A careful observer can not fail to notice in some of these patients a definite eagerness to be catheterized and an hyperesthesia of their urethral membrane. During catheterization, the patients frequently display, along with slight erection, a typically blissful facial expression, although at times they may try to hide their pleasure behind a façade of pain and discomfort. The urosexual tendency may also become strikingly evident in senile psychotics of regressive type, who wet their beds, defecate in bed, and smear feces all over themselves.

But this involves the anal sexuality, which will be discussed below. Although urosexuality and anal sexuality usually go hand in hand, we have grouped the latter, for reasons of exposition, into a separate unit.

2. Ano-Erotism

To Freud goes the credit for having called our attention to the tremendous importance of infantile ano-erotism. Among the erogenous zones, the anal region has a paramount significance. In all probability the infant derives great pleasure from the normal act of defecation, and it soon learns to prolong the sensation by means of retarding the act (Freud). The pleasurable sensation is produced by the pressure of the bulk of scybala against the mucous membrane of the rectum and is quickly converted into a complex libidinal sensation.

The peculiar intermixture of pain and pleasure is found in many manifestations of infantile sexuality, and it is quite in line with this phenomenon to find, with Hitschmann, that the passage of solid fecal mass produces just such a combination of pleasure and pain. The constitutional component of the anal erotism manifests itself in, or is enhanced through, a diarrheic disposition, and even the painful tenesmus may thus become a source of pleasure. Adult patients tell of erections induced by the painful strain.

Anosexuality also meets the child's primitive olfactory desires. The odors of the feces and the flatus had been sexual stimulants to primeval man, and still are to some of the present-day primitives and to many culturally inferior members of our own society. The child's interest for the toilet and his preoccupation with the smells emanating from the bodily functions of the adults are infantile manifestations of this olfactory sensuality.

The inappropriate sensations inherent in our ways of managing children lead to an intensification and a fixation of sensations originating at the anal zone. Many mothers have the habit of administering to their children daily enemas and generally of fussing too much about the cleanliness of the baby's buttocks. The recollection of all the pleasurable stimulations obtained through mother's salving, oiling, and rubbing, added to the indigenous mucosal impulses of the rectal membrane, may lead the child to concentrate on an anal form of masturbation. The finger or pointed objects are introduced into the anus, or external rubbing and whetting is used to produce stimulation. The latter is a wide-spread form of the child's misdemeanor and is a sure indication of exaggerated anosexuality.

There are probably few people of whom it may be said that they have completely outgrown their anal sexuality. A certain erogenous sensitivity of the anal zone constitutes at all times part of our erotic experience. Some prostitutes insert a finger into the anus of an impotent client to improve his erection.[1] It is also well known that a good bowel movement with the evacuation of solid scybal is an effective sexual stimulant. Not only homosexuals practice the anal form of intercourse; there are women, too, who are completely insensitive to vaginal coitus and achieve their gratification only the anal way.

Ivan Bloch, in his basic work, *Das Sexualleben unserer Zeit,* says:

Case No. 72: "Hammond reports the case of a young cigar store owner in New York, who, at the age of seven, had acquired the habit of inserting stick-like objects into his anus and derived great sensuous pleasure from the performance. According to this man's own words, he had come upon the idea while watching mating dogs and had assumed the canine act to be an anal one. The first object he had used, a plain pencil, caused him both pain and pleasure; later on he used an oiled tooth brush handle for this purpose. At the age of ten he began to submit to boys and remained a passive homosexual ever after. His appearance

[1] This device seems to have been played up in the ars amatoria of the Middle Ages. Aretine describes it in great detail in his *Colloquies.*

and behavior became more and more feminine (his garments resembled ladies' clothes, he modified his name to give it a feminine sound, and so forth), and he grew completely apathetic to women. Schrenk-Notzing reports another case of early anal masturbation with the aid of a pencil, which has likewise resulted in homosexual propensities."

Hypochondriacs and compulsion neurotics manifest the strangest distortions of anal sexuality. There are people to whom digestion and bowel movements constitute the essence of life. They either want to concentrate their attention on the progressive stages of the digestive process or they imagine blockages at certain spots of the tract (one of my patients, a physician himself, complained of a blockage in the flexura sigmoidea); some are afflicted with chronic constipation and sometimes have several enemas daily; others are so greatly concerned over the cleanliness of their anus that they compulsively wash after each movement, are anxious about the texture of the toilet paper, inspect their feces, etc.

Some anal erotists spend most of their waking hours in the toilet, as they almost constantly feel an urge to move their bowels; and do so in tiny "installments" accentuated by abundant flatulence.

Another expression of pronounced ano-sexuality is the affliction known as mucous colitis; and so is, on another level, the well-known phenomenon of partialism for buttocks, wrongly classified as fetishism.[1]

Many buttocks fetishists become sexually aroused at the mere sight of a well-formed backside.[2] To children, the posterior means a great deal, as it frequently substitutes for the genitalia; in their games of exposure and inspection it is

[1] Cf. Sadger's paper on "Buttocks Eroticism" (Gluteal Eroticism) in Internationale Zeitschrift fuer Psychoanalyse, 1913.

[2] I can still remember the ridiculous ladies' fashion called "Cul de Paris." Every woman à la mode had a padded derriere, as vast as a club chair, and the contemporary buttocks fetishists complained of having been robbed of their most cherished delight—the sight of a natural backside.

often the part of the body which they both display and view in the nude. And then there is, of course, the common infantile assumption that babies come into the world through the anus.

Bloch has collected a great mass of material on the scatologic rites among primitive peoples; and the studies of our scholars, as gathered in the *Anthropophyteia,* prove that the European peasants are not very far behind in this respect. Does it come then as a great surprise to learn that scatology and anosexuality play an important part in various forms of psychic infantilism?

I have stated again and again that the natural man is squeamish neither about the human anus nor about the end products of his digestion. No one will deny that babies eagerly delight in pawing their feces; by the same token, psychotics who have shed the restrictions of culture and live by untrammelled instinct relapse into the habit of smearing excrement all over themselves.

Case histories of neurotics frequently mention the performance of anilingus in childhood. Certain idiomatic expressions and "invitations" hurled at one's adversaries may be found in any tongue. The Balkan Slavs include, in the ingenious elaborations of the ano-lingual invitation, not only the person addressed but his parents and grandparents. All these lusty adjurations make us believe that the contact between the tongue and the anus must have been once considered as an expression of love and affection.

I saw once in the Antwerp Museum a Rubens painting, "Venus, the Frigid." The explanatory text in the catalogue called attention to the squatting positions of Venus herself, the cupid, and the satyr in the background. There was also a comment on the satyr's stuck-out tongue: *"Il semble se moquer de la déesse en tirant la langue."* (He seems to mock the goddess by showing her his tongue.) And the text concluded: "The meaning of this painting, known also under the name, 'Jupiter and Antiope,' is best rendered by the saying, 'Sine Baccho et Cere friget Venus.' " (Without Bacchus and Ceres, i.e., without food and drink, Venus' love freezes.) I could not help disagreeing with the entire note. To this day, I believe that the "sine Baccho" is partly contradicted by the satyr's fruit-filled horn; but what seems to me more important, the position of the three figures, especially that of the cupid, is clearly one of defecation. The painting is plainly an ano-sexual orgy, and the satyr's tongue suggests anilingus. This particular Venus seems to be frigid only toward normal approach.

Of all infantile forms of gratification, anilingus is the one most easily repressed, and its presence manifests itself only in neurotic distortion. Following is a case of such a neurotic transformation.

Case No. 73: **Mr. D. S.,** Civil Service clerk, thirty-seven, complained of agoraphobia. The illness started six years ago, following a gonorrheal infection.

The patient had a prostatic condition and went daily for a massage, after which he felt so much better that he could not do without it. It was evident that he was deriving pleasure from the stimulation of his erogenous rectal zone.

As analysis progressed, it was revealed that his desire for massage has been for some time past intricately connected with a general psychosexual regression, which had ensued in a rather round-about way.

At first the patient had suddenly become aware that his anal region was all too frequently damp and moist. (A not unusual complaint with ano-erotists.) This condition made it necessary for the patient to resort to regular washing and rubbings. (We recognized this as camouflaged masturbation.) He began to postpone every bowel movement as long as possible with the flimsiest of excuses, for his defecations made him feel faintly orgastic. The physiological procedure became a distinctly pleasurable performance. Then, one day, driven by an unbearable itching sensation in the anal region, he went to a prostitute and made her perform a lambitus on him. The sequel of this act for the patient was a dilemma: on the one hand he was afraid of getting into the habit of the paraphilia and, on the other hand, normal intercourse gave him such a weak orgasm that it did not appear to be worth his trouble.

Analysis revealed that in his unconscious, the patient really had the desire to have a man perform this act on him. His agoraphobia was an expression of his struggle against this desire; the presence of an escort, necessitated by the patient's fear of leaving his house by himself, protected him against succumbing to his unconscious craving.

One of his earliest reminiscences referred to an anilingus he had performed on his sister when he was four. The girl was two years younger, and the two children slept in one bed. The game, which the little girl enjoyed, although she never returned the act, had continued for many months.

I have elsewhere [1] described a case of priapism which we were able to trace back to a suppressed desire for anilingus.

The regression to anilingual gratification is not infrequent. Prostitutes are in a position to demand a "stiff" price for their anilingual services, since men who have acquired the habit of lambitus usually become "incapacitated" for the normal approach. Among the overt anilinguists whose cases I had occasion to study was a man who had accidentally learned the paraphilia in a brothel and had then become addicted to this form of sexual activity.

The next case exemplifies a strange linkage of several infantile traits:

Case No. 74: Mr. J. L., a Dutch attorney, complained of various forms of fear and of vague pains. Among the first was a fear of being alone, of getting lost, and, most of all, a great anxiety preceding his every appearance in court. As for his pains, he grumbled over a stabbing ache in his loins which disturbed him in his sleep, complained of periodic inflammations in his nose, with puffiness and abundant flux, and of the most vexing of them

[1] *Impotence in the Male,* Liveright Publishing Corp., New York, 1927.

all—the daily mucous colitis spells which made him run from doctor to doctor in search of help. The patient came to me after an unsuccessful analysis by another psychiatrist. It was an extremely difficult case, mainly because the patient was thoroughly acquainted with the psychoanalytic literature and offered great resistance to penetration. He was least of all willing to surrender his daydreams.

At this point I want to make it clear once more that no analysis is complete unless the patient has submitted his daydreams to analysis. Many neurotics take refuge behind such alibis as lack of awareness of any daydreaming on their part or the impossibility of putting the reveries into words. This is nonsense. What these neurotics lack is not the ability but the willingness to tell their fancies. The fantasies are their most precious possessions, and they refuse to part from them. Besides being cherished relics of childhood desires they are, as a rule, very infantile, something of which the patient feels ashamed, as they usually revolve around ani-lingus, enemas, irrigations (performed by mother or a mother figure). Such relics of infantile wishes resist even the sincerity of bona fide love, and constitute a sanctum into which not even the loved one may be admitted. Very often the infantile yearning proves stronger than a latter-day attachment, no matter how real this attachment may be. Many a love tragedy, presumably due to faithlessness, is actually based on such a "betrayal" of the present in the name of the past. The patients must be made to relate their fantasies, for only through ventilation and analysis can the reveries lose their magic significance. But it must be admitted that some neurotics would not part with their infantile fantasies even after their absurdity and insignificance has been exposed.

At the time of consultation the patient was a happy child of healthy parents. He showed no signs of disturbance during his youth. His neurosis broke out relatively late in life—two years after his marriage. True, there have been a few premonitions shortly before that. Immediately before the wedding there had been a period of doubt and vacillation. On his wedding day, just before the ceremony was about to commence, he fell asleep, and his bride had a hard time waking him. During the first three weeks of his married life he was impotent, although he loved his bride very much.

The patient's sexual life never became quite normal, although he finally managed to have penetration. He had good erections only during the playful introductions to intercourse, such as kissing, touching, and manual manipulations, but the prospect of inserting his penis would, as a rule, throw him back, and the erection could not be sustained.

Despite this, and despite his constant lamentations about his pains and aches, his marital life was very peaceful, thanks to the intelligence and devotion of his wife.

The patient's reminiscences disclosed his childhood fixation to his brother, two years his senior. The boys had been inseparable. They slept in one bed at night and played together in the daytime. Not only had they worn similar clothes but, later in life, they chose the same career.

The patient did not remember any intimacies between him and his brother, although he had many homosexual relations with a cousin and the cousin's friends. He had his last homosexual experience at the age of sixteen. At eighteen, he made an attempt at normal intercourse, but had premature emission.

Analysis of his dreams revealed a strong criminal tendency at the basis of his anxiety. (He hated everyone who stood between him and his brother.)

His mind was dominated by the fixed idea of sharing his brother's life. In his fantasies he offered his brother his anus as a substitute for any possible vagina.

The toilet occupied a central position in the patient's daydreams. In the toilet vacated by his brother he experienced pleasurable moments. The toilet, of course, had been used also by his father, a heavy smoker. The odor of tobacco combined with that of feces was one of the pleasant memories of early childhood. The patient's pains in the coccyx and in the nose were conversions, symptomatic expressions of his psychic pains over the impossibility of reliving those childhood pleasures.

When his brother married, the patient married, too—out of spite. Of course, there was also the positive moment of real love for his wife, but actually he could never forgive her because she, and not his brother, shared his life. He had fantasies of murdering her. One of his reminiscences referred to an incident when he had seen a kitchen knife and was seized with horror that he might plunge it into his wife's body. He was impotent because he visualized his penis as a dagger and was afraid to kill his wife with it.

Among the patient's habits was the irresistible urge to beg for his brother's worn-out trousers. The idea that the trousers had held his brother's buttocks gave him a thrill; the mere smell of the old trousers aroused him.

Speaking of anosexuality, one cannot help thinking of Freud's study "Charakter und Analerotik" contained in his *Kleine Schriften zur Neurosenlehre.* According to Freud, the sublimation of anal erotism counts for much in the development of human character, so that we are entitled to speak of an "ano-erotic character," the main features of which are orderliness and neatness, a pedantic trend and stubbornness.

Unfortunately, Freud's paper produced an immense crop of the most fantastic elaborations on man's "anal character." I. Sadger and Ernest Jones, to name but two, were studious on the subject and drew some far-fetched conclusions on the relations between anal sexuality and creative ability, anal sexuality and general character structure and the like.

The truth of the matter is, however, that the character formation has nothing to do, in any specific way, with anal erotism. Every neurotic is a victim of regression and is dominated by overpowering drives. Implicitly, every neurotic is also in the grip of strong ano-sexual impulses which are part and parcel of all primitive sexuality.

Pedantic formalism must not necessarily be a self-erected protection against the specific ano-sexual drive, and neatness need not be a compensating conversion of mysophilia—both are entirely conceivable sublimations or moral reactions against *any* inacceptable sexual drive. And as to spite, it is certainly a trait common to all neurotics. Spite is the strength of the weakling.

All compulsive neurotics display the presence of strong sexual drives and of deep-seated criminal propensities. Their unbridled egocentrism leads them to hate everyone who surpasses them or stands in their way. Jones elaborates on one single source of hatred. "We never hate any one," he says, "who is not to some degree our master." And he rightly goes on to evolve the idea that unfulfilled erotic aspirations may be converted into hatred. Here Jones should have gone farther and spoken of the incessant struggle between the neurotic and the world about him, of the neurotic's fight against his own criminal disposition, of his frequent tragic choice of a compulsion which represents a caricature of self-improvement and self-mastery.

But instead, at this point Jones falls back on his pet theory and tries hard to trace all compulsion to anal erotism. According to him, then, the child encounters his first real outside resistance in the process of defecation. The necessity of curbing the sphincters is every human being's first submission to force, and the evil consequences are but the result of this enforcement. Mother's interference with baby's anal erotism is the prime source of his hatred, and "it can hardly be expected that later on in life the person who had alternately loved and loathed his mother should act differently toward other love objects. Perhaps we also touch here upon the reason why compulsive neuroses are so much more frequent among men than among women." I most emphatically disagree with this last statement. Women are just as often afflicted with compulsive neuroses as men are, perhaps even more often, since men, in circumstances leading to compulsions, tend to become fetishists.

And then Jones goes on to draw one of his most daring conclusions, thus proving that the clearest head may at times get lost in the fog of its own vagaries. Referring to Ferenczi's statement that every child passes through a phase of exercising omnipotence by means of magic gestures and signals, Jones assigns to the flatus the most prominent place among the token actions. "The flatus," he says, "is the child's main device of asserting himself. It is in the light of this insight that we ought to view the above-mentioned relation between the infantile omnipotence feeling and the ano-erotism of compulsive neurotics." And Jones then adds his astounding statement that "the flatus plays an important part in the development of speech, both in the individual and in the species."

There is no doubt that the flatus is of some importance in the psychic make-up of the neurotic personality and in the mechanism of regression, but Jones' generalizing assumptions are absurd.

Now let us look at a case from my own files, a case in which buttocks erotism, to use a term coined by Sadger, plays an eminent part.

Case No. 75: Mr. S.I., an office clerk of twenty-seven, complained of compulsive actions which made him the laughing-stock of everybody. Although gifted by nature and far from lacking physical attractiveness, intelligence, and many natural talents—he spoke fluently several languages and played the violin extremely well—he always acted in such a way that every one thought of him as being a complete fool, and he was fired from one job after another. He was obsessed with the desire to look at the backside of women and to masturbate at the sight of their behinds. This desire was always present in his thought during the working hours and made him drop the job at hand and run the streets in search for gratification.

His father owned a large manufacturing plant, but being considered an idiot, the patient had no chance of ever becoming his father's assistant and successor. In fact, this job had been already disposed of in favor of the patient's brother, seven years his junior.

The patient described his perversion as follows: Several times a day he would run the streets until he saw women bending over (window display workers were his favorite objects). He would watch from a distance, stare at the contours of the buttocks, and masturbate. He had a hole in his trousers pocket, made for the purpose of reaching the penis with his hand.

Two previous psychotherapeutic interventions by other physicians had been unsuccessful.

The patient's initial story revealed that a certain Mr. B. played a very important part in his life.

The patient was sixteen and a student enrolled in an out-of-town "Business Academy" when he met B., a "precocious and original personality." B. made the patient go to a brothel for the first time, but the attempt at intercourse was without success. Whereupon B., presumably out of friendship and with the sole purpose of investigating the matter, masturbated the patient and even introduced the patient's penis between his buttocks, "perhaps even into the anus." The patient himself presumably had no clear idea of what it was all about.

Analysis proved very difficult. The patient would talk incessantly but skillfully avoid saying anything concerning his childhood. It became evident that he went on playing the fool. Here as elsewhere he played the fool first to disarm all critics by admitting in advance his silliness, and secondly to surprise everyone the more by his brilliance. He had once proved to his family that he was able within a few months' stay in Switzerland to master a difficult subject and to learn three languages.

He did not want to give up his affliction, which he had accepted as punishment for his criminal feelings toward his father. The patient's silliness, his implicit inability to manage the plant, was to disprove that he wished to inherit it as soon as possible.

Only so much light could be shed on his sexual development as to see that he had, by sheer willpower, converted his homosexuality into heterosexuality. The homosexual component was much too strong to be completely subdued, however. The patient's first sexual fantasies revolved around the fine contours of boyish buttocks; the patient himself had for a while acquired homosexual mannerisms.

Most harmful was his relation with B., who obviously had but one goal: to make the patient, even sexually, completely subservient, in order to have him at his mercy when he inherited his father's riches. B. had, of course, strongly objected to the patient's consulting me, and as he was unable to prevent it, he constantly attempted to disrupt the analysis by keeping the patient away from my office for long stretches of time. Finally, I had to give up this case. The patient left me with the assertion that he had improved. I knew perfectly well that it was a very limited improvement which was confined to a certain adjustment to work and to a slight moderation of his habitual horseplay.

I referred the patient to my assistant, Emil Gutheil, who later reported on the case as follows:

"The patient suspended his visits for a while, then came back. In view of the old experience that patients, refused treatment, often soften up to yield more data and to give up some of their resistances, Dr. Stekel instructed me to make a further attempt at therapy.

"First, I cleared up with the patient a few current difficulties. B.'s father was made to pay the money back which his son had extorted from the patient. The latter's relations with his family have been restored, and the question of a steady job was successfully solved.

"However, the patient's evasive horseplay at the sessions went on, and it required a great deal of patience to clear a path to the patient's mind. The only data to go by at first was the fact that the patient's sexual attention in the initial period of his neurosis was directed toward young boys.

"Slowly, it could be established that the patient's attitude had been predominantly masochistic. Thus, for instance, one of his recollections referring to a bodily threat at the age of nine contained the acknowledgment that he had not at all endeavored to avoid the expected beating by an older fellow student but had made preparations to undergo the punishment. And neglecting all other parts of his body, he had padded the bottom of his trousers.

"I was certain that this episode, the main features of which had been already established by Dr. Stekel, pointed at another, much earlier experience, since the episode clearly contained the moment of expectancy and desire. Significantly enough, the patient's memory of the years preceding his ninth year was a complete blank.

"The development after the episode at nine showed a marked reversal at the age of fourteen, when the patient—presumably craving for vengeance—turned out a strong sadistic component. His favorite game, at the time, consisted in whipping younger and weaker boys with a bamboo cane over their buttocks. There was only one little girl to whom he administered the cane with equal sensations of great sensuous pleasure: his youngest sister, with whom he had shared also other sexual experiences. Simultaneously, the patient learned to resort to imaginary whippings, if and when reality failed to supply actual ones; these imaginary sadistic reveries had the added advantage of allowing the patient to whittle down the age of his objects at will. At that, his passion for canes remained real and practicable; he had an assortment of them and cherished his collection greatly.

"At last, analysis was able to bring forth the following stubbornly suppressed memory: When the patient was four or five years old, his governess, a statuesque girl he had adored, locked him in alone in a room after having first vigorously spanked him with a bamboo cane over his buttocks. The episode occurred in the wake of some misdemeanor on his part and presumably caused him a whole gamut of emotions, such as rage, pain, humiliation, and a burning desire for vengeance.

"Thus the determinative childhood experience was finally uncovered. Whether the patient's later conversion to female objects was due to the fact that we generally bestow pleasure upon others in the manner we would like it to be bestowed upon us, or, as Freud would say, the initial trauma was abreacted through repetition and transformation into activist forms—the fact remained that the patient's central daydream—and ultimate compulsion—has been disengaged from the repressed primary sexual goal, and the connection was lost from sight.

"Significantly, the patient's intentional rerouting of his sexual interest toward women had to be undertaken by him via his own self (a transitional period of transvestism and feminism). I was able to establish that the patient, in his transvestist span—when he used to put on feminine garments, stand before the looking glass, and whip himself—preferred tight and short dresses. Indeed, he wore blue dresses of his younger sister (incestuous component of his sadomasochistic paraphilia).

"To summarize it briefly: In his psychic infantilism, the patient was projecting onto his sexual object, in a specific and rigid form, the original pleasure-pain experienced at the hand of a cherished person. The feminine ideal of his compulsive visualization was a montage picture of the blurred governess memory, his own self as seen in the mirror, and the first female object. The gap between his fantasy world (life at the age of four or five) and reality was expressed in his bipolar attitude of asserting his adulthood and playing the part of a fool. His fear of the discomfort at being addressed as 'Mister' and his unfounded assumption that his penis was too small belonged also in this dichotomic formation. His very strong homosexual component was due, it seemed to me, to his assuming, in his specific revery, the role of a female. His search for a partner was a search for his masculine counterpart, that is, for himself. His friend B. must have sensed and exploited the nature of the patient's fixation."

To my assistant's analysis I might add a few remarks outlining my view of the way the traumatic experience had been operative.

Besides the strong sensation of pleasure, the patient had also experienced in that childhood episode an overwhelming desire to avenge his humiliation and to hit the governess on her naked buttocks. Later on, when he was actually doing just that to small boys, he projected his infantile self into the boys, while his adult self became the governess.

A feature peculiar to the patient was his infatuation with his own buttocks. Even during the disciplinary episode he must have been certain that the governess was impressed by that part of his body.

Rage and pleasure converged into one sensation. In his search for reiterations of the experience, he cherished most of all the sight of maidservants in the act of caning and dusting rugs in the backyard. The rug-beating probably evoked in him most strongly the old sensation, while his bolstered ego-feeling (his stare, he said, made the servants turn and tug on their skirts which had been deranged while they had bent over to hit the rugs—a truly magic stare) allowed him to convert his childhood role into an active one.

The buttocks fetishists are recognizable at a glance. They walk differently. They have a certain swagger, a way of swinging their hips and buttocks, as though they were calling the attention of the world to the beauty of that part of their body.

The phenomenon of playing the fool deserves investigation. It is very common with children, and the tragic nature of this exaggerated gaiety is evidenced by the almost inevitable crying scene which usually follows immediately after the strenuous horseplay.[1]

The regressive form of "childish foolishness" is present in various types of infantilism, and its psychological motivation is quite clear. Infantilism emerges ordinarily in the wake of a severe blow to the ego, and the forced gaiety is compensatory, an attempt to drown out the defeat and disappointment. It is as though the patient were saying, "Look, I don't mind it, I am laughing about it myself."

The above patient was basically prone to dejection. Most specifically, the presence of people (whom he always appraised on the merit of their sexual availability) made him want to cover up the hopelessness of his real cravings with the mask of slapstick humor.

It is hardly possible to exhaust the great variety of expressions of infantile anal erotism within the limits of these few pages, and I shall mention briefly only a few common types. There is, first, the type of the flatulent person who by means of aerophagia obtains a welcome means of producing many "gases."

[1] We find an extraordinary presentation of this type of buffoonery in the person of Karamazov, the father, in Dostoyevski's *The Brothers Karamazov.*

I have been told by some patients that they like the smell of their flatus and actually derive from it a pleasurable sensation. It is possibly one of the sources of the love of perfumes; and it is certainly not without significance that aphrodisiac perfumes resemble certain animal and human secretions in that they are all caprylates. A homosexual patient complained of what he called a "ridiculous erotic sine qua non"—his male love partner had to prelude the erotic act with several flatuses. The patient remembered that his father was past master at prodigious flatulent performances. Another patient, a compulsive neurotic who had been in treatment for a lengthy period, displayed a very strange form of anal sexuality.

Case No. 76: In his early childhood, the patient had the habit of collecting toilet paper that had been used both by himself and by other members of the family. When he was thirteen, a member of the family had stumbled upon his collection and had burned it. The patient felt so deeply ashamed that he gave up his "hobby" for some time. At the age of thirty-two he married, but his marriage was a failure. He relapsed into his old condition of daydreaming and, one day, he suddenly felt a resurgence of his old passion to collect used toilet paper. After some struggle against this urge, he gave in, and again began to spend hours on end playing with the collected toilet paper and losing himself in reveries. Simultaneously, he developed other infantilist traits, such as a peculiar twitching of the nose. The tic proved to be related to his olfactory urge, and analysis was able to free him of it.

Coprolalia likewise belongs to this sphere. The four-letter words are part of the vocabulary of every man who is preoccupied with anal matters.

Some children are in the habit of soiling their clothes and keeping them on for a while. In the opinion of the parents, such children are so absentminded or so engrossed in their games that they don't even know what had "happened to them." This is not true, of course. Such children are pronounced anal erotists, and traces of their condition may stay with them forever. Their underwear will always be somewhat soiled. And given a psychosexual regression, they may relapse into anal erotism, even if they had originally outgrown the anal erotic phase.

Case No. 77: Mr. U.T. in his early boyhood had been in the habit of holding back his feces as long as possible and, after defecation, of playing with his feces. He would let some through the sphincter and then draw it back, deriving great sensuous pleasure from this practice. His trousers were frequently soiled, and he was punished for it. He learned to be clean only when he was ten, but his games with feces went on until he was fifteen. After that he apparently lost all interest in these games.

At the age of twenty-five he went through a period of despondency due to a romantic disillusionment. He began to brood heavily, and his anal sexuality re-emerged. He again began playing with his excrements. His favorite form of procedure was to have a tip of the fecal column protrude from his rectum against the seat of his underpants and to enjoy the feel of its presence for hours. For reasons of discretion he usually had to destroy his shorts.

One of the most baffling forms of anal sexuality is *coprolagnia,* which involves enjoying the sight of defecation by another person. While such enjoyment is not surprising if found among children, its appearance in adulthood carries with it all the characteristics of a paraphilia. Morbid fixation of certain childhood experiences is at the core of these severe forms.

Following is an excerpt from a case reported by Moll.

Case No. 78: The patient said: "After what I have said, you will understand the way I would use a boy to get the greatest gratification. Let us assume I have at my disposal such a boy and all the necessary accommodations. I would bring the boy into a specially arranged room and first give him a bath and inspect him thoroughly, concentrating my attention on his lower half. I let my hands glide along his thighs up to their juncture, pat the boy's buttocks, and put my finger between them, in the crena. Then I feel his stomach, trying to imagine that it is full of feces. If, upon my question, the boy confirms my suspicion, I become so aroused that my hands begin to shake. I keep on caressing the boy's belly, in a delirium of sensual joy and excitement. I have the boy take all sorts of positions which bring his buttocks and anus into full view. If the boy avowedly has but little bulk in his intestines, I feed him bulk-producing dishes, such as potatoes, course bread, leguminous plants, fruits, and the like. I feed him perhaps two or three days in succession without letting him move his bowels, until at last I shall be able to reach the summit of all sensuous gratification: watch a good, long-lasting defecation, the dropping mass being as solid and well-formed as possible, and the boy changing positions at my will." Moll, l.c., page 301.

And here is a case from my own files.

Case No. 79: Mr. S.C., thirty-five, an army officer, was a bathroom fiend. He spent hours on the toilet, smoking, studying, reading newspapers. Watching a defecating woman was one of his greatest pleasures. He had a chance at such a gratification on hikes or when stationed in villages. By way of preparedness he always carried along a little drill to bore holes in the wooden walls of country privies. According to him, he is not an exceptional case. As a matter of fact, he nearly always found that someone before him had already bored a hole in the privy wall. Of prostitutes, he asked nothing but a chance to watch them move their bowels. The patient had repeatedly nibbled at the feces of women.

The habit of some mothers who take their children along with them to the toilet, out of fear of leaving them for a few minutes without supervision, may lead to such fixations. Avoiding such practices is one way of preventing them.

Chapter Six

THE ANIMAL IN FANTASY

Chapter Six

THE ANIMAL IN FANTASY

1. ZOOPHILIA

Friendless people are inclined to seek the companionship of pets. Little wonder that among most ardent lovers of animals we find many lonely, unmarried people. Ordinarily, their zoophilia is mild; it is essentially an outpouring of otherwise untapped emotions; and as objects of such emotional expression the animals fulfil the function of serving as objects for the emotional catharses of human beings.

These are well known facts that need no further elaboration. Perhaps I should add one significant detail, however: admirers of animals often fall back on baby talk, like lovers, when addressing their pets,[1] and they speak of bunnies, chickens, pigeons, pussy-cats, and other animals when they address children affectionately.

---

[1] Many artists and poets are warm friends of animals. Baudelaire addressed many poems to cats; indeed, he needed the presence of a cat for inspiration. Byron immortalized his dog in verse and in a moving epitaph. Hebbel's writings are full of zoophilic passages. He cried disconsolately when his pet squirrel died. After he had picked up the creature's body, he kept it warm in his armpit. One of Octave Mirabeau's heroines was passionately in love with her stallion.

Less widely known, however, is the fact that in many instances, pets serve as sexual objects, or as instruments of sexual gratification. Many a charming lap dog has been trained to perform cunnilingus.

The line of demarcation between love of animals in the broadest sense of the word and overt "sodomy" is fluid, as Havelock Ellis has justly stated. We shall rather subsume all proved instances of sexual abuse of animals under the heading "zoophilia," knowing that this is a widely spread aberration and that it evolves out of normal relations to animals through intensification, sexual starvation, the yen for variety, and other morbid trends.

It goes without saying that in ancient times zoophilia was more talked of than now. Not that our culture has become less zoophilic, but the aberration is less overt—or rather, it has been crowded into the realm of fantasy which accompanies a masturbatory act.

Literary allusions (in the Bible, in the writings of Herodotus, Strabo, Ovid, Virgil, and Juvenal), various scenes on murals and vases, and many little sculptures show the preoccupation of ancient man with zoophilia.[1] The sources quoted refer to sexual contacts of women with donkeys and dogs, and even with he-goats and stallions.

Here is an excerpt from the material assembled by Erich Wullfen for his *Sexualarchiv,* V. II:

"Sodomy is indigenous in all parts of the world. There are recorded tales both in Africa and South America of voluntary sexual intercourse between apes and human females. An old Peru legend tells us that syphilis, originally a disease of the Alpacas, has been transmitted to man through sexual intercourse between men and llamas. Sodomy prospers in India, Kamchatka, and Anam. Many passages in the Bible speak of sodomy in Canaan. . . . Egyptians practiced devo-

[1] The reader may find many references in Ivan Bloch's *Der Ursprung der Syphilis* (Origin of Syphilis), Gustav Fisher, Publisher, Jena, Germany, 1911.

tional sodomy. . . . Part of the adoration of the he-goat at Medes consisted of sexual gratification of the animal by female worshippers. The religious significance of this animal in Hellas and Italy is also due to its place among the sexual divinities, and may be one of the reasons of present-day frequent use of goats for sodomitic purposes in South Italy (Bloch). Although sexual intercourse between shepherds and goats in Southern Italy and on Sicily is so frequent that it may well be described as a local custom, it is absolutely void of any pathological component. According to Mirabeau, sodomy was widely spread in the region of the Pyrenees in the XVIIIth century, and the Southern Slavs allude to extant sodomy in their folk songs."

Havelock Ellis argues as follows:

"Three conditions favored the establishment of the sodomitic habit; first, the primitive way of life that almost effaced the barrier between man and animal; second, the strong intimate ties between the peasant and his cattle, coupled with occasional forms of seclusion on the part of the female population; and third, the influence of various popular beliefs, such as the superstitious assertion that venereal diseases could be gotten rid of through copulation with animals."

Is it surprising then to hear of shepherds or ostlers or swine-breeders using their animals for sexual gratification? The population of many regions does not think it is. Mirabeau, quoted by Wullfen, tells us that with Basque boys the sin of sodomy is the most frequent subject of religious confession; and the stories told by present-day war veterans reveal that the situation has not changed significantly.

The only really surprising fact is that even city-dwellers who have so little contact with animals are yet so frequently affected with zoophilia. Only exceptionally do we find a neurotic whose history and reveries do not reveal any zoophilic elements. Well, after all, flies, butterflies, dogs, cats, and similar living creatures are within reach of the city-dweller.

It is the animal that often supplies the child with the first display of sex life, and we have learned enough from Binet to know of what tremendous importance the first impressions are, especially in regard to sex. Many girls get their first lessons in the "facts of life" by watching mating dogs; others are so overwhelmed by the sight of copulating flies or beetles that their entire future is forever keyed up to that signal impression.

A patient of MacDonald, a boy of fifteen, confessed to the following scale of arousing stimulations: (1) copulating flies; (2) mating horses; (3) the sight of women's underwear; (4) flirting boys and girls; (5) bovines in heat; (6) female statues with nude breasts; (7) the touch of his own governess, especially her bosom; and last, (8) intercourse.

It seems to me that the only reason why flies should occupy place number one in the potency scale of stimulants with this boy was that these insects were the first to stir his curiosity and imagination.

I know instances of entirely unconscious reactions to flies; a person would half listen to the buzz of a fly in the room and suddenly become sexually aroused, wondering why and how this erotic feeling came about.

Masturbators often link their act with the visualization of coupling flies. I reported three cases of this type in *Zeitschrift für Sexualwissenschaft,* V. II, 1916, and I quote from my paper, "Flies as Sexual Objects":

"I am, by chance, in a position to report on two instances in which sexual stimulation leading to masturbation came from flies.

Case No. 80: "Mr. O.R., traveling salesman, aged thirty-eight, complained that buzzing flies aroused him sexually to such a degree that he could not refrain from masturbating. Every time when this happened he was in a strangely dreamy condition, mostly extremely pleasurable, but occasionally saturated with sadness. He became addicted to this form of masturbation at the age of twenty-two, after he had left the parental house. His father was the owner of a small restaurant, and the premises were always full of flies. Apparently, the buzzing of flies was linked in the patient's mind with childhood experiences; no further data, however, could be obtained, as the patient consulted me only once.

"The second case was that of a patient in treatment at my office, and I am in a position to comment on it.

Case No. 81: "The patient, a lawyer, aged twenty-six, was in the habit of catching live flies and pressing them to his penis while masturbating; squashing of the insect, orgasm, and ejaculation—all these joined into one vehement climactic experience.

"The patient masturbated to the accompaniment of the fantasy of a sexual crime. The fly was the symbolic substitute of a young woman he fancied he was murdering. The consequence of his criminal tendency was an absolute impotence in the presence of slight and weak women, an impotence which obviously served as a protection against temptation. Only with husky, robust women did he feel both safe and potent.

"The strange combination of masturbating with the aid of flies and copulating with masculine women, apparently contradictory, was easily explainable. The patient kept on masturbating despite regular intercourse with women, because his masturbation was primarily a means of gratifying his criminal rather than his sexual impulses. The use of a fly was not a *sine qua non* of the act; the destruction of an insect only augmented the voltage of gratification."

It is entirely possible that many people permanently regard sex as something beastly because their first sexual impressions were those of mating animals. A case reported by Havelock Ellis suggests such a possibility. I shall quote here a few lines from Ellis' presentation, which is based on the data supplied by the patient, himself a trained psychologist:

Case No. 82: "The patient began to masturbate when he was five years old. He masturbated very frequently, rubbing his penis with oil for the act, and all his mother's warnings and admonitions were of no avail.

" 'A few months later,' the patient went on, 'one of the maids began a series of games with me, from which she expected sexual gratification. It was summer, and I played all day long in the barn. She came to the barn regularly, and tried hard to introduce me into full sex life. I was a bad pupil, however. The proceedings left me cold; I looked upon them as interference with my own games and disliked the maid's play with my genitalia. Strange as it may seem, cunnilingus was less of a nuisance to me than her attempts to introduce me to the art of intercourse.

" 'About a year later I began to experience the first stirrings of sexual desire, which I did not connect, however, with the previous stimulations by the maid. The peculiar characteristic of my first spontaneous sexual stirrings was that I experienced them usually while I was maltreating animals. I do not remember how I first noticed the connection, but I most vividly remember that I went to all sorts of troubles to provoke those sensations, such as fastening nails to the end of a broomstick to hit the dogs, cats, and calves the harder.

" 'At that time I conceived also my first ideas about sexual relations, as I eagerly watched the mating of animals. Those ideas were wrong, inasmuch as I thought that the anus was the female's recipient. But my excitement at the moments of observation was great; it involved not only my genital organs but also the anal region, as I feverishly fancied myself a female animal, in an ecstasy of both pederasty and sodomy.

" 'Between the ages of fifteen and seventeen I practiced *coitus inter femora* with my brother; then I had a resurgence of my sodomitic fantasies and tried many times to abuse animals. Both experiences gave me pleasure far below my exaggerated expectations. In fact, ever since I was sixteen I have fought my impulses, although with only intermittent success.

" 'I know now that the feeling of depression I had after every single act of sexual aberration was not due to the loss of semen, as I had naively thought at the time, but to the deep sense of my moral degradation.' "

The patient who reported to Ellis the preceding lines was barred from normal sexual life. Like all infantilists, he lived in a strange dream world, gratifying his desires in masturbation and its accompanying fancies grown out of fixated childhood experiences. He distinguished, in his confession, between earthly (beastly) and heavenly love. Apparently, he had not freed himself from his early zoanthropic and zoophilic cravings.

Zoophilic tendencies sometimes manifest themselves merely in accentuated specific sensations evoked by the ordinary act of caressing or petting animals. Cats are known to be pre-eminently able to arouse sexual sensations, but for certain obvious reasons this phenomenon has been described under the heading of fur fetishism. Some [1] women, however, become aroused also when stroking a hen or a lap dog, without pursuing the act any farther.

The following are a few cases of individuals who showed strong interest in large animals at the expense of normal erotism. The first case is quoted by Krafft-Ebing from Hane.

Case No. 83: Y., twenty, intelligent, well-educated, of good stock, healthy, except for a distinct urethral hyperesthesia and some neurasthenic manifestations. Allegedly, he has never masturbated. His fondness for animals, especially dogs and horses, dated from early childhood, and has grown stronger since puberty. No sexual component was ever involved (patient's data).

On the occasion of his first horseback ride, the patient experienced a strong physical sensation, and when he mounted a horse for the second time, fourteen days later, he had an erection. A subsequent ride brought ejaculation. The patient, disgusted with himself, gave up horseback riding. From then on he had emissions nearly every night.

[1] "With one boy of twelve I knew, love of furs had its origin in the boy's habit of sleeping occasionally with his dog. The phases of development were: coincidental masturbation and feel of dog's coat; sufficiency of feel of dog's coat without manual masturbation; and, finally, fur-fetishism."—Ivan Bloch.

The mere sight of horseback riders (and dogs) began to cause him to have erections. He consulted a doctor, and got some relief through the improvement of his urethral condition. Reluctantly, he followed his doctor's advice and made a few attempts at normal intercourse, but they were all unsuccessful. (Dr. Hane, *Wiener Medizinische Blätter,* 1877, No. 5.)

Bloch describes a similar case.

Case No. 84: A farmer, forty-two, of stately appearance, very healthy-looking. Personal and family history revealed no data to account for his strange sexual development. The family, however, was afflicted by unhappy marriages. The patient's own parents, too, were an unhappy couple. The patient disliked his mother, an extremely dominant woman, and made a special point of his having been raised "on the bottle," for which he blamed his present indifference toward women.

When the patient rode a beautiful horse for the first time at the age of twelve, he experienced a great sensuous pleasure. Ever since, his whole sexual life has revolved around beautiful horses and riding. In fact, his only gratification for many years has been a weekly ride, and the concomitant orgasm and ejaculation.

The patient regarded normal intercourse as "something bestial," and he despised women. (Ivan Bloch, "An Unusual Case of Sexual Perversion—Zoophilia," *Medizinische Klinik,* 1906, No. 2.)

And here is another case, this one reported by Hirschfeld.

Case No. 85: G., of a family of lawyers, studied law himself but backed out before taking the bar examinations. He accepted work in an office. Although mentally very alert, he had neither the will nor the perseverance to conclude any project. He had the appearance of a boy of sixteen, and, as he said, felt that age, especially in the company of nice, elderly ladies. One note of his read: "I need a woman who can see the boy of sixteen within me, whimsical, spoiled, and in need of education. To instruct me, she would have to make use of my erotic imagination. For instance, should I misbehave during a walk, as I certainly would, she ought to be able to describe to me very vividly the beating I would receive, and thus fascinate me into obedience."

Another of his notes described his desire to be a schoolboy bringing faulty homework to class and being punished by a lady teacher—slapped in the face, scolded, threatened, and spanked on his naked behind. The patient had a large collection of paintings and drawings—mostly of British origin—of boys undergoing whipping by women.

The patient was also disturbed by another compulsive idea, the absurd nature of which he perfectly well understood, although he was not able to dismiss it from his mind. He visualized himself as a horse, "and by no means a noble, racy prancer, but a miserable decrepit nag, driven by a woman." He became strongly aroused at the mere sight of women drivers. (Hirschfeld, l.c., pp. 48-49.)

Now let us turn to those severe cases for which Krafft-Ebing coined the term "Zoerasty." One of them, reported by Boeteau, presents a combination of zoophilia and sadism.

Case No. 86: A., sixteen, gardener by trade, was an illegitimate child. He never knew his father; his mother suffered from a severe hereditary affliction (hystero-epilepsy). The patient himself showed a congenital skeletal deformity and asymmetric cranial structure. Very small for his age, he was sullen, apathetic, retired, extremely irritable, and almost pathologic in his vehement manifestations of affect. His imbecility was indirectly enhanced through constant masturbation to which he had been given since early childhood. Among his symptoms, we also ought to mention his reduced field of vision, dyschromatopsia, low degree of olfactory perception and taste, impairment of hearing (on the right side), low sensitivity of his right testicle, clavus, etc.

The patient has been accused by his employer of masturbating and sexually abusing dogs and rabbits.

According to the patient he had at the age of twelve watched boys masturbating a dog, and he, himself, became addicted to this habit. Later he also masturbated cats and rabbits, and widened the scope of the tortures inflicted on the animals. The bestial habit acquired gradually the form of obsessive spells, occurring always in the same manner, in intervals of about eight weeks. In such moments, the patient felt an uneasiness, a sensation as though his head were splitting. He struggled frantically against the oncoming anxiety and the ever-growing, hammering headache. Then came a climactic ringing in his ears and a clammy perspiration, and his knees shook. Finally, his resistance collapsed, and he sneaked over to the rabbit warren of the nursery where he was employed and there he indulged in his passion. The spell always occurred at night, and the morning thereafter the body of a female rabbit turned up to testify to the boy's violence.

These bestial acts were the only ones of which he was capable, and according to him even these never gave him any real sexual enjoyment; they only brought a temporary relief from the dreaded spell. (Boeteau, *La France Medicale,* Vol. 38, No. 38, as quoted by Krafft-Ebing.)

Wullfen, in his "The Sexual Criminal," quotes Rohleder's case of a single woman in her thirties who used to let a male parrot gently peck at her face and bosom until she went through all the phases of sexual suscitation. At a certain climactic point she stroked the rump of the bird. It is not known whether she achieved orgasm in the act or not, but the scene was definitely of a masturbatory nature.

Rohleder rejected a fetishistic interpretation of this case because according to him, the primary source of pleasure was not the feel of the bird's feathers but rather what may be called its caresses.

It is often hard to draw a line between zoophilia and veiled sadism. I am personally inclined to see in some zoophiliacs latent sadists and lust murderers. (I believe that for the boy quoted above, rabbits were only substitute victims for women.) A case out of my own files seems to substantiate my view.

Case No. 87: U.B., a thirty-five-year-old physician, beset by anxious apprehensions, told me that his sexual gratification was subject to two conditions: The woman had to agree to an *immissio in anum* and to suffer pain in the act. The more pain he inflicted, the stronger was his orgasm. During the war he turned sodomist, but even then he chose small animals and destroyed them in the process.

His states of anxiety originated in his impulses to kill women while making love to them.

Of much greater value for the understanding of the aberration are the instances of complete identification with an animal for the purpose of a successful performance of the sexual act. They are expressions of zoanthropo-sexual infantilism in its purest form.

Among the clients of the Viennese houses of prostitution there is the well-known type of "chantecleer" who stages, with the help of the woman, a perfect and expensive imitation of rooster-love.

The high degree of identification with an animal is well-illustrated by the following case of masochism.

Case No. 88: The wife of an army officer consulted me about the strange, and only, way her husband was able to perform his masculine duties. She had to put a dog's collar around his neck, talk to him as though he were a dog, and walk him up and down the room on a leash. He would first do a few "tricks," then perform a cunnilingus on her, and only after all these preliminaries would he be ready for the sexual act.

Merzbach (*Die Krankhaften Erscheinungen des Geschlechtssinnes,* Alfred Hölder, Publisher, Vienna, Austria, 1909) reports a similar case.

Instances of this kind are by no means rare; it is only that they are seldom brought to the attention of physicians. The women involved are ashamed of being a party to the act, while the men, who stubbornly cling to their infantile gratification, have no desire to consult a physician. Prostitutes are familiar with many details of these practices, for it is part of their profession to cater to paraphiliacs.

2. A CASE OF ZOOPHILIA

Case No. 89: Mr. T., twenty-three, a clerk, complained of a severe compulsive neurosis and ensuing difficulties at the office where he worked. He was always in doubt whether he had done his duties the right way, whether he had followed all instructions correctly. He had to pass over in his mind again and again all the details of the completed job, and it took him hours before he could start on the next assignment. The situation was even worse when money was involved.

To cope with his insecurity he spent his evening hours making notes, reviewing the events and activities of the day, and fixing the precise schedule of the morrow. Even while doing so, he was tormented by doubts, vacillations, and indecisions.

In addition to this trouble he was also beset by a strange form of zoophilia and sadism, with strong sexual content. In fact, it seemed that his pedantic preoccupations with his work, that is, his compulsive ideas and actions, were there as an insurance against lapsing into unacceptable sexual reveries. For as soon as he was at last through with his daily series of compulsive reflections and acts, he helplessly succumbed to his hallucinations and fancies.

In the center of his daydreams was the figure of a horse. The patient was either riding the horse or was driven in a carriage. (In real life, he has never mounted a horse.) A powerful tyrant, a king, he rode through throngs of people, or upon their backs, trampling men, women and children into the dust, so that their blood covered the path of his triumphant passage. Every now and then he had men and women pull his carriage, while to both sides stood the humble worshippers of his divine majesty.

Divinity and immortality were the attributes not only of the patient himself, but also of his mother (and of her alone—of all the members of his family) and of his horse. The latter was curried, bathed, and perfumed by twenty virgins; the excrements of the animal were the delight of the patient's subjects, whose job it was to clean the horse's anus with their tongues.

Occasionally, the patient rode on top of a woman who was in turn stretched on the back of the horse.

The very first questions revealed that the patient, who has allegedly never masturbated, went to sleep nightly pressing a pillow (surrogate for horse) between his thighs.

He came out, however, with the statement that his pillow caused him many worries: He was afraid his brothers would become infected if they touched it, as though his neurosis were a contagious disease. The tendency to regard neurosis as infectious, like syphilis, is not uncommon, but in this particular case it had the added significance that the patient had thus for the first time established a connection between his fantasies and his family. He followed up the initial step by stating that he also fancied mixing some of his semen into his younger brother's coffee.

This brother, who is two years his junior, was also disturbed; he, too, was still being helped along by mother when dressing in the morning, and tucked in when going to bed.

The younger brother's fantasies, according to the patient, were of a masochistic nature. He identified himself with a horse, and was driven and whipped by severe coachmen.

The patient reported the following incident: He and his office boss were in the vault. Through his mind suddenly flitted the idea, "What if I killed him right here and now!"

He remembered dreams in which *he was riding on brother's back.*

He had two older brothers. The elder of the two was irascible and had often spanked the patient, and they still had fights. Once the patient said to this brother, "I have read in Stekel's books of a woman who killed her husband in his sleep. You'd better be careful with me."

He remembered distinctly that in his boyhood he once had suddenly found himself in that brother's bed without knowing at the time how he had gotten there.

His two senior brothers had pushed him around, and he hated them. He used to dream of taking his revenge on them.

Until recently the patient doubted whether he was a man. At times he appeared to be afraid of becoming impregnated. He had allegedly no idea what female genitals looked like. His younger brother also was naive.

This statement was in contradiction with many of his associations which had revealed that he had both explored the matter himself very early in life and had been enlightened by his elder brothers, by maids and playmates.

His ignorance had all the characteristics of repression; as though the genitalia he knew nothing about were those of a definite person. His earliest reminiscence: He was sitting in a poorly lit hall and his mother was naked down to her waist.

Two data revealed his preoccupation with the size of his penis. He remembered having slept in grandfather's bed admiring the penis of the old man.

He recalled having read in a biography of Pirogov that the Russian had a childhood fantasy of a pencil that grew and grew, and of a worm that could stretch and stretch.

The patient dreamed:

"Mr. Z. tells me that he will have someone else in the office to take dictation, since I am so poor at it."

Mr. Z. had already appeared in the patient's dreams several times. He was the patient's superior in the office, although the two men had begun work simultaneously and as equals.

In this connection the patient spoke of his clumsiness. He was not good at anything, whether it was closing a door, buttoning his shirt, or typing. He was convinced he would bungle everything if he went to bed with a woman.

That was why he always needed the help of his mother, even when he was dressing in the morning.

Not only he himself but the entire household behaved in strangely childish ways. The oldest brother dropped his eye glasses once, and because the other boys burst out laughing, he furiously hurled a precious china bowl to the floor. Every one of the four sons wanted to dominate the rest of the family, and all four fought over their mother's love and attention; if one of them vexed the mother, the others tried to outdo one another in kindness to her.

The patient had short intervals of dreamy, semi-conscious states. In the electric street car he could lose himself in a revery, and what was worse, the same happened to him in the office, causing him trouble.

This was one of the reasons why he distrusted his memory and was always swamped with little notes. All his pockets were full of notes, both on things done and things to do. These notes obviously served two purposes: (1) They were proof that he was right. (2) They expressed his desire to forget and at the same time to retain some childhood experience or experiences.

He dreamed:

My uncle speaks of telephone numbers, and I tell it to my brother. Brother repeats the numbers, but I am not quite sure. He leans against my bookshelf and causes one book to fall onto the floor. I tell him, 'Pick it up!' He refuses to do so, and I threaten to drop some of his books, and I also say something like, 'It came, as it had to come!' Perhaps, it was, 'Let it come then!' I see a rope round my brother's neck, the end of the rope is in my hand. Then I see myself sitting on the foot end of my bed, the end of the rope in my hand again, but I don't know whether the boy at the other end is my brother or his friend. I do, however, pull and jerk the rope, with the feeling that this is the way the police extort confessions.

The uncle in the patient's dreams always represented the moral authority. In association with the word "telephone," the patient remembered a German pun using the word "telephonism" for "masturbation." The first part of the dream meant: "I had been masturbating, and my brother, too. But I am not quite sure whether it was my brother or his friend."

The book associatively reminded the patient of his brother's sarcastic remarks about me and my books. The patient is opposed to analysis because it stressed the importance of his childhood experiences. The book was the container of his memories. It held an episode when the patient had an orgasm, when he had "come." ("It came as it had to come.") His fixation to his brother was symbolized by the rope.

At this point, though, the patient advanced another association. His brother's friend had once remarked that the patient's and his brother's penes were "as thin as threads" (cf. the Pirogov reminiscence above). In the patient's dream the penes thickened and became like a rope. He tugged on his relations to his brother

—the police, the analyst, wanted him to confess, to tell the truth. The following is a dialogue between the patient and me:

P: "I once spent my vacation in G. There was an open privy there. I was always afraid of spiders and bees, and I went for days without moving my bowels."

I: "Were you afraid to be stung anywhere or at some particular part of your body?"

P: "I was afraid the bees might sting me in the rear end. This reminds me of a joke. A stutterer could not say, 'I like your *assortment.*' [1] It always came out, 'I like your ass—ass. . . .' That's true, one of my greatest fears is that a bee might get into my trousers. Did I tell you that my sister (the only girl in the family who had died) stuttered something terrible? I used to stutter myself, especially when I prayed. I wonder why."

I: "Maybe your conscience was not entirely clean."

P: "I still stutter at times, especially when my elder brother asks me something to test me. Now I remember. I was once in G. with Grandfather. As soon as he went to the privy I had an urge, too, and had to go on the chamber pot."

I: "Was this the grandfather whose genital you saw?"

P: "Yes."

I: "Did you watch him?"

P: "No. I always closed my eyes when he urinated."

I: "How is it you remembered your grandfather while speaking of bees?"

P: "I thought of the sting and then of Grandfather's penis. I am afraid of the bee's sting as if it were a penis."

I: "But you're afraid that a bee might sting you in the back."

P: "I am afraid someone might introduce his penis into my anus."

This dialogue showed the patient's fear of an anal penetration. But there was more. He feared the phallus because with him the phallus was an instrument of aggression (sting, hurt). The patient harbored strong criminal desires.

The frequency of the grandfather's presence in the patient's dreams was amazing. In one such dream, *"Grandfather lies in*

---

[1] This word has been changed to make the point clear in English—*The Translator.*

bed, and I tell him, 'You ought to be glad to be in bed.' Then he says reproachfully, 'It was not right what you've done.' "

The patient's first horse fantasies occurred in the year 1914, when his grandfather was very ill. The whole family went to live in the country, and the sick old man was often driven in a carriage in the fresh air. The patient enjoyed those rides enormously.

Soon the patient himself became sick. His fantasies ceased and returned only later when grandfather was dying.

Frankly, I was surprised to hear this story. Usually reveries, of the kind the patient had, become more intense in periods of illness; why should the patient have behaved differently?

Additional details brought the explanation: He had been jealous of his grandfather who, while sick, had the full attention of the patient's mother. His first horse fantasies were connected with death wishes toward his grandfather (the horse is a symbol of death; death is also a rider—"Death rides every breeze"). When the patient himself became sick, grandfather was relegated to a secondary position, if not farther back. The patient was getting an overwhelming amount of care and attention, and needed not the consolation of his fantasies. As soon as he got well again, and his grandfather was near death and again the center of attention, the patient's fantasies recurred.

The patient remembered clearly that he had wished his grandfather would die; he also remembered being surprised and feeling guilty over his indifference and calmness when the grandfather had died.

The patient's neurosis was apparently connected also with the death of two other close members of the family, his father and his sister.

In relation to this was his own fear of death. Even the ticking of the clock reminded him of death, and vexed him. On the way to my office he had to pass a poorly lighted corner of the stairway, and it made him nervous. He visualized death lurking in wait for him in that dark corner.

He had a pocket watch his grandfather had given him one year before he died. The watch reminded the patient of his wickedness and his egotism. It let him know that he was the harbinger of death. He wished death upon everyone who stood in his way or who laughed at him. He cursed constantly. His favorite ditty was, "Drop dead."

The patient had a dream about *an attempt at sexual intercourse with his mother. He had a lengthy discussion with his brother on the difficulties of the venture and the possibilities of a failure.*

Following the report of his dream, the patient went on to a lamentation on the blackness of his sexual life. He claimed that he had never masturbated, never even as much as made an attempt to approach a woman. He felt that he was too clumsy and awkward; he was afraid of defeat.

He has never known happiness, he said, except in his reveries about horses. Life held no joy for him. He had no friends, no one with whom he could associate. The fellow workers in the office teased and mocked him all the time, so that he avoided talking to them outside his line of duty. He was completely apart from the rest of the world and never went out. Of course, he shunned the company of women for fear of being ridiculed.

He had only his books and his mother. Unfortunately, he had to share her love with his brothers. How could anyone wonder why she means so much to him, why her attention was his everything?

He did not suspect that his mother was also in the center of his sexual desires. She was the horse he was riding. He had envied his brother's being carried around in mother's arms and had kept asking for the same favor under the pretext of tiredness. He kept this wish forever. His zoophilia had but one sense: He wanted to be a child again, and again be carried by mother.

He dreamed: *The world collapsed in a tremendous cataclysm. All human beings—those of the entire universe, not only the inhabitants of our planet—perished. I believe it was more than one hundred billion people. I was very furious and said to myself, 'How could the World Spirit ever allow such a thing to happen?'*

The interesting point about this dream was that the patient apparently survived the cataclysm. He was the only one to survive. Being the only living person, he could do anything. He had no longer to fear any competitive comparisons (Tannenbaum's *Noah Complex*). Even as a child he wanted his mother all to himself and wished death upon everyone (siblings, grandfather) who had title to her attention. Every death in his family (his father's, his sister's, his grandfather's) was the result of his magic wish, and he felt guilty for it. This guilt contributed to his feeling of inferiority which colored his every move.

His fantasy world was the only one where the entire situation was reversed, and he could indulge in all his megalomanic aspirations. Not only was he omnipotent, he was immortal. He survived every one.

One of his pet fantasies ran like this: A very rich girl, heiress to an immense fortune, wanted him to marry her. He let her beg for his consent for quite a while and at last formulated his conditions: (1) Her father was to hand over to him all his fortune. (2) The girl was to permit him all sorts of sadistic acts. (3) She must take care of him and of his horse and serve as his chambermaid. (4) He is to have absolute sexual freedom and as many women on the side as he wants.

In actual life the patient shunned women, was afraid of impotence and ridicule, feared his wife's infidelity, her whims and lack of concentration; in his fantasy everything was settled to his satisfaction.

The patient admitted that the girl had the features of his mother. For the understanding of neuroses it is absolutely essential to comprehend the phenomena of affect displacement and distortion. The fluidity of the dividing line between symbolization and reality is conditioned upon these phenomena.

One day the patient told me that he disliked eating his lunch, a sandwich, in the office. Only when his hunger became unbearable did he take out his sandwich, but then he ate it avidly. At that, he felt a great anxiety and his heart pounded as though he did something wrong.

Associating freely, he first talked of the day before and said that mother had presented him with a tea cup. He enjoyed the gift very much and immediately put it on his desk, which was his kingdom.

By way of rationalization, he explained that stingy as he was he would never have spent the money on a cup himself. He

seemed completely unaware of the obvious displacement of the
affect from mother to cup.

The patient's second association referred to his habit of re-
citing poems to himself when at home (presiding at his desk).
He would recite one bit of poetry endlessly, while working
through his notes or before going to sleep (and checking mentally whether he had done everything according to the notes that
day). Again, the patient seemed to ignore the connection between the notes and the poems.

On the preceding day, the patient was muttering constantly
to himself Schiller's verse on hunger and love. It was another
confirmation that his hunger was hunger for love, for a pro-
hibited form of love bestowed upon him by his mother in the
form of a drinking cup.

A succession of other associations also revolved around his
mother's love. He quoted another poem: [1]

> "And so runs on the time and on the changing tide!
> In all this misery and shame
> Abide with me, my comfort thought, abide:
> I shall forever be the same.
> The same eternal child!"

Our patient has often the feeling that his life is a dream.
Reality and fantasy fuse in his constant pursuit of infantile
revery.

He dreamt:

*In my office I broke a water glass. I think I must repay the
loss. Then I think that you will ask me how and why I have
broken the glass. I decide not to tell you about it. Then I say to
myself, 'This is only a dream, and I don't have to tell you
anything.'*

The patient struggled with the idea of suppressing some facts
from his history. He recalls that a dream dealing with his brother
has preceded the above dream. From his associations to this
dream, I conclude that he is determined not to permit me to
gain insight into this area. However, the above dream symbolizes
the collapse of his neurosis portrayed as a glass. He cannot admit

[1] What follows is a free translation of the poem—*The Translator.*

that he has changed. The horse fantasy is gone, he can work more efficiently.

What is it that he has succeeded in retaining? He sucks on a corner of his blanket before falling asleep; he must also occasionally make a note or think over the events of the day.

Can he get well? Only if he accepts reality. Only if he abandons his social isolation and replaces his infantile fantasies by more realistic ones. He must not sacrifice his life for the love of his mother. Marriage might be a way to his liberation.

3. ZOANTHROPY

The following condensed autobiography of a thirty-five-year-old engineer gives us a measure of insight into the development of a zoanthropic aberration.

Case No. 90: "The younger of two boys, I grew up on a farm, in the country. Very early in life I developed a great interest in animals, especially in birds. My first toy was a little metal cock, actually a sort of whistle. My brother and I played animals for hours. Animal figures were our favorite playthings. Some of them we associated with fairytale figures such as enchanted princes. I still preserve a little cloth monkey, and were I not afraid of being laughed at, I would even now take it with me to bed, as I used to when I was a little boy.

"I got my knowledge of the facts of life watching mating animals. Once I tried to abuse a hen, but the fowl raised such a ruckus that I became frightened and gave up at a very tender age, and always visualized myself as an animal in the act. It did not matter which animal; I was every one of them in turn. Besides fairy tales, it was Kipling's *The Jungle Book* which strongly spurred my imagination. I read the book a hundred times if I read it once, and I wished I had grown up among wolves.

"When I was in high school, I was constantly puzzled by the 'strange' propensity of my classmates to run after girls. I thought of dogs and horses, and dreamed of getting rich and having a corral filled with animals. My first introduction to sexual intercourse at the time, although successful, was a disappointment as compared with masturbation accompanied by visions of animals. But I soon came across one prostitute with a bird's face, and I became her frequent guest. I had begun to notice animal features on human faces at an earlier period.

"A performance of Rostand's *Chanticleer* gave me an opportunity to acquire a discarded rooster-costume, and an 'ad' in the paper brought me the acquaintance of a girl as confused as I, and the two of us enjoyed a glorious imitation of a poultry-yard romance. Unfortunately, the girl soon left Vienna, and I was stranded again. My attempts to play the rooster with prostitutes brought only humiliation and mockery.

"My unhappy state became acutely tragic when, at the age of twenty-seven, I became engaged to a very nice girl. I was impotent on the wedding night, and with tears in my eyes confessed everything to her. She was willing to put up with my impotence, but she would not 'debase' herself—and our love— with animal personifications.

"I looked up a well-known hypnotist, in frantic search for help. Unfortunately, I was not susceptible to hypnotic influence."

The analysis revealed a strong sadistic component in the man's make-up, and brought him relief. His potency was restored, and his zoanthropic fixation slowly subsided.

The *Alienist and Neurologist* for the year 1906 brings Kiernan's description of a remarkable case of zoanthropy.

Case No. 91: Two prominent citizens of the Russian town of Vladikavkaz, on trial for abduction of several girls, were found to have perpetrated their crimes in a state of senile mental regression, and were committed to an insane asylum.

Their last victim, the daughter of well-to-do parents, was kept by them for a period of about a year, after they had carried her off from her house in a very elaborate fashion. They abducted her in the dark of night in a carriage; both men wore masks. All year long the girl, who was dressed up by the men in a costume made of feathers, was kept in a large cage; every morning one of the men—she never saw the other man—looked at her through the bars of the cage, gave her breakfast, poured some water into a pan, and said invariably, "Take a bath, Birdie."

It is hardly possible to enumerate all the insensate tricks to which zoanthropists resort, but the underlying cause is always a fixation on a childhood experience (sometimes enhanced by the profound and lasting impression of a fairy tale, such as the German one entitled "Fittcher's Vogel" [Fittcher's Bird], in Grimm's famous collection).

Women, too, are susceptible to zoanthropy (usually a form of masochism), but they may not indulge their paraphilias in bawdy houses, as men do. The female's zoanthropy manifests itself much more subtly in a fascinated preoccupation with the animals in the zoo, or in a partiality for "exotic," animal-like men.

Zoanthropic fixations, such as I was able to uncover in many cases of male impotence, come to the fore only very late in analysis. Careful attention should be paid to dreams revolving around animals. So-called "love at first sight" may spring from latent zoophilic tendencies. It is a rather common occurrence that human faces often show strong or faint similarities with certain animal types. (I have known a man with pronounced ornithophilic tendencies, whose wife had a strikingly bird-like appearance.) Perhaps it is somewhere within this area that we ought to look for the reason of the profound impact upon us of certain ugly faces.

And above all, the possibility of reversal should always be kept in mind. I have demonstrated elsewhere [1] that repressed zoophilia may take on the form of zoophobia.

[1] *Conditions of Nervous Anxiety and Their Treatment,* Chapter on "Fear of Animals: Analysis of a Case of Dislike for Birds," Liveright, New York.

Chapter Seven

DETERMINANT OF AGE

Chapter Seven

DETERMINANT OF AGE

1. PEDOPHILIA

Pedophilia, a common form of infantilism, is very close to being a normal component of our sexual drives. Nearly every one of us at some time or another is bound to discover in himself a pedophilic trend, which normally is subdued, of course, with all the moral force (and indignation) at the person's disposal.

The sexual appeal of children is the more astounding if we consider that our culture has for thousands of years desexualized and sanctified childhood.

I for one have been for years the recipient of many confessions by both plain and outstanding people that they had been shamefully tempted and had had "sinful" thoughts at the sight of children.

Such temptations, naturally enough, tend to present themselves to the mind of the normal person in a cloak of negation. Thus one gentleman, prominent both as a poet and as a man of sterling qualities, told me that he was once watching his six-year-old daughter at play, when the thought flashed through his mind, "How is it at all possible that people *do* abuse children!" The very occurrence of this thought testified to the presence of some obscure and vague pedophilic stirring within the man.

Goethe, in his *Erlkönig*, has beautifully expressed a boy's homosexual fantasy, but the creative act must have been Goethe's own discharge of such a suppressed desire. A similar conation served Thomas Mann for the creation of his gripping story, *Death in Venice*.

The use of the child as "sexual plaything" is demonstrably present in several primitive cultures, but we would be merely deceiving ourselves if we indulged in the supercilious belief that we have completely outgrown those "savage" ways of life. My daily contact with patients proves to me beyond doubt the phenomenal ubiquity of pedophilic tendencies.

Before I make an attempt to inquire into the psychological roots of pedophilia, I should like to bring a few observations on its normal—non-neurotic—manifestations. Much of what appears to be "friendliness toward children" is really latent pedophilia, which may occasionally erupt in its full force and meaning, to the consternation and dismay of the unsuspecting agent himself. It is because pedophilic urges overcome the individual so suddenly that we ought to be made fully aware of pedophilic potentialities within the individual.

Case No. 92: A physician, thirty-four years of age, wrote to me as follows: "I am not conscious of harboring any morbid inclinations. That is precisely the reason why the incident I told you about scared me out of my wits. I shall gladly comply with your request to put down the experience in writing for you.

"I was on my way home from Vienna with a girl cousin of mine seven years of age whom I had been asked to take along. The journey took nearly twenty-four hours, and my fellow-travelers on the train admired my way of handling the child. In the course of the trip I also had to take the little girl to the ladies' room several times, and my kindness and patience aroused even my own admiration—I had never before shown any particular interest in tending to children.

"When evening came and the girl became tired, I seated her on my knees and rocked her to sleep. All of a sudden I became horrified—I had a powerful erection. I quickly put down the girl, although she protested vehemently.

"I noticed with a sense of relief that by that time all the other passengers had left the compartment; I arranged a whole bench as a bed, put the child to sleep, after taking off her shoes and loosening her clothes, and made myself comfortable on the opposite bench.

"To my great surprise I could not sleep a wink. My erection would not subside. I tried to comfort myself with the argument that I have always experienced riding on a train as a sexual stimulant.[1]

"As time went on, my erection became almost painful. I was not thinking of the child. At least consciously I made every effort to divert my attention to other erotic images. As it happened I was very much in love at the time, and within ten or twelve hours I was going to be with my fiancée. I tried to think of her, visualized her meeting me at the train, and anticipated our embrace.

"Suddenly, the child moved in her sleep. It was a warm summer night, and the girl threw off the cover I had tucked her into. Her little skirt was deranged, and I could see her well-formed legs. I was swept by a desire to get close to her, to hug her, and to stroke her body. Furious at myself, I ran to the door of the compartment, when the girl called after me, 'Please, Uncle, don't go! Don't leave me alone. I am afraid.' She put her little arms around me and pressed her lips against mine. It was not the kiss of a child.

"The sudden shock of the train stopping at a station brought me to my senses again. A lady passenger, laden with grips of

[1] This reaction to riding on trains is by no means unique. There are men who feel potent only on a train. Train attendants have always known the heightened sensuousness and lowered resistance of women passengers. That bridegrooms prefer to spend their wedding nights on railroad sleepers is probably partly due to the same infantile predilection. Apparently, we all carry within our grown selves the pleasurable memory of the perambulator.

many sizes, came into our compartment. I made room for her, deeply thankful for the rescue. I shivered at the idea of what might have happened.

"Ever since that dreadful night I refuse to remain alone with children.

"Except for this single experience I have never felt anything remotely similar, and I am not conscious of having at any time dreamed of children this way, but I certainly dare not condemn any one who has ever succumbed to such a temptation.

"I should also venture the assumption that that girl had been willing to meet me half way, that she had, perhaps unconsciously, tempted me. I'd say that she expected some sort of love-making, because she too appeared sexually aroused."

A closer look at the incident just described reveals first of all that the man was in a state of erotic preparedness, that he was warmed-up for love. He was in a period of courting, and he was on his way to see his beloved. Coincidentally, he was also on his way home, and "going home" is always, to some extent, a journey into childhood. The presence of the little cousin only accentuated the atmosphere of re-infantization, and enhanced the man's desire to be a child, to feel like a child. In all of us there is a greater or lesser readiness to relapse into a state of infantilism, even though we are not necessarily neurotic. Neurotic aberrations in adults, as I have shown repeatedly, are only *compulsive* regressions to the childhood phases of development.

The fact is well known that pedophilic tendencies erupt with greatest force in old age. Our newspapers bring frequent accounts of pedophilic acts committed by elderly people, and we must never forget that only an insignificant part of such occurrences becomes public. The point is that in old age we are most susceptible to regressions, and especially to the sexual regression known as pedophilia.

Before I make a further attempt at elucidation of this phenomenon, I should like to report the confession of another patient, an artist, for whose strength of character and moral stamina I can vouch personally.

Case No. 93: "I was spending my summer vacation in G. together with my wife and our two children. It was the forty-ninth summer of my life, the eighth year of my happy marriage, and I enjoyed being with my family. My seven-year-old son soon found several friends, boys of his age, but my daughter, a girl of five, was rather lonely until I finally succeeded in ferreting out a girl of approximately the same age who was docile enough to stand the tyranny of my somewhat "bossy" daughter.

"One day, when the two girls played in the garden and I watched them amusedly, my daughter's friend sat down in such a position that I could see her genitalia. All of a sudden I became shamefully aware of the fact that I could not turn my eyes away from the sight. Moreover, I had a vehement erection and could not resist the temptation to take the girl into my arms. My daughter grew very jealous, and I let the girl go. I had done nothing in particular, but I must admit that I had a strong desire to touch the girl's genitalia. I have never had such a desire toward my own child. The incident depressed me all the more as I dared not tell my wife the shameful story of my weak moment.

"The temptation recurred several times during the summer months, and I had to admit to myself that the girl, who had something very feminine—or, if you'll permit me to say so, something courtesan-like about her—fascinated me sexually. A few times, and with unspeakable pleasure, I stroked her hair and her well-formed legs. I also made several sketches of her, and they still are among the best I have ever drawn. This confirms my belief that an artist paints best when he is sexually attracted by his model."

Various workers in the field have found many reasons for the phenomenon of pedophilia, but all of them agree on the point that a man's professional preoccupation with children, like that of a teacher, for instance, is very conducive to the development of pedophilia.

Now, it seems to me that this is a clear instance of reversing cause and effect. As I have shown elsewhere,[1] there is a sexual motivation in the very choice of occupation.

In my experience with pedophilics I have found assumed sexual inadequacy to be the most frequent motivation, as may be seen from the following case.

Case No. 94: Mr. V.B., forty-six, a small, ugly, hunchbacked shopkeeper, was known in his hometown as the "good uncle." His pockets were always full of sweets which he distributed freely, or he took the children to the candy store, and gladly played "uncle" to every child he met. For fear of failure, the man has never known sexual intercourse, and he has masturbated since he was fourteen. He dared not make love to girls or women of good standing, while at the same time he abhorred the idea of having anything to do with a prostitute. Ever since his adolescence he dreamed of having sexual intercourse with little girls, and he regarded it as quite justifiable in view of his allegedly small genital. But he was, of course, averse to getting into trouble. He made by chance the acquaintance of a "madam" who enabled him to meet in her house child-prostitutes between ten and fourteen years of age, but the immediate danger of a scandal and legal entanglements made him give up the visits, and so he went on masturbating and being friendly to children.

At this point, I should like to include a most emphatic word of warning against such "uncles" with their inexhaustible amounts of sweets. By far the greatest number of them are pedophilics, and they are apt to lure children into their homes or to some secluded places. Any one who invites strange children into his home in order to treat them to ice-cream or sweets may be suspected of pedophilia.

It is safe to assume that a pedophilic's craving for children is strong, as the ubiquitous plague of child prostitution proves most clearly.

[1] *Impotence in the Male,* chapter on "Choice of Occupation and Sexuality," Liveright, New York.

During World War I, the regions around the military bases were infested with child prostitutes. An Army officer told me that he had been accosted by a girl of eight and invited to come to see her "pretty mother." The officer accepted the invitation in order to report the mother of the girl to the police. His indignation grew even stronger when the mother actually offered him the sexual services of her eight-year-old daughter. But great as the officer's indignation was, he evoked only laughter at Police Headquarters. There was not room enough in the local prison to harbor all the pandering mothers and all the prostitute daughters of the neighborhood.

Child prostitution is not confined to exclusive "houses of joy." On the streets of many large cities men are approached by juvenile prostitutes (in many instances, the purpose is blackmail). Experienced streetwalkers, who know the tastes of many men, dress so as to look like school girls, or they ply their trade in partnership with a child prostitute. In slum districts, where children as a rule are sexually precocious, the girls build little gangs and ply the trade in a group.

I had once a refined neurotic lady patient who in her early youth had been a streetwalker in a city of Czechoslovakia. I learned a great deal about juvenile prostitution from her. The money earned by the girls is usually spent on sweets. The services required of them almost never exceed manipulation of the man's penis. Many exhibitionistic men don't even require that much contact, but now and then one of them will demand fellatio.

However, money is not the only driving force behind child prostitution, although in some of these cases the parents make their children go out to get money by any means. What money there is at the child's personal disposal is spent on sweets. It is often curiosity or the child's own sexual desire that drives her to prostitution.

In many instances it is the child, not the adult, who is the seducer. Little girls stop men on the street, under such a pretext as asking for the time of day, and look up at them very suggestively, or beg for alms, in order to be "picked up." Once I saw a boy of five who had been infected venereally by his ten-year-old sister who, in turn, had been infected by a soldier.

The most inveterate seducers of children are to be found among the service personnel and the people entrusted with the supervision of children, as Rétif de la Bretonne had already known long ago.[1] My own files are filled with instances of such "domestic" seductions.

I have on another occasion called the attention of my readers to the nefarious habit of wet-nurses and servants of tickling the genitalia of infants in order to quiet them, and I want to add here only that such manipulations are often undertaken by adults for reasons of their own sexual gratification. I knew a lady of the highest social stratum who was wont to play with her little daughter's genitalia to make her laugh, and I had very good reason to believe that the lady was not aware of the sexual motivation of her habit.

Bloch cites several characteristic examples bearing out this observation. "In one instance," he says, "a lady accountant provoked a four-year-old boy to participation in lurid and persistent sexual games; while in another instance, horrible as it may sound, a lady prompted her own son of five to arouse her sexually and even tried to induce him to perform a regular intercourse. The boy then performed the same manipulations on his three-year-old sister, and when caught in the act he revealed who had been his teacher.

"In still another case, a four-year-old boy was seen playing with his genitalia and making coital movements. Once he assayed the same movements while snuggled up to mother, and when the frightened woman questioned him insistently,

---

[1] In the story, "Madame Baptiste," Maupassant describes the poignant tragedy of a little girl seduced by the valet of her father.

the boy explained that the servant had taught him to do all this."

Magnan tells us of a twenty-nine-year-old lady who seduced her nephew of five.

I am personally convinced that all the jails in the world would not suffice to hold all the adults who had at one time or another misbehaved with children. Bloch justly points out the very active part played by the feminine half of our adult population, and Havelock Ellis echoes him in his statement that many more men are seduced by women than there are women seduced by men, if we count the early erotic experiences.

Psychoanalytic practice has revealed the frequency of early traumatic experiences of a sexual nature, and there can hardly be any doubt that erotic contacts between adults and children are, unfortunately, more frequently practiced than we dare to believe.

Here are a few examples from my own files.

Case No. 95: A lady patient told me that nursing her first child always gave her an orgastic thrill, and that, therefore, her whole attitude toward the child was tinged with a crazed, excessive adoration. Even after the second child was born, the first one continued sleeping in her bed, and she allowed him to touch every zone of her body. Later on she encouraged him to ply his little feet between her thighs, a procedure that stimulated her sexually. Her resistance was so weak that she also allowed her second child, a girl, to do the same. Her third child liked to play with her breast, and up to the age of four went to sleep with her nipples in his mouth. All three children were spoiled, precocious, vehemently jealous of each other, and obviously disturbed.

Case No. 96: In a state of extreme excitement a fellow physician consulted me about the following predicament. For quite a while he had been in the habit of permitting his eight-year-old daughter to touch his penis with her hand. One day his wife discovered what was going on, and she made him come to me.

I demanded that before I begin the treatment the girl be separated from her parents under some pretext. Both father and mother refused to comply.

Case No. 97: Mrs. M.B., in analytical treatment, complained of strange temporary constipations, which plagued her as soon as she went to the country on vacation. Thus she had to stay in town all summer. Analysis revealed that at the age of nine the patient had spent the summer months with her relatives in the country. A twenty-five-year-old cousin had seated her one day on his lap, and tried to introduce his penis into her. She had cried and run off in a panic.

She had completely repressed the memory of that experience, but it lived on in the disguise of a neurotic symptom. The real meaning of her constipation was that she both feared and desired to be "plugged up" by a man. This unhappy and sexually starved woman used to go for walks in the loneliest places, with the unconscious wish to be raped.

I could go on endlessly with this random selection from my files. Every analyst has a similar lengthy list of instances. The objection that so many of the cases are pure imagination does not remove the true situation, as we have reports from the other side, from the adult seducers, themselves. It is an undeniable fact that pedophilia is very widely spread among men and women.[1]

Following are several examples of information coming not from the dubious admissions of the victims but from those of the perpetrators themselves.

Case No. 98: Mr. A.S., forty-five, married five years ago a lady with whom he had had premarital sexual relations. Three years after the marriage the man became impotent, and has been so for the last two years. Although he had erections, especially in the mornings, his erection always gave way whenever he attempted a penetration. (I have on other occasions demonstrated that such a symptom ordinarily points to the presence of another

---

[1] Erich Wulffen reports (in *Der Sexualverbrecher*, p. 415) the interesting case of a woman who trained a girl of ten in precoital stimulation of her impotent, pedophilic husband.

—unconscious—sexual goal than the one at hand.) Analysis revealed that the man had strong pedophilic tendencies which at the time of affliction became acutely intensified through the presence of two factors. The man was in love with the twelve-year-old son of the landlord of the house, and he was greatly disturbed by the flirtatious attention his wife was paying to a young friend of the house.

Case No. 99: A lady of forty-two complained of an overwhelming sexual interest in adolescent boys. When she was eighteen she tried to seduce a boy of fifteen, but he was so clumsy that the affair never advanced beyond petting. The lady's hope that marriage—and later motherhood—would cure her of her passion was not fulfilled. She seduced the twelve-year-old brother of her husband. Together with the only friend who understood her plight—the wife of a teacher and owner of a boardinghouse for out-of-town students, who herself had seduced nearly every boy inmate—the patient went on systematic chases for young victims.

There was a period when she was attracted by her son. Under the pretext of caring for him while he was ill, she went as far as manipulating his genitalia, but she had enough strength of will to stop in time.

Analysis revealed the patient's fixation to her brother, by two years her senior, who had engaged her in vehement sexual play when she was ten years old. For two years the two children indulged in frequent mutual oral contacts, when the boy suddenly had a change of mind, became very pious, and stopped all sexual activities.

Remarkably enough, the lady was teaching her boy partners the same forms of sexual gratifications she had learned from her brother.[1]

Whether a pedophilic had a traumatic experience in his childhood or only fancied he had one, he is eternally hunting some childhood love relation, which he relives in a state of revery. It is well known that epileptics are apt to indulge

---

[1] Both the French author Catulles Mendès and the Austrian, Arthur Schnitzler, have treated love relations between ladies and adolescent boys in their novels, *Sa première maîtress* and *Frau Beate und ihr Sohn,* respectively.

in pedophilic acts while under a spell, and so are men under the influence of alcohol. A single slip in an alcoholic state may work as a trigger act and cause the eruption of a dormant tendency.

I know the case of a country teacher, unused to drinking, who on his way to school had been treated by a farmer to a considerable amount of wine, whereupon he suddenly discovered that the children in his class aroused him sexually. He had one of the girls help him carry the papers to his house, and he indulged in heavy petting with her. Next day he felt so mortified that he was afraid to go to work. It was a great relief to him to be greeted by the girl with a smile. Apparently she had not told anyone what happened the day before. The teacher swore never again to taste a drop of alcohol. A few days later, however, he again invited the girl to his house and, in a completely sober state, again played with her. From there on it went down hill. Soon the affair became known, and the teacher was tried at court.

In another, similar case, the perpetrator was a clergyman. Here, too, the initial collapse of inhibitions under the influence of drink paved the way to a full regression.

Very many impotent men show pedophilic tendencies, as they are usually incapable of normal intercourse because of fear of failure, or because they imagine they have inadequate (too small) genital organs. Such a tendency is often tinged with the vindictive (sadistic) desire to defile the purity and innocence of children; it often also lurks behind the quasi-progressive demands for forthright sexual education of our children.

Such a derogative tendency sometimes goes hand in hand with a passion for deflorating virgins with subsequent abandonment of the victims.

Case No. 100: Mr. L.K., a lawyer, twenty-five years of age, complained of agoraphobia. He dreaded to leave his house without an escort. Analysis revealed his phobia to be a neurotic protection against a strong pedophilic urge. The patient's history was replete with unscrupulous seductions of virgins, which often involved breaches of promise.

It was anamnestically established that the patient, at the age of twelve, had deflowered his sister, who was only nine at the time.

Significantly enough, the outbreak of agoraphobia occurred while the patient came to stay in the house of this sister, by now happily married and very much in love with her husband.

It was obviously the image of his sister which the patient sought in children and virgins. His frequent acts of "jilting" meant that he could not stay with the girls once they were deflowered and no longer identifiable with the virginal sister-image.

During World War I, a great many cases of confessed abuses of children came to my attention. Even more frequent were the incidents reported by members of the armed forces with the crimes attributed to someone else, particularly to the enemy. These stories always contained an element of sadism. I intend to dedicate a separate study of sadism,[1] and, among other aspects of it, to the strange phenomenon that juvenile individuals are so prevalent among the victims of the brutal acts. Here I shall report only one instance, illustrating the specific conditions of war-time and their influence on sexual behavior.

Case No. 101: Mr. K.R., thirty-six, former army officer, complained of impotence which had persisted ever since the end of the war. Prior to that he was a very happy husband and father.

During the war he had served in Serbia and in Romania. Morals were at a low ebb everywhere, and sexual orgies were very common. For a loaf of bread one could have many a woman whose husband was in the front line, and the woman's young daughter to boot. In Bucharest, he frequented a house whose specialty was child prostitution, and ever since that time he

[1] *Sadism and Masochism*, Liveright, New York, 1929.

craved sexual intercourse with children. The stories of sadistic acts influenced his thinking to such a degree that he was dreaming of brutalities. Fortunately, he fell ill, and was confined to a hospital for a long time. All he could actually do was masturbate, visualizing himself in the act of rape or lust murder.

These sadistic wishes subsided by the time he came out of the hospital, but the craving for children remained. In addition to becoming suddenly impotent in his marital relations, he was tortured by the idea that his own children might tempt him to an immoral act.

This man, too, felt he had an undersized genital organ, and he had even before his affliction always regretted that he was unable to penetrate his wife "fully and forcefully."

I am inclined to believe that actual or assumed inferiorities, such as an underdeveloped penis or low potency, predisposes men to succumb to pedophilic temptations. However, high potency and normal structure by no means preclude overt pedophilia, as may be seen from the two following instances.

Case No. 102: Mr. G.K., forty-three, was sentenced to two years imprisonment for immoral conduct with minors. It was the man's first offense; he pleaded an irresistible urge. He claimed he had acted in a daze, and the fact that he had confessed to his wife the sexual play with two little girls before it became publicly known was in the defendant's favor.

The man's physique, except for a malformation of his ears and microcephalia, showed no signs either of degeneration or infantilism. His genital organ was overdeveloped. He had had nervous disturbances in his earlier life (bedwetting, pavor nocturnus, slightly compulsive habits), and in his childhood he had been designated as a "woolgathering" daydreamer. He developed many talents, though, and after he finished high school he entered an Art Academy. His achievements fell far below everybody's expectations chiefly because of some strange peculiarities. He devoted too much time to his various collections and to his hobby of pasting and binding.

He had masturbated ever since he was twelve, and neither his religious scruples nor his marriage at the age of twenty-four—and bafflingly frequent marital intercourses—cured him of the habit. Never before his proved misdemeanor had he tangled with children.

Analysis revealed that the man had repeatedly played sexual games with his sister who had died at the age of ten. It had been for that sister that he used to paste and bind things. The man obviously had a fixation to the memory of his sister; it needed only an opportunity to make his latent pedophilia break through.

Case No. 103: Mr. J. was accused of immoral conduct with minors, two girls of ten and eleven respectively. The man's assertion that he had been encouraged by the girls themselves won no credence with the judge. Nor did my testimony of the man's psychopathic disposition and pathological psychic infantilism save the defendant from a jail sentence.

To me, however, the entire history of the forty-six-year-old man was a typical instance of arrested development. As it happened, the man was in comfortable financial circumstances, and he was not even disturbed in pursuing the life of a child. He never worked, and he spent his days either sleeping (twelve hours a day), or daydreaming, or playing with childish toys. Every now and then he still wetted his bed. Despite repeated daily intercourse with his wife, he masturbated—also two or three times a day. He had a child's intelligence and knowledge, and was completely disinterested in anything besides his petty hobbies. His pockets were full of rocks which he picked up wherever he went, and which he sometimes displayed in battle array like toy soldiers.

At this point I should like to make it clear that I have found traces of pedophilic tendencies in nearly every neurotic I have treated. They are part and parcel of the neurotic's general longing for his childhood days. And I am inclined to believe that no man is absolutely free from similar infantilist longings.

I have shown elsewhere that pedophilia may combine with

misopedia (pathologic hostility toward children). The classical literary example is given in a story by Dostoyevski. Among the great writer's papers a manuscript was found which so minutely described the rape of a little girl that the publishers hesitated to include it in the posthumous collection of his works. I venture the assumption that Dostoyevski had visualized the perpetration of that crime in his epileptic spells. If this is the case, then Raskolnikov's murder would represent a transmutation of the victim from a child to an old woman. Such transmutations are by no means alien to the psychogenesis of human passions and paraphilias.

But this is a subject which requires more than a passing remark.

2. Gerontophilia

The erroneous belief that sexual attraction toward old persons is much less frequent than that toward children is based on the fact that gerontophilia, unlike pedophilia, is easily obscured and more apt to appear in sublimated disguises of respect, admiration, and similar acceptable attitudes.

Gerontophilia is, basically, a psychosexual infantilism, a libidinal carryover from childhood, and entirely out of place in the emotional life of the adult. It is often to be found in combination with pedophilia, and I for one do not consider this combination to be paradoxical. Experience has taught me that what the neurotic usually avoids is the facing of sexual relations on a par. Consequently, he looks for his love objects either at one of the age extremes or—indiscriminately and simultaneously—at both.[1]

The two main reasons why neurotics shun the sexual partnership of contemporaries are fear of failure (subjective) and a certain indefiniteness of sex in both boy and old man

[1] A patient wrote: "To me, both the boy and the old man, like spring and autumn, represent ultimate beauty, the beauty of blossoms and of falling leaves."

which affords a gratuitous homosexual gratification (objective reason). Yet, there is more to it. The general trend in gerontophilia is still heterosexual; that is, boys fall in love with mature women, while young girls dote on elderly gentlemen.

There can be no doubt that elderly persons represent parental images to neurotic adolescents, and the abundance of gerontophiliacs in recent times can only be understood on the background of the spreading "small family system." In fact, gerontophiliacs are mostly to be found among those who grew up as only children in a circumscribed family constellation. Such children are, as a rule, in contact predominantly with adults, mature earlier than most children, and look down upon children of their own age.

I know men who entertain sexual relations or enter marriages (sometimes repeatedly) only with women older by at least two or three years. On the other hand, many girls fall only for mature men. The usual rationalization of the tendency is that the older person is more stable, more experienced, and will be able to serve as a dependable guide through life. At times, the desire for a mere platonic relation is advanced as chief reason for marrying an older mate. An experienced psychologist will discard all these attempts at justification, which only cover up the eternal pursuit of an unconscious father or mother image.

But the point is that a 17-year-old girl falling in love with a man of forty-five can hardly be classified as a gerontophiliac. Only when a youngster of sixteen or seventeen feels passionately in love with a person of sixty or over are we entitled to speak of gerontophilia.

We find in our literature a few pronounced cases of gerontophilia in which a childhood fixation is clearly discernible. Such is, for instance, the case reported by Féré.

Case No. 104: Mr. M.B.X.'s mother tried to persuade her son to marry a very rich and beautiful girl, but a deep-seated aversion toward young women made it impossible for Mr. X. to comply with the wish of his mother.

Although only twenty-seven years of age, he loved very mature or elderly ladies. His current "girl" friend was a woman of sixty-two, and she had just rejected the young lover's marriage proposal.

The patient's gerontophilia could be traced back to an experience at the age of four when he was nursed by a friend of his mother through a period of scarlet fever and subsequent convalescence. During that time he became passionately attached to the young lady's mother, a woman of over fifty, in whose house he lodged.

The boy used to come into the old lady's bed every morning, and he was always intensely thrilled at the touch of her soft, fine skin. The lady was relatively reserved toward the boy, and when she noticed once that her touch caused him to have an erection he was quickly sent back home.

The image of that lady stayed with the boy forever. His relations with girls and young women gave him no pleasure; in fact, he had to think of that lady before he could complete a coitus. Finally, he gave up young women entirely, and looked only for elderly ladies, whose skin complexion, color of hair (grey), and agility resembled that first lady at least remotely. He broke up a few relations for the sole reason that the respective ladies, though old enough, suddenly decided to dye their hair.

This case shows us the poignancy of early impressions and their occasionally fateful influence. It is, of course, an idle speculation, but an analysis might have discovered a deeper-seated initial mother fixation and possibly brought the man relief.

Wagner Jauregg reported, in the *Wiener Klinische Wochenschrift* (1907) a very interesting case of gerontophilia.

Case No. 105: A young man was tried by the district court of Upper Austria for the rape and murder of a sixty-four-year-old woman. About that time seven similar sex crimes had been committed on women in the age range fifty-three to sixty-eight. The defendant himself was known to have attempted rape on two women, one aged sixty-four, the other seventy-six years of age. In both cases the cries of the attacked women attracted the attention of passers-by, and the women were saved.

A cell companion of the defendant reported that the latter often talked, in his sleep, of sexual brutalities and of old women. The defendant himself admitted dreaming of old ladies. In those dreams things did not necessarily come to physical relations; sometimes he only hugged and petted the women, or he indulged in some other form of purely infantile sexuality.

Significantly enough, the defendant's parents were both relatively old when they joined in marriage; his father was sixty-three, and his mother was forty years old. The defendant has always adored his mother.

Of equal significance was the data that the defendant had had his first sexual intercourse at the age of seventeen, when he was seduced by an old woman.

However, we must not be misled into assuming that such plain and obvious patterns are discernible in the genesis of all cases of gerontophilia. The presence of a multiplicity of factors is the rule rather than the exception, as the following instances make amply clear.

Case No. 106: Mrs. E.L., thirty-six, lost her husband in an automobile accident. Her marriage had been an unhappy one, and widowhood was a new lease on life. She resumed her pre-marital studies of art (painting and music) and read extensively, in an effort to achieve the self-realization she had been unable to aspire to while her drinking, gambling, venereally-infected husband was alive.

Then all of a sudden she fell in love with her music teacher, a man of sixty-seven, and forgot so completely her firm decision never to get married again that she herself offered her hand to the old gentleman. Upon his steadfast refusal she became depressed and came to consult me.

The patient's fixation on her father, who had been forty-six years old when she was born, could be easily established. But in addition to this it was found that her love for the tyrannical father had a strong component of fear and hatred, that these emotions had been greatly enhanced in the period of marital connection with her brutal husband. In other words, in the patient's gerontophilia, a strong desire to be dominant was also operative. She was unconsciously attracted by her teacher's weakness. (Some of the man's utterances, as related by the patient, as well as other indications, pointed to his actual impotence.)

Interestingly enough, the patient was simultaneously in love with a boy of seventeen, that is, a male to whom she might also feel greatly superior.

We should always watch for this component of fear, especially in female gerontophiliacs.

The following is a very interesting instance of gerontophilia based on a homosexual, instead of the usual heterosexual fixation.

Case No. 107: Mr. E.U., a young American gentleman of twenty-eight, complained of spells of acute anxiety and of a general inability to work steadily. He was in a state of legal war with his father, a very rich man, who refused to support his idle son, and doubted the authenticity of the young man's numerous medical certificates attesting to his neurotic condition and some sort of presumably epileptic spells.

When the patient was five years old, his father often stimulated his genitalia, sometimes repeatedly on the same night. The procedures came to the attention of the patient's mother, who made a terrible scene and called her husband "a criminal." Angrily, the father left the house, and the patient's parents were separated for many years. Although formally reconciled at last, the two parents continued to lead their separate lives.

The patient's fixation to his father was so complete that the latter became his sole love object. However, as long as the patient was young, and father lived separately, things were not too bad. The moment father moved back to the house, and again took up what the patient believed were marital relations, the states of anxiety set in. Besides vehement jealousy of mother there was also the tormenting fear that father might beget another child. (By that time, the patient's desire for father's exclusive love had assumed the form of wanting father's money and support.)

The situation at home became so strenuous that the patient moved out of the family house and came to live in the house of a family friend, a lady of about eighty-three, who had always been very fond of the young, talented boy.

Despite her old age, the lady was very vivacious, and she still preserved traces of her former beauty.

One evening, the young man was seized by a spell of anxiety and entered the lady's bedroom. She allowed him to lie down beside her until he would calm down. As the young man lay there in bed facing the lady's back, he became suddenly aroused, and intercourse took place.

Ever since that night the young man became crazed with a passion for elderly ladies, and his aberration grew so violent that his eighty-three-year-old friend herself supplied him with the means to go to Europe and to seek cure from his erotic fixation.

In my practice this has been a unique case in which a homosexual fixation to the father was transferred into heterosexual gerontophilia.

We can often trace gerontophilia to a fixation to grandparents, as Abraham has pointed out. Such a fixation is often facilitated by the fact that grandparents are apt to have developed sufficiently strong pedophilic tendencies and to indulge in sexual stimulations of their grandchildren. ("Jocular" and "innocent" manipulation of their genitalia.)

Case No. 108: Miss J.L., twenty-six, felt attracted only by old gentlemen with grey whiskers. She had been deflowered by a very old man, and thereafter entertained relations with him for more than two years, until the man died of a heart attack in her arms. She looked down upon her subsequent suitor, a "brat" of merely thirty-four, and could not even think of marrying him.

The girl's history revealed that her parents died when she

had barely outgrown her babyhood, and that she had been raised by her grandfather. Until the age of twelve, she slept in her grandfather's bed. Blushingly, the patient admitted that the old man had the habit of touching her genitals, and that she used to be aroused by these manipulations.

Fixation to grandparents is sometimes of a purely spiritual nature, especially in those instances when stern parents drive children to seek refuge with the more indulgent grandparents.

Chapter Eight

THE SELF AND THE MANY

Chapter Eight

THE SELF AND THE MANY

1. Narcissism

There is a difference between normal self-love and narcissism. The feel of our own physical and spiritual self is pleasurable. We are all egoistic. All our thinking and feeling is self-centered. Such appreciation of one's self is present in every emotionally healthy person and is characteristic of the dynamics which encourage object love.

Narcissism, however, is infatuation with and ecstatic rapture over one's self. Healthful self-love is always under the controlling influence of reality. A sober look around us shows us that there are people who surpass us in beauty, shapeliness, intelligence, and moral conduct. But the narcissist, like the child, negates reality. Just as an infatuated person sees perfection in the beloved and worships him as the personification of an ideal, so is the narcissist blind to his own blemishes. He idolizes himself; he is the incarnation of his own ideal. The narcissist is much more than a "conceited fool." His self-love embraces every minute particle of his being. He loves the odor of his body and the body's secretions. He admires his genital organs. And, of course, the narcissist considers himself the finest of all lovers, and sometimes expresses this belief by practicing "mirror masturbation."

Case No. 109: Mr. J.L., thirty-nine, is able to copulate only when he can see himself performing the act. His interest in his love partner is secondary. His most ardent wish is to have the walls and the ceiling of his room covered with mirrors. He maintains a miserly existence as he saves money in the hope of fulfilling his fantasy in the grand manner. In his masturbation fantasies he always sees himself in such a mirror-lined room. He usually masturbates while looking at his mirrored image.

He is a "mirror-man." He carries several pocket mirrors and holds them before his face frequently. He spends much of his waking time admiring his reflection. His stay in the bathroom on mornings is prolonged by the convenient looking glass. He combs his hair meticulously as he views his head from every angle. With uncompromising vanity he is determined to be the most elegant man in town. He envies quick-witted men who radiate socially. He has collected a little thesaurus of "smart" sayings which he uses in his conversations. He fancies himself as the great master of *repartee*. He loves to tell jokes and often pretends he has authored them. He is a member of many clubs and social circles, knows all the rules of etiquette, and would be mortified if he were caught in a *faux pas*. He is overgregarious. Despite his avarice, he once readily paid a high fee to get his by-line on top of another man's newspaper article. He, himself, never wrote a line which was published.

He remembers that his mother spent endless hours before the mirror fussing with her hair-do. The patient was a pampered only child. His parents died when he was fifteen, and he was taken into the home of an aunt who treated him with indifference. It was in this cool setting, that contrasted with the excessive warmth of his earlier life, that he developed his severe narcissism.

Narcissism often flourishes as a continuation of a childhood which has been marked by pampering, or by parental coldness which drives the love-hungry ego to feed on itself.

If a child is not loved or pampered by others, he may resort to self-pampering.

Sometimes, as in the case just cited, pampering and coldness both participate in forming a narcissistic symptomatology. Like any other form of infantilism, narcissism may be a perpetuation of an early development (primary narcissism) or a regression to an earlier stage (secondary narcissism). In the secondary form, we observe vanity, the will to shine, the wish to undress, fears of aging, ugliness, and illness. Also a tendency toward hypochondriasis; but, above all, *affectedness*.

Many flirtatious women want only to catch a man's eye, solely to have their own favorable opinion of themselves confirmed by the eagerness of a man's eye. They consider themselves attractive and are happy when they provoke desire, although they have little passion. They are often surprised and annoyed if the man wishes to make further advances.

The male narcissist, too, is amorous in manner; he is usually only a verbal Don Juan, rarely an actual one. He shows many feminisms for which he compensates by strong desires to be a "full-blooded he-man."

Neurotic distortion may convert narcissism into discontent with one's own body, into a feeling of inferiority, fear of public opinion or of being the object of ridicule. A narcissist may have the feeling that every one looks at him critically, that something is the matter with his clothes, that people mock him or exchange whispers about him. Paranoid traits of this type may accompany narcissism for a long time until they deteriorate into regular paranoia.

The narcissist will undergo humiliation if that will attract attention. He manifests a severe neurosis to evoke pity. His need for loving kindness is so great that, if he cannot do any better, he will *extort* pity. He is usually passionately engrossed in his illness. He takes an unconscious pride in his sickness which is similar to the pride of the hypochondriacs who are narcissists in their own right.

A narcissist is resentful when another sick person is the focus of attention. He must be the most interesting case. To him, all other patients are shameless pretenders and "fakers." By way of outdoing a rival, and in order to secure all the attention for himself, he will appropriate the symptoms of other patients.

Féré's classic example of such a neurotic is illuminative. We quote it in part:

Case No. 110: "For ten years I observed a neurasthenic whose only manifestations of mental disturbance were indecision and self-incrimination. He was able to win prolonged respites from these symptoms by environmental changes, but a marriage proposal on his part reversed the trend. He so bitterly regretted his marital intentions that he went through several nervous crises and thus finally had to cancel the engagement. Through an extraordinary combination of favorable conditions, however, his mental self-torture ceased, and he married in 1895 under the most auspicious circumstances. His unperturbed state lasted eighteen months.

"He was thirty-two when I saw him again in May, 1896. His complaint was that for the last ten days he vomited daily, either in the morning, shortly after waking, or after lunch. In the mornings, he disgorged, with striking regularity, about a half-pint of a thick light-colored fluid. After lunch he threw up the food he had eaten. The vomiting was always preceded by a sudden attack of nausea. Unprompted, he advanced the reason behind his trouble: His wife was in the third month of pregnancy. On the day before his first vomiting attack she came home from a walk and told him that she had become nauseated and had vomited some mucous matter. The wife's story had a deep effect on my patient because—as he said—all the pregnant women in his own family, his mother, aunt, and two sisters, had nausea. At a later date, the patient's mother confirmed his words, but she also said that my patient's wife had only had seven or eight attacks of nausea in all, and that they had all occurred in my patient's absence and, with the exception of the first one, had been unknown to him. Nevertheless, he kept on vomiting for three weeks and, as the attacks were always abrupt, he never had a chance to take the prescribed precautionary measures. The nausea ceased when he moved out of the house temporarily and they did not recur after his return a week later. Everything was fine until the month of November when his wife began to complain of pains in the small of her back. Immediately, the man became afflicted with aches in his loins and developed a feeling of weakness in his lower limbs. Within two days, he had trouble walking, his head ached constantly, and he could not sleep at all or his sleep was interrupted by brain cramps which made him howl. He was taken to the house of his father in a state of severe neurasthenia characterized by persistent fits of anxiety: now he saw his wife in mortal danger, now he was tormented by too much light, by noise, and even by evil smells. Every change of position caused him acute backache and made him cry with pain. The skin on his abdomen and chest became hypersensitive. Completely absent were such hysterical traits as sensitive testicles or modified patellar reflex. Informed of his wife's successful delivery, he quieted down somewhat, but major improvement did not come until he was reunited with his wife three weeks later. From then on his recovery made rapid progress.

"In 1898 his wife again became pregnant. The family took every precaution to hide from him any occurrence of nausea or vomiting, but one morning his wife had an attack of nausea in his presence. It happened after breakfast. He reacted immediately, throwing up what he had eaten. And again he was vomiting mucus upon waking for ten mornings in succession, until he moved out of the house. He returned a week later without any after-effects. His wife, who had been generally subject only to mild and infrequent attacks of nausea, was completely free of them by then. However, in the last days of October, and this time without any external stimulus, his nervous crises and anxieties reemerged and kept on until last February, on a pattern only slightly different from that of the previous occasion." (*L'instinct sexuel,* pp. 93-95.)

The identification of the man just described with his wife is remarkably strong. But what is the motive of this identification?

Because of her pregnancy, every member of the family and every friend paid his wife increased attention. But to be the center of attention was his desire, and to achieve his goal, he went the "whole hog," including simulation of childbirth. He outdid his wife in suffering and pain and relegated her to a secondary position. The case is of great psychological significance and throws some light on the strange primitive custom of *couvade,* according to which a man takes to bed when his wife comes down with a child.

Another form of narcissism is presented by those who hate to see happy people about them. These neurotics *wish to be needed.* They want to help, to advise, to console, to pour out their love on others. They are infatuated only with themselves, but they cherish the pose of a prodigal Spender of Love. During the war I had occasion to observe many examples of this type among nurses. One of them, a very intelligent head nurse, gave me the following description of herself:

Case No. 111: "I am forty-eight now, and I may as well confess that I know no greater joy than that of seeing a grateful look in the eyes of a well-cared for patient. It's like an opiate. It's the only form of 'orgasm' I am capable of. I have never cared for romance; all I really want from anybody is appreciative gratitude. Ever since I was a young girl I had but one ideal: to care for a man who is dear to my heart and incurably sick. When I was nineteen, I married, against the wish of my parents, a forty-two-year-old man who had a severe myelitis. I was happy beyond words when he patted my hand and looked up gratefully at me. Handsome men never attracted me. Passion means nothing to me. After the death of my husband, I yielded to the pleas of a college student, out of pity, because he threatened to commit suicide. I had no sensation at all at the intercourse, I was only glad to make him happy. Sometimes I reach a sort of orgasm watching the partner's orgasm. I have had numerous relations with men, but I never loved these men. My love is only for my patients. I give myself to men only out of compassion, and enjoy only their contentment.

"I will admit I am a vainglorious nurse. I wish to be loved and admired by all my patients. I like to walk through the ward with the feeling that I am a good, tender-hearted fairy, bestowing love and happiness upon every one. . . .

"But there is also a reverse side to my character. Happy people leave me completely cold, or else they irritate me. I have a younger sister, for whom I did everything I possibly could as long as she was having domestic troubles. As long as she was unhappily married, I was willing to give her everything I had to the last penny.

"She used to spend nights lying in my arms and crying bitterly. I patted her and called her endearing names. Her husband was a brute. He infected her with a venereal disease and after a while neglected her completely. Night after night, he either played cards or was out with a girl. I pleaded with my sister to leave him and sue for divorce. I visualized how I would care for her, how my love and attention would change her life for the better, and she would appreciate my sacrifice. Like that pelican, I wanted to give her the blood of my heart.

"Well, she up and fell in love with the physician who was treating her. I had brought her to him, too. He was known as an excellent psychiatrist, and I wanted him to free her of her depressions. I paid the stiff fees, in the feeling that I was doing my utmost to save her. As it happened, the doctor reciprocated her love, and she cheered up. Gradually, my jealousy grew. The previously idolized doctor was now, to me, a brutal and mean egotist. I called him a woman chaser to his face, and accused him of seducing my sister with false promises. I fought quite hard, but I was not strong enough to make them sever their relations. They got married, and my sister brimmed with happiness. As for me, I broke off relations with her completely. She simply did not exist for me any longer. By way of substitution, I took into my home another miserable girl to whom I meant a great deal. But let me tell you something. Deep down in me there's the dream that one day my sister will come back to me, disillusioned and heartbroken. I'll welcome her and give her all my love. I shall prop her up, and again be everything in the world to her.

"Now, you say that I am a narcissist and love only myself. How right you are. I have many narcissistic traits. I am always admiring myself. When I prepare a meal, I like to think that there is no better cook in the whole wide world. Therefore, I enjoy cooking or, rather, I enjoy enjoying it. I am deliriously happy at the idea that the meal will be excellent and that people will praise me for it.

"I have the unpleasant habit of talking of myself all the time. I have studied foreign languages to show off my condition. I take singing lessons and entertain my friends with songs in order to be gaped at. Lately, I have also begun to woo for their pity, and I discover all sorts of diseases in me.

"I seek the friendship of important people to have the feeling that I am of importance myself; I have learned the skill of impressing favorably practically every one. I have assumed the role of a chipper, positive, forceful character, with a bewitching voice and an irresistible eye twinkle. I put myself in the other person's shoes, agree with everything he says, and by making him happy win his affection. Unfortunately, I can't hold all my conquests. Some people seem to fathom me quicker than others, and they desert me despite all my efforts to hold them. Oh, these efforts of mine! There is probably no other woman trying as hard as I do to help people, to lavish favors upon them. I am capable of running myself to death in the service of a person, for the sole purpose of seeing that appreciative gratitude in his eye. I hate people who owe me nothing.

"Perhaps it will interest you to know that I not only experience the greatest joy when a patient presses his lips against my hand, but am also in the habit of kissing my hand and sucking at its skin myself before I go to sleep. It's the only way I can fall asleep. You may be able to understand this infantilism of mine better than I, and I only regret I have never had a chance to be analyzed by you."

The infantilistic habit of kissing of one's own hand is mentioned in psychoanalytic literature. Some neurotics suck their thumbs or play with their tongue or lips, by way of prelude to sleep. The nurse's self-kissing is not of infantilistic nature; it is only the reproduction of a daytime act for which she has constant craving, namely, that of a patient kissing her hand in reverent gratitude. The kiss of reverent gratitude has become her *idée fixe,* the leitmotif of her life.

In this connection, it seems appropriate for us to consider another case reported by Féré as a typical example of "pseudo-narcissism."

Case No. 112: When Mrs. M., now twenty-nine, was born, she weighed only five pounds and was weak. Her mother, who had breast-fed three children, could not make this infant take to her breast, and so she resorted to the bottle. The infant was in the care of a wet-nurse, a person overburdened with children of her own and, although honest and devoted, not particularly well-mannered. The growing baby developed a dislike for her mother; she cried and showed other signs of displeasure in her presence. On the other hand, she was very friendly to her father, aunts, and uncles, not to mention the nurse to whom she was greatly attached. Her mother dismissed the nurse when the baby was thirteen months old, but no change in the baby's attitude occurred. The mother had to use force to make the little girl accept a kiss, and could by no means get one in return. The child soon learned to take advantage of the situation and exacted pampering and sweets for every endurance of fondness, without ever granting her mother a sign of spontaneous endearment. Mother's indulgence assumed even greater proportions when the child, at the age of two, developed nervous symptoms of waking with anguish by night and turning pale at daytime.

"The girl was four years old, when, one day, her mother had a heart to heart talk with her, replete with promises and tears, and the little girl at least seemed to be willing to bestow upon her mother a kiss. Ostensibly reluctant, she puckered her lips, and drew her face closer to mother's, when all of a sudden she raised her little hand and shoved it between her lips and the cheek to be kissed. The girl's lips touched her own hand, while she burst out crying, 'I can't do it! I can't!' The mother gave up any further attempt. She was a very busy woman, and a disciplinarian both in the household and in the small manufacturing plant she owned and managed. The girl cooperated willingly, was obedient, respectful, and friendly, even genuinely attached to her mother, but she stubbornly shunned every manifestation of love.

"Some time after her unsuccessful attempt, the mother became aware of smacking sounds of kissing coming nightly from the girl's room, and, upon entering it, found the girl in her bed, kissing the back of her hand in her sleep. The scene recurred on many nights thereafter. As the girl grew older, she developed a spiteful attitude toward her mother and brothers, in complete contrast to her behavior toward servants or strangers. At the age of eight, the girl came into the habit of withdrawing to a far-off room or to a deserted corner of the garden where she sat dreamily for hours, her lips on the back of her hand. It could be observed that she was in the grip of a strange exultation in the act. Her face turned red, then grew suddenly pale, and then the kissing stopped, leaving the girl in a sort of stupor. The brothers began to tease her, and she seemed to desist from her 'mania' only to become more skillful in hiding it from unwanted observers.

"The girl began menstruating at the age of thirteen. Her first few menses were painful, but, after three or four months, they were completely normalized. Several months later the girl became ill with neuralgia localized in the right side of her face. The indisposition lasted for months, and, after a pause of several weeks, a right intercostal neuralgia set in and lasted as long as the first one. The pains, the cause of which could not be made clear, made the girl so irritable that no family meal went by without a fracas. Her attitude toward servants and strangers still remained friendly, though. One day, while she bitterly argued with every member of the family, one of her brothers called her 'Miss Cuckoo,' because as he explained, she was laying her eggs into someone else's nest. In a rage, the girl turned on him and screamed, 'I am sure I'm not your sister! My flesh hates you so!'

Suddenly, she fell backward onto the floor and writhed and cursed wildly for a while, and then, just as abruptly, began to kiss her hand tempestuously. The kissing continued for a few minutes, when her face turned pale, and the girl fell into a stupor; then she calmed down gradually, stood up, and went into her room, her usual self again.

"After that seizure, the only one she has ever had, her behavior showed a marked change: she no longer quarreled with the family, and extended to all of its members the even-tempered friendliness previously reserved for strangers. She suppressed every manifestation of annoyance at mother's endearments, although she herself remained a passive.

"She seized upon the first opportunity offered and got married. She was nineteen at that time, and her husband, an industrialist, was twenty-eight; but despite the age difference, her affection for him augured a happy marriage. She maintained correct, although unemotional, relations with her family. She talked very little about them to her husband, but he could easily guess that she did not particularly care for them.

"Of the four children born to her in the first six years of her marriage, two boys died of cramps; two last-born girls were also beset by cramps and teething difficulties. The older girl is still bed-wetting at the age of five; the four-year-old younger girl shows no visible disturbance. (Incomplete data on husband and his family.)

"Young Mrs. M. had no mental disturbances in the periods of pregnancy, confinement, and breast-feeding. While suckling her fourth child, she began gaining weight, and became rather plump.

"Following an illness from shrimp poisoning in June, 1895, she had a neurasthenic condition, and three weeks later, after having witnessed, from a great distance, an accident in the street, she showed signs of anxiety, dreaded to be in the street or to die abruptly and without her soul being protected by Extreme Unction.

"She became gloomy and withdrawn, and her husband found her several times in the act of kissing the back of her hand. The strange scene, and the even stranger incidental circumstances, worried him greatly.

"At the time of consultation, Mrs. M., herself perturbed, said that ever since that day when, forced by her mother, she was about to kiss her and her hand came between her lips and mother's cheek, kissing her own hand, especially the part of the back touched on that occasion, gave her great pleasure. At the age of eight the pleasure became sexually tinged, and the accompanying excitement of her genital organs often led to a regular orgasm and, later on, to vaginal secretions. When her 'mania' became known, she began to practice this form of masturbation secretly and kept at it until she was married. And even then, although she loved her husband and responded to his advances, she actually began enjoying intercourse to the full when she reverted to her old practice. She had to kiss her hand in order to reach orgasm in the course of the act. Her husband had been always perturbed at the sight of her self-kissing and the subsequent paroxysm, and at last the expressions of abnormal lust on her face during her period of depression gave him an inkling of the nature of the kissing performance.

"The many cures she undertook brought her some relief as far as her sleep disturbances went, but her agoraphobia and irritability lingered on." (*L'Instinct Sexual. Evolution et Dissolution,* par Ch. Féré, Médicin de Bictre, Paris, 1899, Ancienne Librairie Germer Bailliere et Cie, Félix Alcan, Editeur, pp. 257-261.)

This very interesting case, into which only analysis could have brought further insight, demonstrates first of all the power of a fixation, that is, a repetitive pattern resulting from an experience. It may be assumed that the experience was rooted in a *spite reaction* which was motivated by the affect of jealousy. The hand became the symbol of the mother. Yet, it was the girl's own hand. Freud's explanation would be that the girl's libido, unable to flow toward its object, became fixed upon her own body. In any event, the case shows clearly how parts of one's own body may become "narcissistic fetishes," and carry a charge of libido that was drawn from other objects.

I have known for quite a while that the solution of the problem of the "minor" fetishism lies in the fact that preference is given to those erogenous zones of the partner's body which had pleased one most on one's own body. The foot becomes the fetish of one who had been sucking his own toes (Adler), or the hand may become the fetish of one who derived his first autoerotic pleasure from sucking his own hand. This preference is also the root of the so-called partial narcissism (or partialism). A partial narcissist is infatuated with one definite part of his body and critical of all the rest, which he would like to change. The ears, the legs, the figure, the face, the nose, and above all the genital organs may be objects of his predilection. (The love for one's own genital organs, which plays such an important role in the psychogenesis of neuroses, is also one of the roots of exhibitionism, *q.v.*)

Freud [1] points at the castration complex as the main cause of the primary narcissism. I, for one, cannot go along in this evaluation of the importance of the castration complex. In my own analytical practice I have come upon the castration complex every now and then, but never with the regularity ascribed to it by the orthodox Freudians.

On the other hand, I agree with Freud on the significance of the relationship between narcissism and the ideal. According to Freud, the child finds his ideal in his own self. "The neurotic's ideal is only a substitute projection for the lost narcissism of his childhood when he had been his own ideal."

But the trouble is that it is rather difficult to comprehend what Freud means by the term "ideal." "The construction of the ego-ideal, under the watchful eye of conscience," says Freud, "has been first stimulated by the voice-borne critical influence of the parents and then later reinforced by that of

---

[1] Einführung zum Narzissismus. Schriften zur Neurosenlehre.

the educators and teachers and of the incalculable, indefinite multitude of all the other people of the ambiance (social contacts, public opinion)."

I see here a contradiction. Are we to say then that the child, prior to its training, has no ideal, that he cannot be his own ideal, that it is training, the extrinsic (Otto Gross), which creates the ideal-ego, that the self knows of no ideal-ego and is content with the reality-ego and does not reach out for the higher and better?

An "ideal" is the personality one wishes to be, or the love object one wishes to possess; one may idealize the man who has subdued all his drives or the man who dares to let his drives reign supreme (the Renaissance Man, the criminal, Napoleon—any or all of them may serve as ideal).

The narcissist is his own ideal. As one narcissist once said to me: "You wouldn't believe it, but I actually envy myself." This man's state of mind was an overcompensation of an oppressive inferiority feeling. He was, in certain aspects, a cripple; his idealization of himself was made possible only through a neurotic fiction.

The child usually adores himself because the adults about him incessantly praise his beauty, his charm, and his intelligence. Freud says: "To become again his own ideal, which includes also the things sexual, to regain the childhood state, that is man's goal and idea of happiness." And why does the child's infatuation fade away? Because his conscience creates in him, and nurtures, a feeling of inferiority. Thus we see that education builds up an ideal after first having destroyed the child's self-erected one.

The narcissistic process may lead to either physical or mental self-love: that is, one narcissist will be infatuated with his own body (specifically, with his genital organs), another narcissist will adore his psychic personality, his intellectual abilities, and other properties of this order. In many instances, the two aspects merge in varied combinations. One narcissist may feel certain to approach very closely to his bodily ideal and smart under the gap separating him from the spiritual ideal; others regard themselves as physically repellent, but they are full of admiration for "the beauty of the inner personality" which they are sure to possess.

All narcissists have in common a deep-seated *faith that they are immortal*. They simply cannot conceive of the idea that they will ever really die, like the "rest of them." They believe they are in possession of divine powers, and they display marked traits of the "Christ neurosis."

Following is the analysis of a narcissistic case from which we may derive some insight into the character and psychogenesis of the affliction. It is the case of a man from the former Austrian province of Siebenbuergen, a teacher whom I analyzed at great length. The man was concerned with the obsessive idea that he was losing his hair. He used to stand for hours before the mirror, perturbed about his "vanishing beauty." It became evident that he was infatuated with himself. But before I embark upon the analysis, let us have a look at a few condensed passages of the man's diary.

Case No. 113: Childhood Reminiscences, etc.[1]

"Born 1884. My father was a teacher. My mother, rigidly educated, but a strong-bodied and pretty girl, was a member of the church choir when she met my father. They fell in love with each other, my mother became pregnant, and I was born before my parents got married. Father was a jolly fellow and liked to drink. Even now, at the age of sixty-six, he is hardy, lusty, and basically very healthy. As far as health goes, my mother isn't any worse off than he, but she was only seventeen when she came down with me and she must have suffered a great deal at the time. Father, who was in debt up to his neck, would not think

[1] In accordance with my policy of leaving the reports of my patients unaltered, I have not tried to improve on the style or grammar of these excerpts. Such as they are, they offer a true and undistorted picture of their author.

of marriage, and thus he caused another great anxiety. In fact, he was forced into marriage by state authorities. My mother told me many times later that it would have been better for her if he had succeeded in his intention of jilting her.

Impressions at the Age of Two

"When I was a child I used to spend much of my time in the house of our neighbors, a doctor's household, where I was treated as one of the family. My brother Charlie was not liked by our neighbors, and they nicknamed him 'Charade.' At home, on the other hand, the situation was reversed; Father, and Mother, too, I believe, preferred Charlie to me. My brother was, and still is, taller and stronger than I. Father was very proud of him. At the house of our neighbors I was always treated to sweets, although I never sat at their table. I used to go along with the doctor when he went to his orchard outside the city limits. But Charlie was the favorite with the ladies in town, and I was envious and jealous of him. Even as a child I loved the company of ladies, but they did not like mine. They kept on disliking me when I entered school. I was of a much more serious disposition than Charlie, and the ladies held that against me. There was, however, one lady who totally disapproved of Charlie and liked me very much—my grandmother on father's side. I used to go to her house daily. Although living on a small pension, she always found something to give me. At her house it was Charlie who received less than I or nothing at all. I was also driven to Grandmother's by the fact that we never ate well in our house and because Father used to come home from school highly irritated, scolded Mother for being late with the meal, made a gloomy face, slapped us, and was generally so much more feared than actually loved that we were happy when he left the house. He went daily to the village bar with complete disregard for the fact that he was a poorly-paid school teacher, and if he came home late there was usually a fracas which upset and frightened me, and Father called Mother names, like 'beast' and 'tramp.' He often told us boys never to marry a 'termagant' like her, for she'll make our life miserable. Every time Father stayed too long at his friend's, the town baker, and was late for dinner, there

was a quarrel at the table, because Mother was of the opinion
that Father ought to look for better company (she was wrong
there—the baker's was a respectable family). Mother was snobbish.
She always thought that with her beauty she herself could have
made a better marriage choice. On such occasions, Father raged
with anger, broke dishes, came dangerously close to apoplexy,
and we cried and pleaded with Mother to leave him alone. Father
always made a point of the fact that he gave mother his entire
salary (a ludicrous reproach, in view of the size of the poor devil's
earnings). When in a fury, Father used to shout that he was
going to keep each one of us from studying. Mother had an
extremely tough time, what with having to raise six children
under such conditions and with her antiquated ideas of a country
girl who had been prematurely burdened with marital responsibilities. Father never missed a chance to remind her of her
inadequacies and called her names, like 'feeble-minded goose'
and such.

"Mother's health was not always good; she had had rheumatic
fever when a child. She talked to us of death as being the most
horrible and dreadful thing, knew from hearsay something about
Christian Science, liked to describe other people's ills and sudden
strokes. These stories made me conceive wishes to be spared
every disease. Longevity—that was Mother's highest ideal, and
she spoke again and again of cold rubbings and baths.

"Mother imbued us with religiousness. I felt keenly the difference between her makeup and that of Father, who was rather
cool toward religion and almost never went to church. I dreaded
the flames of hell and shook with fear when the holy wafer stuck
to my teeth (a mortal sin, according to F.H., our landlord's son
and false friend of mine).

"When I displeased Mother, or sided with Father, she prophe-
sied back luck for me in all things to come.

"I remember that I often stood before the mirror and appraised
myself favorably. I expected my looks to secure for me in the
future a good standing in the world, particularly in the world of
women. I was happy at the thought that I was better-looking
than my brother, but not because I did not wish him to be
handsome; I had an idea that beauty, to him, would only be a

liability. Anyway, there never was any doubt in my mind that my physique was far superior to his.

"In my childhood I was greatly attached to our neighbor, the doctor, who was for me a father substitute. Characteristically, I have, both then and after, looked for protectors, and have never been able to feel strong and independent.

"As early as my first school year, I listened eagerly to talks on sexual topics and, desirous to see things, always preferring the company of women. And even before that, in my pre-school years, when I still slept in my aunt's bed, I used to look at her genital organs while she was asleep. I fell in love for the first time at the age of ten, and when I was thirteen or fourteen, I secretly adored three girls, whom I intended to marry when the right time came. When I was in love, I could spend hours waiting behind my window, and as soon as the girl appeared on the street I ran quickly to the piano and played so that she could hear me. I never dared, though, to talk to the girl I loved; her beauty overwhelmed and intimidated me. In all my later life the story repeated itself; the beauty of every girl I loved was too much for me; it made me so timid and over-awed that I dared not speak of my feeling for her.

"Father began teaching me music when I was six. I developed such a passion for the art that I ran to the piano as soon as I came home from school. I was very fussy about my piano playing, and fancied myself a future virtuoso. F.H., the landlord's son, also took music lessons, and played much better than I, causing me a great deal of suffering and humiliation. He also boasted of a finer approach to women and predicted that I would never make a hit with them. He was popular in school and rarely missed a chance to show his superiority over me.

"Later, when we were both students at the teachers' seminary, he was still impressing me with his tall tales.

"A school friend taught me to masturbate when I was thirteen. Sometimes F.H. joined us in the act, and the three of us masturbated until we ejaculated. Father talked to me about masturbation once, stressing the dire consequences of the 'vile habit.'

"We masturbated rather infrequently, once or twice a week, our cue being usually the sight of a girl we liked, walking down the street. To this day, I masturbate very seldom, if ever. At the beginning, the practice caused me no trouble at all, but, as time passed, a feeling of guilt and sin depressed me on the days we indulged in the practice. I became shy and hardly dared to look straight into anyone's face for fear he'd see through me. In my college years I tried to escape the consequences by interrupting the act before the ejaculation came. When our Professor of Divinity censured me in front of all the students for my vanity, implicit in my long, curly hair and the pince-nez I wore, he never failed to include some remark about the dark shadows under my eyes.

"My brother was a poor piano student. But the head teacher at school, in the presence of both of us, praised him and upbraided me (my brother, though younger than I, was in my class.) I have a feeling that my brother and I liked each other, just the same.

"The teachers in our grade school were bad and taught us little. My father was teaching the fourth and fifth grades while I was in those grades, and he often slapped me in front of all the children. Even before that, he had always talked to his pupils about us and about our misconduct at home. He never had a good word to say about us. He was never a real father to us; instead of being our guardian and protector, he believed every stranger's denouncement of our behavior and was prompt to chastise us, unless Mother saved us from his wrath. In moments like these I wished every ill, including death, upon him. Even in high school he gave the teachers free hand to treat us as they pleased, and we were handled roughly and unjustly. I, especially, was subjected to a most severe regime. I grew even more timid than I had been, and my standing with the school boys was very low. As an indication of the poor teaching abilities of our masters I want to mention here that they never talked freely to us, but read from the book or had one of the pupils read the assignment. One of my high school teachers was openly hostile to my father and vented his feelings on me, calling me 'brat' and similar insulting names. I was so deeply afraid of him that I learned absolutely nothing from him. That year my self-esteem suffered a severe set-back. I felt physically weak and incapable of achieving anything at all. When I was thirteen, I fancied having tabes, but I soon got over it.

"Wrong ideas about the social position of teachers made me wish to become a teacher myself. I did not know then how hard their life was; their boisterous manners made me think that they were important and prosperous people. Even as a little boy, I liked to cut out little paper manikins, and range them at will; I could not imagine a more pleasant occupation than that. Father wanted me to become a businessman, but Mother insisted that I study. I, too, was for scholarly pursuits; I liked the idea of being a college student one day. My father finally gave in, rather thoughtlessly, and has never as much as tried to dissuade me from becoming a teacher. My mortifications and humiliations as candidate were heart-breaking, and my social standing was pitiable. Mother had not fostered in me a feeling of self-reliance; on the contrary, she imbued me with the silly notion that it was hard to converse interestingly with women. Her influence on me was so great that later on, although attracted strongly by women and craving to please and to impress them, I was never able to open my mouth in the presence of the girls I loved, and felt awkward and embarrassed.

"Studying was not easy for me, but I was a hard worker. Our Divinity Professor was very strict. He taught us—for hours and hours—religious subjects, and history. His method of teaching was highly academic. I dreaded his classes, but the other teachers weren't very different, inasmuch as they all told me to my face that I would never amount to much.

"Of my seminary years, I can only say that the load of studies was too hard on me, that I lived in constant fear of a venereal disease or of a testicle eczema, and that I was torn between excessive love for a girl and a similarly excessive hesitancy to approach her, for fear that I would not be able to keep up a conversation.

"In my childhood, I had thought I was destined to achieve greatness because I fancied myself very beautiful; I believed in my personal immortality, because of my firm belief that God would never let me die. At the age of four, I was also convinced that I was strong enough to withstand death."

It is of utmost significance that narcissists keep diaries or write memoirs. Convinced of their personal importance, they are self-engrossed, analyze the minutest traits of their makeup, trusting that future generations will avidly read their notes. Destined for immortality as they believe themselves to be, they bequeath to posterity the perennial monument of their soaring thoughts. This analysand has filled many notebooks with accounts and meditations on everything that has ever happened to him, intended for transmission to the "coming generations."

His biography is first and last the history of his competitive struggle with his brother. The few persons who, like the doctor's family, gave him preference over the other boy, are his sacred patrons, saintly individuals. All his life, he wished to excel his brother in physical beauty, intelligence, riches, and above all in popularity. He wanted in every situation to be the first and foremost man and could not endure being overshadowed by someone's greater success and achievement.

His most acrid words are for his former teachers, and he never omits to sideswipe his father in the process of denigration. We note, however, an early identification with father in his desire to become a teacher like his father and in his early consideration of teaching as the highest profession.

He takes note of every humiliation he has endured. Every freshman joining a fraternity goes through a rather harassing initiation process, but our analysand takes all the pranks as personal insults and never gets over them.

He displays self-infatuation, a consuming desire to shine. In his search for love, which his parents denied him, he found both the doctor's family and himself purveyors of sympathy and attention. The school, on the other hand, forced him into a situation of inferiority, nurtured his grudge and envy by holding up against him better looking and brighter fellow pupils. The following is another comment in his diary.

The Genesis of My Illness

"At the age of twelve I dreamed of death. An inkspot on my lips evoked in me fear of poisoning, and someone's description of an apoplectic stroke generated in me ideas of guarding myself against something of the sort. When I was in high school, I imagined having *tabes,* because one evening I felt a stabbing pain in my shanks. As soon as I could, I read all about the disease in an encyclopedia. But I was young and peppy, and the idea, though persistent, did not oppress me too much. In our school years, we were never by ourselves even in our room, which we used as a passageway to other rooms. The peremptory and whimsical orders of the boarding-house manager irritated me. Generally, I was on good terms with the other boys in the house, although my roommate, a brilliant student, kept on vaunting his superior qualities. The manager, an assiduous newspaper reader, exchanged views only with my roommate, so that every one knew that I was but a mediocre student. I had been poorly prepared for the advanced studies, and flunked three subjects at the first examination. I began working harder than ever and caught up with the class. I had my greatest troubles with the Divinity Professor. Despite all my cramming, I could never top the 'satis-factory' mark. Besides, he always moralized about my vanity, and made dark allusions to my sins in front of all the boys. The first year in school I did my evening prayers kneeling on my bed; in the second year, I was so exhausted by my daytime studies that I could only pray in a lying position.

"Unlike the high school pupils, we, the students of the teachers' seminary, enjoyed no social prestige, and this circumstance was in utter contrast to my pre-school dreams. We were not even allowed to enroll in a dancing school, and I had to forego the privilege of meeting pretty girls, who I missed so much. On top of this, there were the severity of my teachers and my constant cramming (which I felt compelled to do, as I wanted so much to show everyone that I was as good a student as anyone else).

The Actual Genesis

"I was a sophomore in the Teachers' Seminary when one day I noticed a node at the root of my genital organ. The swelling soon turned into a herpes and spread all over the scrotum. I hesitated to go to the doctor, first because I was terribly ashamed, then also because I was afraid he would diagnose an incurable disease. When vacation came, I looked up an encyclopedia, read all about 'Suppurative Inflammation,' and became gloomy and depressed. From then on I became a regular reader of encyclopedias. My state of mind did not escape the attentive eye of my Divinity Professor.

"As time went on, I noticed that my capacity for study diminished. Unlike the other boys who boisterously enjoyed their vacations, I was reticent and depressed. In 1903, I fell seriously in love with a girl and wanted to marry her. I wrote to Dr. H. about my condition, and he sent me a powder and a salve. For months and months I washed my scrotum daily. During the Easter holidays I went to consult Dr. H. He sold me several contraceptives and recommended sexual intercourse. It was at that time that I felt the above-mentioned weakening of my mental capacities. I was masturbating at the time, but not too frequently. Eggs were an important item of my diet. In May, my neck began to hurt, and I was certain I had meningitis, as the pain extended down my back and legs and radiated toward my arms. Up until September I lived in the conviction that I had *tabes,* and the more I read about the disease the more convinced I became that I had just that. Of course, it was only the initial stage of my neurasthenia.

"It was at that time that I wrote a betrothal letter to a girl I liked, a girl who insisted that I should write to her two letters weekly, each letter at least eight pages long. I knew through her that her mother was wicked and tyrannical and that she was strongly opposed to our engagement. I was upset about the meanness of the woman and also tormented by conflicting emotions, as I had no desire whatsoever to ask her personally for her daughter's hand. The lady, by the way, had become very rich through an inheritance. It is worth mentioning here that my brother who had met, through me, my girl's sister, married her five years later. In the summer of 1903, I spent my vacation at home, and my family tried to 'talk me out' of my ailment. Father was of the opinion that the long love letters were the cause of it all, and he sent me to Dr. N. The doctor discovered nothing, but suggested, nevertheless, cold rubbings. I was without means to undertake anything, and my father was no help either, as he wouldn't move a finger for my sake. There's no doubt in my mind that at that initial stage much could have been done toward saving me. The several steam baths I took that summer brought me some relief.

"My work, upon which I had entered with so much anticipation, was a complete failure; as a teacher assistant I was in a subordinate position, my salary was miserably small, my social standing below par, I was not free to conduct my classes as I considered best, and the principal harassed me with his pedantic trifles and conversations. I had eighty-six pupils in my grade and worked like a galley-slave, only to be constantly criticized and discouraged by him. No matter how hard I tried, I could not achieve the success I craved, and I felt unhappy and was torn by conflicting emotions.

"All through the winter of 1904-05, and the following summer, my nerves were on edge again. I was plagued by a fear of the dying moment. The last split second when breathing stops, horrible to imagine, was exactly what I constantly imagined. My pupils at the time were the worst brats, the graduating class. Besides, I was studying for my teacher's exam. I had hopes to pass it with flying colors, as my thinking was very keen just then.

"In the fall, when I was beginning to feel better, people started talking of the coming war with Rumania, and my fear of death crystallized into a war mania. I saw myself as a rifleman in the battle line, gripped with fear of the onrushing bullets, and so forth. These visions pursued me for three long years (1905-08). At the time of the 'Rumanian Incident,' I became frantic. For five months I was taking two cold baths daily. Slowly, I regained strength, my fear of death subsided, and the youthful vitality returned. Despite advice to the contrary, I stopped the cold water treatment. But in the summer of 1909 I decided to take it up again, and went to W., where a doctor, upon examining me, found nothing worse than a slight weakening of my retentive power. The cold water cure helped me to a certain extent, but it also made me more irritable, excitable, and sensitive. The too low temperature of the water caused persistent pain sensations in my head and forearm. Mere trying to think in a coordinated way could also evoke the same sensations, and I found it harder and harder to do any thinking at all. Father was absolutely indifferent to all my complaints, which lasted for years, until I got relief through the Priessnitz treatment.

"In the summer of 1910, I went again to W., for an eight-day Kneipp treatment, which involved the following daily routine: Dew-and water-treading, washings in the fore- and afternoon, and a second water-treading in the evening. It was then that I began to lose my hair. The washings were a great strain, and I had to lie in bed for hours to recuperate from their after-effects. Toward the close of the treatment my doctor told me that if I did not get rid of the dandruff I would lose my hair completely within six years. From then on I became obsessed with the 'Hair-Idea,' and I have never freed myself of it. People's jokes about bald-headed men had a devastating effect upon me, and it was a shocking blow for me to discover that baldness was also a laughing matter to my mother. She told me once that I had the recessed hair line of Old Man Spouse. Some time before, I had been in love with the daughter of a butcher. She reciprocated my feelings but at the same time went out with many college boys, and all through the two years I had loved her I have never really had a chance of a good heart-to-heart talk with her. The girl's mother considered a teacher to be a poor match. I, in turn, was afraid the girl would not love me bald-headed. Tormented with this idea, I did all I could do to save my hair. It seemed to me that the cold showers were the only cause of my dandruff.

"In 1911, I took, at last, a six-month sick leave. Upon inquiry, a doctor in W. wrote to me that I needed psychiatric treatment, and I agreed. His treatment, however, consisted in his telling me to relax, to stop thinking of my illness, to conceive a counter-idea, that is, that I am as healthy as can be (but I just couldn't conceive of such a thing, it was utterly impossible for me to feel healthy). Each time I saw him, he used to say to me, 'You will certainly get well.' He administered to me a full-scale water cure (whole and partial washings) and packs. The results were nil. And my own efforts to fight the morbid ideas within me were to no avail. In the fall of that year I met a doctor who happened to stay a short while in N. He hold me that my illness (neurasthenia) required only a mild water cure, and that I would be in good spirits again if I bought a work bench and did some manual labor. I took up wood chopping, and my condition improved.

"Let me note here that it was K., a fellow teacher, who is much to blame for my 'hair-idea.' I frequented a certain cafe where K. spent all his afternoons, and he never failed to call to my attention the state of baldness of every cafe guest with thinning hair. I began to avoid him, and, after the war, stopped seeing him altogether. His conversation, which had rather pleased me once, became too unbearable.

"Up until 1906, I was a devout Catholic, but then under the influence of a friend, I swore off religion completely. For the last twenty years I haven't been to confession once."

This patient displays the contradiction between his veiled belief in his immortality and the pathologic fear of death. His illness begins with typical hypochondriacal complaints; a look into the encyclopedia is enough to convince him of his grave malady. He then proceeds from sickness to sickness, from one doctor to another, and tries every available clinic.

After a while, all ills merge into one central "fear of baldness." The imperative sick leave only worsens the situation, since only work can really bring relief to such *malades imaginaires,* only work can distract the patient from his fancies. In the case under analysis, the patient's daydreams were the only cause of his irretentive memory. In the idleness of his sick leave, our patient had ample time to look at himself in the mirror, to watch the steady loss of hair, and to lament about his vanishing beauty.

Unavoidably, his faith in God ("God is with me, I am His chosen one, I shall not perish") gave way to a rebellious attitude. The patient had to become an atheist. And as he renounced God, he also renounced his father and all authority in general; he gave up his Catholic affiliation and joined the socialist underground.

The following excerpt from his next entry will show us that it was his hyper-sensitiveness and his anarchicistic attitude that prevented him from establishing social contacts.

My Relation to School Authorities

"In my teaching career I have worked under ten different principals. Before I had embarked upon my teaching career, I had visualized the school principal as a man of ideals and of profound knowledge, who would be my guiding star. The ten principals under whom I have worked up till now caused me bitter disillusionment, however. With the first one I did not know exactly how to behave. I was in my nineteenth year at the time, imbued with the carry-over idea of the importance of good conversation, and my stupid inability to contribute to the banter in the tavern made me feel silly. The second principal was an old man, and afraid only of one thing—that he would lose to me his job as organist. Otherwise, he ignored me completely. The fourth principal, formerly head of a high school, treated the sixteen members of our faculty as though we were errand boys. He kept feeding us memoranda on his pet theories, peeped into our classes, and was present four times a month at each class to watch us at close range. The staff conferences were interminably long. He was a fool and tried to make fools of us. As a matter of procedure, he upbraided us frequently and reported on us to the district superintendent. At the beginning, he took a liking to me and we made many hikes together. Still, he censured me just the same, and on most insignificant occasions, at that, and I reacted with opposition, even at the staff meetings. I had to endure him for four long years, at a pay of forty-five gulden a month. The other teachers took everything in stride, but to me school mattered too much to acquiesce.

"The seventh principal was a violent and tyrannical person. He put my nerves on edge by his constant scolding, by his incessant 'why's.' (Why were my shoes not polished? Why was the classroom dirty? Why was the door of my classroom ajar?) According to him, I never did anything right. He sensed that I knew more than he, and it made him furious. I had to take a leave of absence at last, because I could stand it no longer. But until then I had suffered for years, and as I was still on probation I was helpless. Toward the end, though, I finally got rid of his 'why's,' by the simple expedient of answering each question with my own repetitive, 'Because I want it so.' While under that man, I was isolated from everyone at school, and my feeling of humiliation oppressed me. I felt like an oaf, and at the same time I developed a sort of anxiety in the presence of my superiors, a fear of compromising my dignity."

The above are only a few lines from the longest entry in the patient's diary. He rages against every one of his superiors. There is not one fair character among all these "pigs, nincompoops, and crooks."

His denigrations serve only the purpose of explaining away his innermost fear of authorities. Just as his love for his father is qualified by paralyzing fear, so is his reverence toward superiors. He bows timidly before them, and yet snarls and scoffs at them. And underneath it all is his burning smart of not being appreciated and loved to a degree commensurate with his worth.

My Fellow Teachers

"Every one of them is a bundle of nerves. Thanks to the laxity of the head teacher, they do not show the proper respect for me, although I am their senior. They always surround the head teacher, gossip, grumble, and ridicule every ordinance, and he nods complacently. They brag and boast about their service in the school systems and have complete disrespect for the supervisor. Unashamedly, they tell the head teacher that they wish it were 4 p.m. so that they could go home. They also tell him that school teaching is only a secondary job for them, and he tacitly agrees with them. They start and dismiss classes when they please. I am in no position to plead with the head teacher for betterment of conditions, because the other teachers all turn against me in the rudest fashion. Specifically, the youngest of them, an arrogant fellow, can push the head teacher anywhere he wants. This fellow demoralizes the whole setup, tears down everything, acts the big wheel, treats me in the most impertinent manner, and the head teacher, who undoubtedly knows what is going on, considers him nonetheless the most efficient school worker. Most of my colleagues lack manners and team spirit, and they make me regret my choice of career which condemns me to be their co-worker."

The co-workers, to my patient, are but unwanted competitors (his brother had been his competitor, too), and he disparages and belittles them. Without exception, they are "high-strung, mean nit-wits." It may be safely assumed that he converts into hatred his homosexual affection for the youngest teacher.

In his relation to his pupils he is also primarily preoccupied with himself and with the desire to impress them. He is lenient toward them lest they dislike him, and he has put but one wish, namely, that they talk favorably of him in their homes.

Relations with Pupils

"I do too much explaining and am too lenient and intimate with my pupils. My excessive jocundity is harmful because it undermines their respect for me. I am also too often indisposed to work and put in too many rest periods or proceed too slowly. I am not strict enough because I curry the children's favor lest they speak badly of me at home. Besides, I tell them, inappropriately, too many things about conditions of life and reality. Since we teachers actually lack power and means to enforce our will, I prefer not to be too strict and too earnest. In general, teaching does not stimulate me any longer; I have been teaching for twenty years now, and have not been spiritually enriched.

"My authority with respect to grading pupils is nil. If I give a student a merely passing mark in conduct, his parents run to the supervisor, who then summons me and the principal; I give in all too soon, although I know I am right.

Relations with Parents and Siblings

"Father was always strict and I, therefore, preserve to this day a strong sense of obedience. I followed many an order of Father's even when I was already a teacher myself. (Father might remonstrate with me for paying too much attention to ladies, or for my insolence toward gentlemen.) My illness does not interest him in the least. According to him, I am running to watering places in search of males. He had imbued me with wrong ideas and expectations. I was supposed to become so popular that many parents would engage me for private music lessons; but teaching is such a hard job that one should not have to look for additional income. We dared not contradict Father, and he usually ignored us completely. At Christmas time, 1904, I made a critical remark about one of the teachers—and a well-justified remark it was, considering the baleful influence the man in question had on my life; immediately, my father began to berate me. He was in such a rage that we feared for his life. Instead of getting up and leaving the room, I gave in meekly, and apologetically asked him to calm down. True enough, I was already sick by then (I suffered from a fear of death) and regretted having followed in the steps of my father who denied me any respect and consideration while he praised Charlie highly. In 1903, before I became ill, Charlie once criticized me, his older brother, and I felt deeply hurt. In 1904, we had a dispute, and Father took sides with Charlie. In 1906, I asked Charlie not to yell at me, and he said to me 'You belong in an asylum!' And it was not his consideration of my worry over my pitiable state that made him say so, either. Being only a teacher, I had no standing with my own family. My mother and my two sisters, who otherwise cared very much for me, despised teachers. No one paid great attention to me. My sisters did not write to me. They thought of my illness as an imaginary one, and they showed no sympathy whatsoever. Even the girls in my family pushed me around; they did not—and still don't—think much of me. Father had once promised to buy the glee club's piano for me, but when our family came into the possession of a little inheritance, it was given to my sisters, and I was doled out one hundred *kronen* and could not get the piano, which cost 500 *kronen*. They could do anything they wanted with me. After the war, the glee club refused to sell the instrument, and I am still unable to make use of my musical knowledge and ability. The failure to get the piano caused me great mental anguish at the time. Was I supposed to come into possession of a piano my marrying just any plain girl, and be forever deprived of feminine beauty? I shall never forgive my father for not keeping his promise that he would get me a piano. Father seems to be aware of what he has done to me; he often invited me to spend my free days with him, and he has tried to talk me into marrying a rich farmer's daughter who owns a piano. He pesters me with questions about when and whom shall I marry. But he does not seem to realize that it is a father's duty to provide his son with such a trade and status that, at the age of twenty-two, the young man should be in a position to marry.

Recent and Present State of Illness

"Weak memory. At times—mostly mornings, or after a meal— there is a dull ache in my forehead, extending from the nose region and gums back to the skull and the shoulders. Likewise, diffuse sensitiveness in the forearm extending down to the fingers (sometimes in the form of an itching sensation), and in the leg.

"Years ago, I had persistent spells of pain in my head and arms. The biting, cold Kneipp showers must have been the real cause of those pains. Intense thinking, too, might have provoked them. They are now gone, however. The present, dull sensitiveness can be alleviated through a light massage of the arm.

"Aversion to thinking and creative mental strain. I can feel the reluctance of my brain nerves to exert themselves. When I am by myself I can still manage to think and to meditate creatively, and on such occasions I feel a great relief; I am gay and buoyant. But when I am in company (especially in the presence of the head teacher or of fellow teachers), and have to strain myself to participate in the conversation, or when the subject of the talk does not interest me, the effort is too much for me, and I feel the dull pains mentioned before; or my fixed idea comes into my mind and makes me despondent. Thus, I am unable to be sociable.

"When I am at home, lying quietly on my bed, I am often cheerful; but rapid walking or hiking brings on the pain and thoughts about the thinning hair, sadness, and despair.

"Upon waking in the morning, I do not feel rested. On the contrary, I feel tired and weak, and do not care to get up.

"Bodily movements tire me, although not always. I do not enjoy nature, music, life—I am indifferent and apathetic and inclined to brooding and daydreaming.

"Very often, mostly after mental work (around 4 p.m.), I am

morose, irritated, and, without any apparent reason, morbidly exhausted.

"I am strongly attracted by everything feminine. Masturbation in spirit. Coitus leads to ejaculation, but brings neither joy nor gratification (this has been so for years). When with a woman, especially at the sight of her nude body, I am excessively aroused.

"In general, I am easily excited and easily tired. Often, I am disgusted with life and long for the salvation of death. Otherwise, I am obsessed with fear of the dying moment. I have always wished so strongly to study, to be a high school teacher, or to read newspapers and to become versed in everything, and to be as clever as the politicians; but I lack the drive, tire easily and have trouble remembering things. I loathe my status and at times I hate my father who should have prevented me from choosing an occupation which is so burdensome, so rewardless, so void of social prestige, and which is the cause of all my misery.

"Spells of anxiety. Specifically, fear of losing my hair and becoming bald-headed. Out of this fear, I get restlessness and morbid depressions, mental turbulence and inability to work. When I comb my hair in the morning and notice how rapidly I am shedding it, or on those rare occasions when I contemplate myself in the looking glass lengthily and see the ravage wrought on my appearance by the receding hair, I am gripped by despair. Thoughts whirl through my brain: (1) What will people say when they see me like this? (2) How will I be able to live, to work? (3) Why did this have to happen to me? (4) No wonder I am such a failure in love now! I'll probably never win the girl I love; with my assets so greatly reduced, I'll never know the happiness of calling her my wife!

"More than anything else I hate greeting people. As soon as I take off my hat, they start talking about my baldness, and I become very edgy."

The preceding excerpt from the diary is of exceptional significance because it contains many psychogenetic phenomena, among which we note the daydream-conditioned "weakening" of his memory, an assortment of symbolic pains, and diminished interest in the outside world, so characteristic of the narcissist.

Inevitably, narcissists turn increasingly inward, concentrate on themselves, and lose all interest in nature, art, politics, and social life. My patient's ability for normal orgasm grows weaker all the time, as he tends more and more toward auto-erotism. He wants to stop masturbating, but he must continue the habit because only in masturbation does he get adequate gratification. He is less and less able to direct his libido toward outside objects.

He accuses his father, the natural scapegoat, of having been the cause of all his misery. In reality, he is homosexually attached to his father, as can be seen from identification with father in earlier years. He longs for marital happiness, but he shuns every opportunity of a permanent attachment. He told me many episodes which prove beyond doubt that he could have succeeded in winning a girl many times. He was never able to hold the girl, however, because he did not want to; his defeats were of his own making. We will have a chance to learn about his love objects later in this chapter.

In love, he also sets his goal too high. His wife is a fantasy creation who must be the most beautiful of all women. It is not so much a question of gratification of his sense of beauty, as the desire to be envied by everyone, to be exalted. This can be clearly seen from the following entry:

Attitude toward Women

"From my earliest age, I have been irresistibly attracted by women. In their presence, however, I was extremely shy and unable to speak. I envisage only very beautiful women whom I dare not even approach, as I am certain they would reject me. I have numerous notes on things to be said in order to impress the beautiful ladies, but I have never made use of these notes. I have known many defeats, mainly because the girls of my acquaintance have turned out to be disappointments. They were not good enough for me. I am sick and tired of messing around with women; those I have really loved have always failed me, and this is what makes me sick and tired."

The "irresistible" attraction of women is a product of the patient's imagination, not a physiological reality. As a matter of fact, he has never experienced a genuine love affair. In most cases, he worshipped his ladies platonically from a safe distance, and wooed and won them only in his daydreams; he never really tried to make his way with them, for he feared failure. He is most clever in avoiding any binding relation. He withdraws the moment he sees that the girl begins to talk in terms of marriage. As soon as the situation becomes "hot," he manipulates and "insults" or doubts the girl's honesty. Once, his courting progressed so far that he was invited to the girl's house. She lived in the country, and he came out to stay with her family. Immediately, he began to gossip with the neighbors about the girl's mother, complained of lack of attention paid to him, scoffed at the girl, and raised such a commotion that he was at last driven out of the house.

He is so thoroughly wrapped up in his infantile fantasies and ideals that he is unable to find the right girl and stick to her. He is too busy with his own self. He demands a sweeping appreciation of his qualities which no girl can ever offer to him. He never speaks of anyone but himself, and of nothing but his troubles, his qualities, the injustices he has suffered, the abilities he possesses, and, of course, of his illness.

Attitude toward Fellow-Men and Society

"When I was visiting with my father in 1907, I was made to live with poor relatives. That was a time of constant humiliation and undermining of my prestige. Besides, my hosts discovered my neurasthenia, and I lost face with them completely. At the moment, I am staying with an elderly, hysterical lady who must never be contradicted. I am at the mercy of her whims and must not complain about anything, be it bad food, lost articles, inferior bed linen, or anything of the kind, or else she flies off her handle and slams the door in my face.

"Ever since my sick leave of 1911, my standing with my fellow teachers has been at its lowest ebb; no one ever seeks my company any more, no one goes for a walk with me. The inhabitants of the town are a sorry lot; they are unfriendly, don't give a hoot about anyone, and, very significantly, looked down on teachers. 'Oh, that one,' they usually say, 'he's just a teacher!' I do all I can to avoid people because I despise them, because I have no luck in this town, and because I do not want to take off my hat to greet them. There are thirty millionaires in this town who have nothing but contempt for the teaching profession. Only our head teacher is admitted into their social circle. The envy and hatred in this town is out of all true proportion. There are only a few decent people here, and none with a sense for beauty and transcendental values."

The above fragment from the diary pictures a man who craves to be on top of the world, a man who regards his modest financial and social position as a personal humiliation. He feels that everyone is insulting him. Envy rends his heart constantly. The central object of his envy is his brother, Charlie. Even his brother's larger stature is an abiding source of unhappiness to the patient. His father, and all men of authority, are objects of his deep dislike. His obsessive craving to shine puts a strain on him when he is in a social gathering; he watches the impression he has produced, and he becomes despondent when—as is usually true—it is the opposite of his expectation that he will be considered the perfect man.

To compensate for his "humiliation," he indulges in ambitious daydreams: for example, he sees himself as the world's greatest conductor, and his glee club is universally applauded. His musical compositions are hailed by the distinguished critics of all countries.

But actually, he is a lazy fellow who takes refuge in sickness, wastes his time on "cures," and neglects his studies. In marked contradiction to his great musical abilities is his failure to acquire the basic knowledge of harmony and counterpoint. What he wants is to win the "jackpot" or to come up with an invention that will make him wealthy immediately. Then he could marry the richest girl and become doubly rich. At the same time, he is afraid of being henpecked by any female. He has nothing but contempt for his fellow men, the philistines.

His earliest recollections concern an episode in which he groped under the skirts of a little girl. He was five years old at the time. As far back as he can remember, he was infatuated with his own penis. In his childhood, he ardently hoped that some time he would have the biggest penis of them all. When he was thirteen, he believed, for a while, that he had the most beautiful genital organ and that no girl could resist him if she saw it. He masturbated in front of the mirror because the mere sight of the reflected penis evoked an erection. He still has a strong exhibitionistic urge that was mitigated only by an equally strong bashfulness.

At school, he engaged in games with handsome boys but never to the extent of getting into serious involvements. He hugged and kissed a boy's cheek, for example, as a "reward" for good classroom behavior or diligent study.

When he was fourteen, he once showed his penis to an adolescent, a girl, and he always wanted to see genitalia of his playmates. He compared sizes of genitalia with his brother and other boys. It was a common game with the youngsters of his group to see which one could urinate the farthest. The patient was heartbroken whenever he failed to win one of these contests.

Seeing women in the nude means more to him than intercourse. He would like to uncover them when they are asleep, just as he had uncovered his aunt when he was a small boy.

He used to think wishfully of undressing children, but he has overcome this urge which easily could have become harmful to his career.

He had a dream:

Father came to my office and scolded me for not marrying the farmer's daughter. I refused to marry her. Then he said, "In that case I will marry her myself."

This dream reveals his high respect for his father, the man that the patient assumed to be the champion in sexual matters. The patient himself does not dare to set up a home with his girl, who is too big and strong for him. He doubts his ability to gratify her. But there is not the slightest doubt in him that his father could. His explanation that the girl is only a country wench and, with all her riches, below his standard, is but a subterfuge. He is afraid of his physical inadequacy.

Another dream reveals his symbolization of hair as a mark of masculinity (Samson Complex). Baldness, to him, is identical with castration. He fears the loss of virility.

He dreamed: *A friend of mine was enraged with an old, tired animal. He wanted to kill it because he had no use for it. My grandmother shielded it from danger, and the animal promised to do more work.*

This dream has many determinants. The "old animal" is his father, a pensioner. The friend who intends to kill the old, retired animal (father) is the patient, himself. Grandmother represents the restraining influence of morals and religion.

And here is a second, weightier interpretation. The "old animal" is his neurosis. The patient wants to kill it so that he can get well and work. However, he also wants to keep his neurosis, and, as compensation for being allowed to retain it, he promises to pull himself together and to improve his work.

We discover yet another track in a third dream: *I and three friends of mine were in a house. A very pretty girl guest attracted me strongly. Then one of my friends said, "The girl is not for you. She will not consent to marry a school teacher." Then I drove with the girl's mother to another place, and we went to the cemetery where one of my fellow teachers was buried. I could see him in the form of a statue. He gesticulated and talked, as though he were alive. The girl's mother and I returned to the house, and the girl walked off without saying goodbye. Her mother made a remark to her, and she said adieu. One of my friends then said, "To get out of here, you have to be stretched out on a bier." (He meant as though nailed to a cross.) I asked the mother, "How far is it to L.?" "A four hour drive," she answered. And I remarked that I'd rather walk.*

With the three friends, the patient associates the three men of whom he was most envious: his brother, a fellow teacher, and a Mr. N. At first he can not associate anyone in particular with the girl or her mother, so he names people at random, stressing his mother and one of his sisters. The cemetery represents an infantile passion which remains alive (the monument talks and gesticulates). The old passion (the beast) in him is still alive. It appears to have some connection with his mother and sister.

He, at first, refuses to elaborate on the strange phenomenon of a live monument. Presumably, he knows of no literary work or folktale which describes a similar wonder. Then he admits that recently he had seen a performance of *The Beautiful Galatea,* the charming operetta in which a sculptor falls in love with his own work of art and brings the statue of the girl to life through the sheer force of his love. He has also reread a scene from *Don Giovanni* while studying Mozart. The two associations belong together. The Statue-Guest of the opera is the voice of conscience. The patient imagines himself be a Don Juan (Don Giovanni) who wanted to kill the Governor (a father image) and to bring the girl to life with ardent kisses. The age difference between my patient and his sister is four years. The town of L. is his goal to which he must walk, and it signifies that he has not given up the fixed idea of making love to his sister, and, in his fantasy, he proceeds toward the goal.

The town of L. is important in still another way. He recently visited in the company of a friend whose beautiful sister, who is a nurse and a nun, lives there. Both men were well-received in the convent; and the patient was also impressed by the Sister Superior, a young, lively lady. The chastity of the nuns aroused the patient's envy.

In childhood he had formed the ideal of becoming a chaste and virtuous man who by being an example to humanity would attain immortality. He wanted to be a duplicate of Christ (Christ neurosis). We find herein the answer to the dream passage of the 'nailing to the bier.' My patient is nailed to the cross of his neurosis.

I asked him to show me the diary entry about his sisters. After I had read it, many elements of his neurosis and the psychogenesis of his compulsive ideas become much clearer to me.

Relation to Sisters

"In my earliest childhood, my sisters had almost no part. I was the older brother and, consequently, treated with respect, although the girls could and did appeal to Father for protection. The oldest girl, Marion, was, I believe, very sweet before she attended school, and I was glad when she joined me in school. She was somewhat slow in learning, but she resembled me in good-naturedness. To this day, I like her very much. I don't remember anything else about my relation to her in those early days. In my later years, however, I was always glad to discover a girl who looked like her. She was in a boarding-school by then, and she was pretty. I once exclaimed in Father's presence, 'Isn't Marion pretty today!'

"My youngest sister, Bessy, is four years my junior. Her raven-black hair had such a gleaming beauty that I was always baffled by it. Her hair and her beautiful face made me think that she could never pass away. God would never allow such a thing. Bessy served me as a yardstick for my own claim to immortality. She was by far more strong-willed and intelligent than either I or Marion. She was a brilliant student. My admiration for her hair blended into the self-admiration of my own locks which I valued above everything else because it made me think of my sister's hair."

This entry, coupled with the patient's oral statements, is of prime importance for the understanding of the psychogenesis of his neurosis. He had been infatuated with his sister and he magically bestowed immortality upon her so that the beauty of her hair and face should never perish from the earth.

He became infatuated with his own self only after he had discovered the similarity between her and him. He had similar hair, similar eyes, and a similar mouth.

Slowly and grudgingly he revealed to me his fancies which had revolved around his sister. There was a time when he imagined that the two of them would live in holy chastity and be the paragon of saintliness. These fantasies merged with incestuous visions in which he and she emulated Siegmund and Sieglinde. How was he to look for other girls if he was unable to attain his sister? She was the feminine ideal of his youth, and he searched his mirror reflection for similarities with her. Was his well-formed nose not the same as hers? Did not their eyes contain the same gleam? Was he not her masculine counterpart? Was she not the incarnation of his feminine complement?

At the center of this identification was the hair which became his fetish. At first he admired his sister's hair; later he admired his own hair.

He loved the personification of his sister in himself. His nar-

cissism grew out of his identification with her, as he himself
gradually became the cherished sister image.

Thus we see that narcissism may have its origin in a person's
identification with his love object, and it will be the task of
further analyses to establish whether this mechanism is general
or presents a special form of narcissism. In the case history
reported by Féré (No. 112 in this volume), the girl identifies her
hand with the hand and cheek of her mother. She loves her hand
as the personification of her mother. We may assume that many
other patients show a similar psychogenetic influence. It may
be in one case the father, in another case the mother, or any
person who is adored by the narcissist through the medium of his
own self. The existence of an obstacle to the love flow, such as
nurtured spite or rejection, seems to be a prerequisite of a
narcissistic transplacement of the love goal onto the ego. But
let us return to our patient.

He reported several fantasies. He had a vision of himself and
his sister in which both were superlatively handsome, pure of
heart, admired and envied by every human being. Ideal siblings!

His mind was set on the idea that he would share his sister's
life. His neurosis broke out when she got married, and his
visionary projects were thus brought to doom. Then he had to
imagine that she was growing older, losing her virginity, becoming a mother, and losing her physical beauty. All such things
were, to him, part of a dreadful process that had beset his sister,
and through affect-displacement his hair became a vehicle for
mourning her ruin and her removal from his life. This conjec-
ture is strongly supported by some of his dreams, two of the
more pertinent of which are presented below:

(1) *I was in a large hall and saw, sitting at a table, Mr. H., the
glee club choir leader (who has replaced me as conductor!), his
brother-in-law, and others. They were drinking wine. I was very
gloomy and could not cheer up. Categorically, I refused to pay
my share.*

(2) *I saw a most beautiful woman. She disappeared for a very
long while, and then she reappeared and sat in her room engaged
in needle work. Beside her stood her beau, a tall, handsome man
whom I envied because of his good luck. I said to myself, 'Here*

goes another chance I could have grasped if I had been at it sooner.' After a little while I saw her again. She passed by, proud and beautiful, without even looking at me. Her beau kept talking to her. I felt very depressed.

Sadness is the basic feeling in these two dreams. He has lost his sister to his brother-in-law, who appeared in the first dream as the brother-in-law of the choir leader. The choirmaster in the dream is, for the purposes of dream concealment, a duplicate figure who also represents the patient's father. Evidently, the patient's first love was for his mother, who was later replaced by his sister. The mother, too, had had beautiful hair; and her beauty had also been admired by the patient.

"They all drank wine." Everyone else has a good time—but the patient is excluded from the joys of life. His depression is the recognition of the impossibility of ever having his wishes fulfilled. He refuses to pay—that is, he denies any guilt and is entirely unrepentant.

The second dream is a variation on the identical theme. The beautiful woman is his sister (and mother). His brother-in-law is represented by the tall handsome man. The patient is also envious in this dream because the man possesses his sister.

I shall refrain from presenting other dreams. As they all revealed a repressed religious tone I asked my patient to show me the passage of his diary which dealt with the subject of religion.

Attitude toward Religion

"My mother had received a strict religious training, and in turn she did her utmost to develop piety in us. We had to pray every night before going to bed. All of us knelt on the hard floor, and mother herself led the prayers. I remember that mother told us about Jesus shedding his blood kneeling on sharp rocks. At times, when we misbehaved, mother slapped us. Kneeling in prayer became a strong habit with us. We never said grace at the table, but mother would make the sign of the cross. She did the same when carving a fresh loaf of bread, or when she saw a flash of lightning. If we laughed at her, she warned us that God would punish us for our light-heartedness, or that we would achieve no happiness in life. We all had high regard for the Day of Judgment, and were even more concerned about the devil and his eternal fire.

"At Communion, I was jittery about dropping the Host or chewing on it. Ernö, our landlord's son, once came into our house right after receiving Holy Communion and he told mother in my presence that I had 'chewed the wafer.' This made me very unhappy because I feared that I had certainly forfeited the ever-lasting bliss of my soul.

"It was in the winter of 1906-07 that a fellow teacher spoke frankly to me about his belief that religion and God were so much hocus-pocus. I insisted that we could not help assuming the existence of God, but he argued against the idea. His arguments made a certain impression on me. At present, although I reluctantly admit that there is something at the basis of nature which we call God, I only go to church and pray occasionally. I often think how happy I would be if I still had faith and could turn to Him for help in distress, especially before going to sleep, and I also wish I had kept the feeling of godhood within me. The World War proved to me the complete absurdity of the God idea. But already as early as 1901 I lived through the bitter experience of seeing the Clerical party and the priesthood oppose the demands of the teachers for a salary increase. Even then I cursed and reneged my faith."

This is an astounding argument. A grown man renounces his faith because the Clerical party is against an increase of the teachers' salary! On the other hand, the patient's severe neurosis can be scarcely understood without the assumption of a concealed belief in God and a fear of guilt, rooted in his faith. To him, his misery is God's punishment. His most priceless possession, his hair, is being taken from him so that the whole world can see his wickedness, his sinfulness. Because he had sinned, the mark of distinction has turned into a stigma.

His relation to God is that of a child; he fears God, yet wants to spite Him. And deep within is the certainty that all his ills are inflicted upon him by an outraged Divinity; his fear of death is the fear of the Judgment Day.

He has the typical attitude of the infantilist with the ego-centered mentality. He denies God his love and obedience because his secret wishes have not been fulfilled; because he is not immortal; because his beauty fades away; because his sister is losing her charms and getting older, uglier, each passing day. He had expected different treatment from God.

The patient himself admits that he is still an inveterate church-goer. At times he even prays; especially at night before retiring he is apt to recite his childhood prayers.

His relation to father is likewise ambivalent. He once envied his father's beautiful hair and, in his opinion, his father was the handsomest, mightiest man in town. He identified himself with his father, entered the same profession and craved to have the same wavy hair. All his life he sought his father's attention and love. We find herein the second determinant of his hair neurosis and the second root of his narcissism. Father preferred to give approval and love to the patient's brother. Consequently, our patient, by partly identifying himself with his father, was able, within his own ego, to get some of the love he so strongly desired.

He loves only himself. He no longer has any fondness for his father, sister, or God. He has shut off all outgoing love. In his whole life he has never experienced romance. When he first meets a girl, he is easily aroused, but the next day he finds many faults with her character and physical appearance. Sometimes he manipulates disagreements with the girl's family. Whatever it is, it is always a means to prevent the development of a lasting attachment. His real goal is not to give, but to receive love. And as he insatiably demands the love and admiration of the whole world, he is extremely sensitive to animosity and humiliation. He is constantly fighting to sustain his ego, and like every narcissist he regards outgoing love as ego-weakening.

Our patient is subject to severe depressions. He often feels lonely and unwanted. Besides, he cannot help being aware that his fantasy of being "the chosen one" (great historical mission!) has no counterpart in reality. The gap between his ego ideal and his real self is too large to be spanned by an illusory bridge.

His future depends on his ability to change his attitude toward himself and toward the world, that is, on his ability to adjust himself to reality.

Undoubtedly, there are certain paranoid features in the configuration. True enough, there are no systematized delusions of persecution, no elaborate hallucinations; but we notice the presence of an overwhelming single idea (baldness) to which all others are subordinate. There is also the sense of being slighted and derided which vies with his disproportionate aspirations; and there is the conflct between what he can do and what he would like to do, a conflict which propels the patient toward a psychotic state; and there is also the narcissistic form of psychosexual infantilism which I consider to be one of the determinants of paranoia. I ought to mention also the polarization of the conscious and unconscious which may lead to a growing split of personality. The patient's attitude toward religion is illustrative of his condition: consciously he is an atheist and a nihilist; unconsciously, he is fearful of God's wrath.

His attitude toward analysis has been that of a skeptical observer. Constantly on the run from the truth, he has really but one goal—to keep his sickness intact. He suspected me of taking advantage of him, of indifference to him, and of an exclusive interest in the fee. I offered to treat him without pay, but he refused to be treated "as a pauper." Finally, we agreed on a nominal payment, and he seemed to be satisfied. But his escape reflex still prevails, and analysis has not yet been able to penetrate to the core of his neurosis. The future will decide whether the treatment will be successful or not, that is, whether the patient will free himself from his delusions or systematize them.

Of great interest are the cases of "temporary narcissism." Nearly every adult person has, at one time or another, gone through a more or less brief stage of narcissism. Especially, is this phenomenon of ecstatic self-admiration common among poets and philosophers and creative people in general.[1]

---

[1] The self-applause of the Viennese is expressed in a song: "We Are We." A frequent American expression which often has a connotation of sheer self-applause is, "That's me, all right."—*The Editor.*

The following case gives us some insight into the psychogenesis of such a transitory regression to the narcissistic infantile state of development.

Case 114: Mrs. Berta, thirty-three, went through a narcissistic period while separated from her beloved husband. Then when her husband returned she was greatly perturbed because her sexual life was not as satisfactory as it had been. Before the departure of her mate, she had always been able to reach orgasm swiftly, and occasionally she had had as many as ten orgasms in succession. Her husband had strong potency, and the couple were passionately in love. Upon my request, Mrs. B. gave me in writing an extremely fine description of her condition. The narcissistic period, in particular, is presented most vividly.

"I have been happily married for five years. Except for a short period at the beginning of our marital life, we were never separated. During that brief separation I was much perturbed. To begin with, I had a hard time fighting my polygamous disposition. Then in connection with my husband's departure there was the worsening of an old conflictive setting. My family had been against my marriage, and the strongest opposition had come from my older sister who had cared for me ever since the premature death of our mother. They had nothing really to object to about my husband, except that they disliked the freedom of his opinions. They were all terribly petit bourgeois, bigoted, and hypocritical. I think it was jealousy more than anything else that made them dislike my husband. Up until I got married I had loved no one but members of my family; I had, indeed, been a real family slave. And here I was about to live my own life, with a man for whom I had more love than I had ever imagined possible. I seemed to live only for him. For his sake I cast off my mental stagnation; I made his interests my own in an effort to rise from a purely animal existence into the sphere of human aspirations. I worked hard in order to equal him in greatness and nobility of thought. My spirit soared jubilantly, and I rejoiced in the knowledge that my love for my husband had transformed me into a different person. At that time, of course, the process of transformation was only in its initial stage. But

I was rising higher and higher, guided by the star of my love, by the strong desire to leave behind me the spiritual poverty of my childhood and youth, to free myself from the shackles of my neurosis, and to walk, together with my husband, the lofty paths of sublime human endeavor. My family, however, disapproved of my determination to change. They were so used to the dumb and sweet little girl I had always been that they abhorred the change. The most discontented of all was my older sister. Her love for me had been a purely egotistic one, and she did not want me to become independent of her. She fought with all her might to hold her sway over me when she learned that I was in love. She would have accepted my marriage to someone I did not love; this seemingly virtuous sister of mine would have welcomed my involvement in a sexual affair if only I did not love the man of my heart. I, in turn, was strongly attached to her and at the same time I was conscious of the harmfulness of the fixation. I did not want to love her any longer. But it was extremely hard for me to eradicate a childhood affection. The situation at home became unbearable, and I had no other choice but to leave the house.

"Soon after our wedding, my husband went on a trip and left me alone. My desire to reestablish contact with my family and to communicate with my sister whom I still loved made me get in touch with them again, and I saw my sister several times. And it was she who at that time nursed my polygamous disposition, whether deliberately or not, I do not know. She enjoyed seeing me at my flirtatious worst and had no objection at all to the unmistakable advances one of my uncles was making to me. And I was so stupidly vain that I felt flattered. All my wicked instincts were reawakened. Lazy as I have always been, it had not been easy on me to put up the constant effort of keeping pace with my husband. Now I could again relapse into idleness, indulge in reveries, gossip; my sister accepted me as I was and put no burden of self-improvement on me.

"My husband returned and understood perfectly what had happened to me in his absence. He helped me to overcome my inner conflicts, and I felt strengthened again.

"Then came the second separation. My husband, who is a

bacteriologist, had to leave for Argentina for a period of about six months. Both of us dreaded the separation. My husband knows me well, and he was afraid to leave me alone, exposed to the danger of an unrestrictedly imaginative life.

"The first days of almost complete loneliness I had but one consolation—the work I was doing for my husband (I was his full-fledged assistant by then). Two or three friends came to see me occasionally, and they were a real help, too.

"A few weeks after my husband's departure, I came down with a severe sinus condition. I was unhappy and missed the care and attention of my husband. Besides, I knew all too well that sickness was conducive to unbridled reveries. And to top it all, I felt an awakening of my longing for my sister. If my husband was not here, I wanted her to take care of me, as she had done so many times in the past.

"I was lonely and I longed for love and sweet attention. After I got well, my sexual hunger became very strong. I lived only for the moment of reunion with my husband. At times I masturbated frequently, always imagining all the sexual joys my husband had lavishly showered upon me.

"As my craving for love and attention grew, I noticed within me a gradual development of something like a loving attitude toward my own person. My husband wrote in one of his letters that he had shown a photograph of me to his Argentine friends and that they all raved about it. The news had the effect of an opiate on me. I delighted in the idea of being admired by strangers. I had to look all the time at the print I had at home, and every time I looked at it I believed I heard the cries of admiration of invisible onlookers.

"My self-adulation grew to almost megalomaniacal proportions. I identified myself with my husband, and looked upon myself as a dazzling personality.

"The more I admired myself, the more I pitied my sister. It seemed to me that she was foregoing too much when deprived of me. My desire to see her again grew stronger all the time. At last, I gave in and wrote to her with such feeling for her that her pride, too, caved in, and she came to see me. I wish now I could undo all the consequences of that fateful letter.

"The first meeting was, to me, rather disappointing. I found her to be hammy and insincere. My conscious mind rebuked her. I abhorred the sentimental tie that bound me to her, my slavish clinging to her. For I had the feeling that the strong trait of homosexuality in me was due to a fixation on her.

"My reawakened neurosis reached its climax when my husband returned. I was torn between my sister, on whose side beckoned a paradisal life, a lazy irresponsible drifting existence, and my husband, who is the very essence of my life."

The narcissist period through which this patient had gone served the purpose of self-protection against an infantile regression. In that sense it was a progression from an infantile ego to an ideal ego. She loved her husband in herself. She looked at herself through his eyes, she addressed herself in his voice, she patted herself with his hands.

The case is of great value for the understanding of the narcissistic mechanism. It not only confirms the fact that identification with the love object may be at the core of narcissism, but demonstrates also that identification with the ideal ego, as seen through the eyes of the love object, may be the substance of a narcissistic formation.

2. PLURALISM

Judging by the accounts of many neurotics, fantasies of orgies are frequently used during masturbation. People who have such orgiastic fantasies are rarely in a position to realize them, however.

I have suggested that this form of paraphilia, in which several participants are involved, be termed *pluralism.*

The number of participants may vary, the simplest case being that of one man requiring two women, or one woman requiring two men. But homosexuals are most prone to this craving for more than one partner, and they indulge frequently in group activities of a sexual nature, such as revelries, secret group meetings, and clandestine orgies.

The pluralistic tendency of homosexuals was widely-observed in ancient Greece. The preserved obscene "Synplegmata" represent such roundels of homosexuals in which each individual is both actively and passively involved in the group act as he turns toward the anus of the man in front of him while offering his own anus to the man behind him.

Needless to say, synplegmata of homosexuals are not the only ones that came down to us from antiquity; representations of orgies of a mixed and general nature are also numerous in Greek art.

It is common knowledge that the oldest known cults contained orgiastic elements, and that to this day orgies constitute an integral part of many sacred or festive ceremonies of primitive tribes. The culture patterns of many contemporary communities retain traces of ancient orgiastic elements, as can be seen, for example, in the unmistakably sexual traits of our various forms of Mardi Gras.

It may be said generally that, whenever and wherever a severe code of behavior restricted all sexual manifestations, there were periodic intervals of relatively uninhibited merrymaking, during which the liberties denied to the individual were granted to the populace as a whole.

Apparently, a dormant lust for the orgiastic experience is present in all of us. No sooner are restrictions lifted than our pluralistic tendencies become clearly manifested. Drinking parties often end in pluralistic sex experiences; but such is also the effect of a real or imaginary communal danger, like the once dreaded "End of the World" earthquakes, the proximity of a battle front, the despair in a besieged city.

The nature of orgies can only be understood in the context of mass psychology. The shock of war experiences has intensified our interest in phenomena of mass psychology. Freud considered Le Bon's *Psychology of the Masses,* published after the war of 1914-1918, to be one of the basic studies in this field, and it served him as a point of departure for his own investigations.

Quite justly, Le Bon stresses the point that the "mass" is characterized by a resurgence of the unconscious, primitive, racial instincts, and by a breaking down of all differentiation. In the mass, the individual as such ceases to exist; he merges and dissolves in the larger unit. And it is this submergence in the anonymity of the multitude, the total shedding of personal responsibility, which makes it possible for everyone to indulge in gratification of instincts which are otherwise under much stricter control. Then there is also the further stimulant of the psychic infection and of the fascination exerted by the leader. Freud reduces the psychology of the multitude to the prime phenomenon of identification with the leader, an identification sparked by a lightning-like infatuation.

However, both Le Bon and Freud overlook the fact that the presence of a leader is not absolutely essential, that any individual may perform the trigger function. The first coward in a panic situation, to mention but one instance, certainly exerts no fascination on the group; he only releases the fear which grips the multitude, whereupon the reflex-like impulse to flee the danger spot springs into action and the normal inhibitions conditioned by fear of punishment, by the feeling of disgrace, by the bonds of patriotism, and similar factors, break down momentarily.

The fact is that the mass easily slips to the lowest level of reaction. This does not, by any means, preclude the opposite possibility; but the instances of the saner reaction carrying the day are rare and far between. The tendency toward the lower depth usually triumphs over all uplifting trends. In a panic situation, the voices of the courageous and cool-headed men are normally drowned out, while the roar of despair prevails. Under duress, it is generally easier for us to regress to our primitive past than to rise to new moral heights.

Le Bon justly ascribes primitive qualities to mass mentality. The multitude, according to him, is driven by instincts; it displays the spontaneity, vehemence, savagery, and also the heroic passion and fearlessness, of primitive man.

It is worthy of note that Le Bon is aware of the similarity between the psyche of the primitive and that of the child; this similarity, in my own view, is the crux of the matter.

The mass is infantile. Its psyche, like that of the child, is dominated by affects rather than by reasoning. And it is precisely in this regression to the infantile stage that we must look for an explanation of mass psychology, which is characterized by a triumph of irreality over reality.

The child knows only the reality of his fancies and covetings. We have to bear this in mind when we speak of the psyche of the primitive horde which, with or without a leader, was childlike.

One of the strongest inhibitions felt by civilized man is caused by his dread of disgrace. He wants to be honored and respected by his fellow men and abhors being socially ostracized. Were it not for our apprehension of what the other participants would think of us many a social party would end up as an orgy even without the stimulus of liquor. What we call civilization is basically a system of well-functioning inhibitions; it is the sum total of everything extrinsic which delimits and controls our impulses. The intrinsic, the innermost ego, may only indulge in dreams and fantasies.

In the mass, however, these inner stirrings burst out into the open exactly because the outside censures break down, because each individual realizes at once that his fellow men are made of the same stuff, and there is no reason for him to hide anything. His overvaluation of society, this strongest prop of ethical conduct, breaks down.

Man's drives yield only grudgingly to the demands of ethical conduct. In his innermost self, man rebels against the shackles imposed upon his impulses. He regards all authority as a hostile force.

Religion, too, is a formidable opponent of sexuality. Orgies which, unlike those of primitive cultures, take place outside the framework of religious rituals, contain elements of religious mockery. Blasphemy adds spice to the orgies. As God is the guardian of morals, while His adversary is the bearer of wantonness, the orgies tend to assume a satanic character.[1]

We are irresistibly reminded of primitive man's habit of chastising his idols when he felt displeased with them.

This revolt against authority, a regression to the blasphemous stage of childhood, is one of the attractions which many sexual aberrations offer to those afflicted by them.

Another aspect of this mutiny against authority is its implied outcry against parental oppression.

Parents rebuke the manifestations of the child's sexuality; they restrain and suppress it by all sorts of "don'ts," and strive to retain their controlling influence in later periods of their offspring's life. The prohibitive influence of state and church authorities is subsequent and secondary. The revolt is directed primarily against the parents. And it is, indeed, a paradoxical situation, for the parents are the child's love objects as well as the prime sources of restrictions upon his will.

From the first, the child wishes to take part in the sex life of his parents. The child's fantasies, inasmuch as they are of pluralistic nature, revolve around the desire for a joint

[1] Goethe displays an intuitive knowledge of the tendency in his depiction of the *Walpurgisnacht*. "Satanic" or "black" masses are celebrated at some places to this day. Schwaeblé, in his book *Les Détraquées de Paris,* describes in detail such mass celebrations as having taken place in a house on Rue Vaugirard, Paris. And similar proceedings are described by Huysmanns in his book *Là Bas.*

love life embracing all members of the family. The first human orgy is a family affair. It is entirely possible that the child preserves a lingering unconscious reminiscence of his babyhood, of those joint, all-family love manifestations when the entire household shared in handling and fondling him, while he himself indulged in pleasurable exhibitionism. I have been able to trace many cases of pluralism to such an intra-family scene.

The fantasies usually designated as womb fantasies are a form of pluralism, perhaps the initial stage of the aberration. Naturally, as time passes, the fantasies undergo changes; they lose their original content and structure and shed their incestuous character in the process. However, a close observation of children reveals the group character of their first sexual experiences. I have been told by many of my patients that they had joined in childhood orgies with their brothers, sisters, and playmates.

Case No. 115: The patient's masturbatory acts are persistently accompanied by images of many couples indulging in sexual intercourse in the same room. From time to time the people change partners. All kinds of paraphilic acts take place.

In the presence of females the patient is habitually impotent, unless from an adjacent room come the sounds of copulation or simply voices of many people. His life history reveals that at the age of nine he played sexual games with his boy friends and girl friends. Some of the girls were the sisters of the participating boys. The patient's own little sister took part in the games. The boys changed partners, and my patient came to play with his own sister. He does not remember distinctly, but he believes that he was capable of coition at that time.

This is by no means a singular case. But here I will merely mention a patient whose sexual potency was adequate only when a friend was performing the act in the same room. He and his friend, therefore, always took two women and retired to the same room. After a while, they exchanged part-

ners. The important data in this case of disguised homosexuality was the patient's memory of having slept with his
sister in one bed. Both children woke to the noises of the
copulating parents and excitedly began to play with each
other's genitals.

The jocular offer to "swap wives" frequently made by men
is every now and then actually put into practice, sometimes
under the influence of liquor. Such a bargain may often
lead to sexual acts characterized by multiple participation.

It is all but impossible to list the endless variety of pluralistic fantasies because of the very nature of these, mostly im-
practicable, fancies. The pluralists are ordinarily reticient
people, brooders with scant vitality. They would be the first
to feel revulsion if given a chance to fulfil their heart's desire. Yet here they are: The dignified man tempted in fantasy by a dozen females at once and indulging with all of
them (the Harem dream!); the distinguished lady with the
streetwalker reveries of a succession of men!

One of my female patients habitually masturbated with
the fantasy of being stimulated by half a dozen men at once.

I have published several examples of a bizarre form of
pluralism of a fetishistic coloration ("The Harem Fantasy
of the Fetishist" in the *Zentralblatt für Psychoanalyse*, Vol.
III).

The habit of many men to frequent brothels in groups of
two or more, an outgrowth of pluralistic homosexuality, leads
often to the strangest act combinations. Two men use one
girl; the men succeed each other with one girl after another,
and so on. The wildest orgies, of an unmistakably infantilistic nature, are often the outcome of such collective raids
upon a "house of joy."

In this connection, a less widely known fact deserves to
be mentioned. Some men and women indulge in pluralistic
fantasies during the sexual intercourse. They imagine other
partners beside the actual one. Persons of high morals, or

persons in love, fight these intruding fantasies, and their love relation is often disturbed in the process.

The commonest form of pluralism is the three-partner act. I remember one patient who consulted me about his practice of indulging with two women in a combination performance of fellatio and anilingus. Another patient of mine practiced the not so uncommon aberration of seeking sexual contacts with sisters. Still another spared no effort looking for a chance to submit a girl and her mother to his will.

In many of such cases I was able to uncover a childhood fixation to two women who had shared in the training of the boy. (Mother and aunt; mother and grandmother; mother and grown sister; mother and wetnurse.)[1]

I also know several women who reluctantly confessed to having had sexual relations with the fathers of their lovers. Presumably, in each case, the men involved knew nothing of the real situation.

I made the observation that pluralism was very frequent among those of my patients who came from large families, and I further noticed that the pluralists were persons who generally disliked being alone and derived no great pleasure from the company of one person. The pluralists like to go on hikes in groups, join all kinds of circles and clubs—in other words, they combine their gregarious traits with their pluralistic inclinations. Other infantile fixations are often admixed, as can be seen in the following case.

Case No. 116: Mr. T.U., thirty-six, complained of compulsive ideas and premature ejaculation. He was in the habit of masturbating while visualizing a grove in the fashion of Greek idyls, with many men and women dancing graciously in the nude. In his fantasy, he joined in the dance, cutting in for one woman

---

[1] Comp. Freud's "Eine Kindheitserinnerung von Leonardo da Vinci." Freud traces the pluralism expressed in the artist's work to the fact that Da Vinci had been attached to both his real mother (his father's sweetheart) and a mother substitute, his father's wife.

after another, until he finally worked up such sexual excitement that he threw one of the girls to the ground and ravished her. The other men then attacked the other girls in the same manner.

The patient displayed many infantile traits. He derived an excessive degree of pleasure from moving his bowels, a strange, crampy pleasure which culminated in a mild orgasm. Urinating produced a similar sensation. At night he used to scratch certain parts of his body—the outer bend of his elbow, the knee, and the ear—until they bled.

He dreamed repeatedly of *playing in a big orchestra of which the members of his family were also members. His father played the viola, while he himself played the cello, which he pressed between his legs until he ejaculated.*

We know that the members of his family, indeed, formed a little house orchestra, but the patient's dream converted the musical performance into an orgy.

Another case (*No. 116a*) treated and recorded by my assistant, Mrs. Hilda Milko, concerned A.M., a girl of twenty-five, who complained of a speech disturbance. She was unable to talk to anyone above her in rank without stuttering. Her office job became almost unbearable as she lived in constant fear of losing her job. She trembled before she actually faced any superior, because she knew she would begin to stutter when the dreadful moment came. True enough, she had been stuttering ever since she had entered school, but the affliction grew in intensity through the years and became most distressing some twelve months prior to consultation.

Although she felt completely well otherwise, she could not enjoy life because of the speech impediment.

Analysis revealed that she had been masturbating for many years and that all her efforts to fight the habit—which she considered a harmful one—were in vain. A causal connection between masturbation and stuttering was easily established in her mind, particularly as the speech impediment had developed soon after her first masturbatory experience.

She also used to think of her speech defect as God's punishment for her sin. She masturbated more and more. At first, she prayed a great deal, asking help and forgiveness, but as her prayers went unanswered, she lost faith in God.

Yet, although she renounced religion outwardly, she remained inwardly the devout little girl, and this conflict contributed greatly to her neurotic state.

The girl complained of a feeling of utter loneliness. It had not been so bad, she said, at an earlier stage, when her somewhat older brother was around. The two loved each other dearly. They used to read and to make music together, go on hikes, and share in other activities. No one understood her better than her brother.

Last year, however, he married, and the relationship changed. She hated her sister-in-law, and could not understand why her brother married this girl in the first place. She hated to go to see her brother, for fear she would have to witness some demonstrations of fondness passing between the married couple.

Quite clearly, the girl's attachment to her brother had the character of a fixation. She herself admitted having pondered a great deal over her feelings toward him.

After a period of strong resistance, she spoke of the things she imagined in the act of masturbation. She had various fantasies.

(1) She imagined sexual intercourse with her brother, and had a feeling of intense pleasure. She also had dreams of the same content, and she was unhappy about them after waking.

(2) She had sexual intercourse with a man who was very fond of her, and he performed cunnilingus and many other paraphilias on her.

(3) She imagined a pluralistic act. She lay with her back on a man who performed a rectal intercourse while a second man performed a normal intercourse.

(4) She saw herself in a brothel and was forced to submit to several men in succession. She felt great pain, but was forced by threats, beatings, and other coercive methods to continue.

The feeling of being coerced was intense, and so was the pain she conjured from her fantasies. She obviously was masochistic. And a part of her fantasies referred to the renunciation of all human dignity in intercourse. She was ashamed of her fantasies, which seemed monstrous to her, and especially of those, the most sinful ones, about her brother.

These latter fantasies took hold of her after a definite experience she had had at the age of sixteen. One evening she was all alone with her brother in the house. She was changing into another dress in front of him without giving it another thought, since the two had grown up together. While she stood there in her petticoat and brassiere, her brother suddenly ran up to her and touched her bosom. At first she was so flabbergasted she didn't know what to do, then she pushed him away and broke into tears. For days thereafter the two avoided looking at each other. But after a while both seemed to have forgotten the scene, and their relations became quite affectionate again.

At that time the thought occurred to her that a brother could be a desirable love object. She became ever more entangled in a net of love fantasies revolving around her brother, and his marriage came to her as a shock, as though he had betrayed her. In her rage, she thought of getting married herself, just to show him that she too could be the mate of someone else.

She was so preoccupied with the matter that she could hardly work. Especially when riding along on a streetcar, she succumbed to her brooding. She avoided longer trips for fear she would become absorbed in her fantasies and miss her destination.

The same was true for railway travel. As soon as she boarded a train, she was overpowered by an intense desire to sleep. Her spasmodic yawning attracted the attention of her fellow travelers. The vibration of the car evoked in her the image that she again was a baby, riding along in a perambulator pushed on by her mother. She was again in that delicious period of life when she and her only slightly older brother were taken out together for a breath of fresh air.

In the dark hours of the evening the girl was afraid to be in the hall of her house. She was afraid she might be overwhelmed by a man. Her anxiety evidenced the presence of both the reminiscence of the episode with her brother and of her desire to be attacked by him.

In her day-to-day life, the girl, who wishfully imagined all sorts of sexual abnormalities, was very prudish. She broke up relations with a man who was courting her, only because he once kissed her "indecently."

The girl was bound to become disturbed: the discrepancy between her conscious ways of thinking and her daydreams was too much for her. Her education had been strict and she had always been afraid of her father, a strict, inaccessible man. She was frightened by the thought that he might find out about her masturbation. She also believed that the teachers at school would learn her secret. Although hankering all the time to unburden herself to someone, she never found the courage.

The reason why the presence of superiors made her stutter was clear. The parents, the teachers, were the representatives of God, the Supreme Judge. She dreaded their anger, their contempt, and their punishment, should they find out how sinful she was. Later on, the higher ranking employees at the offices where she worked assumed the roles of God's representatives.

The main trouble with those office bosses who caused her to stutter was that they were simultaneously the *dramatis personae* of her fantasies. Like so many father images they were the brothel customers to whom she was forced to submit in her paraphilic daydreams. She could not help being intensely embarrassed when called upon to face them in real life. Deep within her was still the childhood belief that God-Father, and all his incarnations, could look into the sinful deviations of her soul.

Analysis brought her complete relief. She stopped stuttering, her attitude toward her brother was normalized, and the pluralistic fantasies ceased to beset her. The prostitution fantasies lingered on the longest, until she reached the stage of discovery that her father and her brother were the owners of her imaginary brothel, and she had sexual intercourse with them, too.

A closer look at the case reveals that all pluralistic aberrations are performed in the confines of an imaginary brothel. I am inclined to assume that it is the general tendency of pluralistic fantasies to provide the gratification of all facets of sexuality in one single act. In view of the great complexity of man's sexual desires, such a craving for an exhaustive, possibly all-embracing form of gratification of the libido components should not be surprising at all. The pluralistic fantasy offers the neurotic a total gratification of all his desires. A normal love relation, on the other hand, could never satisfy one who is beset with a strong homosexual component and with many infantile urges, such as sadism or exhibitionism. Such a neurotic will always complain of a lack of "full satisfaction." There is in neurotics a permanent longing, a drive toward "something else," that is, something more potent, a craving for variation, for new stimuli, which at times manifests itself in the form of hysterical or hystero-epileptic spells. Such spells afford the opportunity to indulge in pluralistic gratification behind the back of the censorial conscience.

The following analysis, performed by my assistant, Dr. W. Bojan, furnishes us with a valuable insight into the psychic workings of an unsophisticated woman and the way she escapes from the reality of her desires into the protective obscurity of hysterical spells.

Case No. 117: Mrs. H.B., thirty-eight, married, has been subject to epileptic seizures for the last twelve years. Every four weeks or so the spells recurred and kept on for several successive nights. At an earlier stage the spells had been more frequent and occurred also in daytime.

The first series of seizures occurred after a surgical operation she had undergone, and they were diagnosed, by every physician she had consulted, as epileptic.

The patient described the spells as follows:

"I have both severe and light spells. While under a severe one, I lose consciousness and don't know what is happening. I can only tell you what my husband has told me.

"When a spell is coming on I feel great anxiety and my stomach turns. I click and bite my tongue. My face turns purple, and I gasp for breath. I kick about violently and am so agitated that my poor husband becomes very frightened. Last night, for instance, he was so scared that he called a doctor. But the doctor said he couldn't do anything for me because it was all hysterical.

"When under a spell I always mutter unintelligible words. I twist my hand in a leftward movement. I urinate surprisingly much, even if I have not taken any liquid before the spell. My bed becomes soaking wet.

"My husband tells me that at the end of one spell the other night I sat up in bed, put my stockings on, and wanted to go somewhere.

"At the approach of the end of a spell I usually smile happily as though I had the most pleasurable feeling. Then, abruptly, I fall asleep, not minding the wet bedding.

"A severe spell ordinarily lasts about ten minutes, whereas the light ones are over in a few seconds. The latter spells cause me only to moan loudly and to gasp for breath.

"The series of spells usually starts with several severe ones during the first night. The following night the spells are less intense, and are completely over within three or four nights."

A physical checkup (Dr. W. Stekel) revealed no clues. The analysis was carried out by Dr. Bojan under my supervision. The following is Dr. Bojan's report:

"H.B. told me of the many 'cures' she had already undertaken—such as water therapy and bromides—without success.

"Six years ago she had entered a marriage of convenience, for the sole reason that she was tired of being single. Prior to her marriage she had experienced many disappointments. She had been a 'man-chaser' and was disillusioned with the poor outcome of all her attempts at a lasting relation.

"She believed that her sickness was due to the many illnesses she had gone through. Eighteen months ago her mother, whom she had loved dearly, passed away. Her mother's death had made her feel depressed; she lost more than thirty-two pounds within one year.

"Normal sexual intercourse gave her no satisfaction; only when her husband 'played' with her (manipulated her genitalia) did she get gratification. Now however, a physician forbade this, on the assumption that this was the cause of her illness. The idea that she had brought on the illness herself made her feel guilty and miserable. For fear of becoming impregnated she had never before her marriage indulged in sexual intercourse and had allowed men only to 'play' with her genitalia. Now she regretted that she had been such a fool and had permitted this to happen.

"On the other hand, she argued, if she was to be deprived of the only gratification, what good was it to go on living or to be married? She might have just as well remained single. It was just too bad that she had gotten into the habit of 'playing' and now could not enjoy any other form of sex.

"She confessed that she had a friend (later on she admitted she had several friends) who came once or twice a month to her house and stimulated her manually. The gentleman was an old business friend of her husband, a married man in his fifties. What attracted her most to him was that, unlike her husband, he treated her with delicate tenderness. She had been spoiled by her parents and had an everlasting craving for love and attention, for a warmth of feeling, which her husband was unable to give her. He never even thought of hugging her once in a while. That is what made her miss her mother so much. She could not go on living without tender caresses.

"She had a young child, but in view of her spells, her husband kept the child with foster parents in the country. Her first child had died a few days after birth.

"She had constant headaches and was unable to do any thinking. She never read anything, housework meant nothing to her. The most distressing thing was her lack of memory. She always forgot things, she could not even remember her wedding day. She wondered why. For the last few years she was in the habit of twisting her head leftward, the way she was doing when under a spell. Another thing that troubled her was her throat. She was often so hoarse she could hardly speak.

"In analysis she spoke haltingly, and her story advanced very slowly. All the time, the complaint kept recurring that she felt constrained to search for gratification. Displaying a somewhat vulgar temper, she talked at times quite blatantly. Speaking of her present sex life, she told the analyst that since normal intercourse did not gratify her, she permitted her husband to approach her *a posteriori* while she obtained her orgasm by digital manipulation. This form of intercourse was practiced until the doctor forbade her to indulge in 'playing.' She had no doubt that her spells were the result of her masturbation.

"When the analyst reassured her that the spells were not the result of masturbation, that 'playing' was not harmful, and that her husband might gratify her the way she liked it best, she advanced the idea that the spells might have been the consequence of a surgical glandular operation.

"At the analyst's question about the time and circumstances of her first seizure, she told him the following story:

"She had a relation with a young gentleman lodger in their apartment in Vienna who responded to her infatuation only half-heartedly. They never indulged in intercourse, they only 'played.' When the man left for his home town, Linz, she and her girl friend went there to see him. He intended to remain in Linz, and it was to be goodbye forever. Prior to the final adieu he spent a night with her in her hotel room. She was very unhappy and angry, although he had really never before shown any intentions to make their relation a lasting one. The day after the final goodbye, she had her first seizure.

"She agreed with the analyst that there must have been some connection between her seizure and that romance. Moreover, she now insisted that the man was the only cause of her illness. However, she did not quite understand the nature of this connection.

"Upon Dr. Stekel's advice, her husband adopted the following procedure: he would stimulate her manually until she was sufficiently aroused, and then, when her orgasm was sure to come, he performed the normal intercourse. She was quite satisfied with the solution and agreed to give up the masturbatory playing with other men. (It was at this point that she admitted having had more than one gentleman friend.)

"The analysis began to stagnate while she came up repeatedly with the statement that she was cured, now that her husband was giving her full satisfaction. She had nothing else to tell the analyst. Or she could not remember anything. When told that her amnesia was rather a refusal to remember, she reiterated what she had said ever since she first came for treatment, namely, that she was not intelligent enough and without any formal education.

"Her first reported dream ran as follows:

I am shopping. I buy milk, meat, eggs and butter. Then I enter a baker's shop and see on a shelf a display of trinkets, tiny figures of dogs, hogs, and such. I tell the baker that I have lots of such trinkets at home, and I want to show them to him. I run home to fetch them. When I return to the bakery, I find there a strange gentleman who makes a move to take the trinkets away from me. I feel angry and argue with him. I can't see why he should want my playthings when there are so many around. I beg of him not to take them, and as he finally agrees, I wake.

"We interpreted the dream as shopping for love. The 'playing' which dominated her thoughts was represented by the little figures of dogs and hogs. The stranger was Dr. Stekel, who had forbidden her to 'play' with men friends. She resented being the one to give up pleasures enjoyed by so many women. In the dream, Dr. Stekel has been finally won over to the idea of moral laxity.

"The patient accepted the interpretation and admitted her anger at Dr. Stekel. She was given to understand the motive behind Dr. Stekel's sternness. She was to avoid mental conflicts. To a devout Catholic like her, infidelity was bound to cause a feeling of guilt and distress.

"The following is a fragment of a conversation between the analyst and the patient:

"*P.:* 'What can I do? I can't think of anything at all. I don't remember a thing. Isn't it a shame, though, I don't even recall the man with whom I had the first intercourse. How can a woman ever forget such a thing!'

"*A.:* 'Haven't you told me that you had no intercourse before your marriage? If that is the case, your husband was the man.'

"*P.:* 'I have always thought I had been a virgin until my wedding day, but the other day my girl friend told me that that night at Linz I had sexual intercourse with the man. It must have been as she says. We must have done this twice; once some time before, and once the night he was in my hotel room.'

"She resumed, insisting that the Linz man was the source of all her troubles. She had never been able to forget, much less to forgive that he had jilted her. She loved him as no one else before or after. She had been spoiled by her parents and used to have all her wishes fulfilled. When the Linz man rejected her, she just couldn't take it.

"She has never again seen the man, although they went on writing to each other for a while. A year or so ago, though, she learned that he was in Vienna, that he was married and had a child. This bit of news made her feel very badly. She began waiting for him to visit her now that he was in Vienna. She hated him for having married another girl after he had said that he would never marry.

"Her conversation made it quite clear that she was quite unable to rid her memory of her experience with the man who had given her the feeling of womanhood and sexual gratification. It was also evident that in her spells she was reliving the scene at the Linz hotel, the scene which her conscious memory had blacked out so completely that she was unable to recall whether she had kissed the boy goodbye.

"In her early girlhood she had been given to reveries to such an extent that her parents had to watch over her. They had often brought her in from the street where she had been standing in a daze for hours.

"She remained a daydreamer to this day. Her cogitations revolved exclusively around sexual fantasies. She could glance at a man on the street and immediately begin to conjure up a romance. Or she would think of her gentlemen friends and anticipate their visits and ways in which they stimulated her sexually. All her fantasies were centered on sexual gratification.

"She implored the analyst to give her something that would strengthen her resistance. The mere presence of a man made her helpless. A man's kind word made her a weak and willing victim.

" 'I could be happy,' she said, 'if I were not ill. I can't stand being alone in the house, and as soon as my chores are done I have to go somewhere. My husband is all right. Of course, he could be a little warmer. He likes me very much, though. But he's not demonstrative, and I can't make him so. At first, my illness upset him, but now he accepts me as I am, and he is kind and helpful when I have a spell.

" 'I was thirty-two when I got married. I simply would not and could not stay single any longer. But when I got married, my spells became worse. Some doctors advised me to get married, some were against it. The same went for having children. Well, I have a child, and still everything is the same. You know something, I am not what you'd call a wicked woman, but I'm so mad at that Linz boy I sometimes wish his child brought him great misery. I want my revenge.'

"Later analysis disclosed that she did relive her Linz experience in her spells. It remained, however, unclear why the experience did not recur in her dreams.

"One day she came forth with the memory of an experience. The memory had suddenly come upon her the day before, and it had struck her as referring to a contributive cause of her illness. She mentioned that at one time she had been capable of being aroused by dogs nestling up to her, especially so when a dog rubbed at her leg with masturbatory movements. Several years ago, she made a dog perform a cunnilingus. Her pangs of conscience at this time were so strong that she felt no pleasure, and she never repeated the act.

"She had a great urge to have her husband perform a similar act on her, but she knew that the mere idea of such an act was disgusting to him. She did not dare ask his permission to perform fellatio on him. While she had a hankering for all sorts of perversities, he was a sexual 'purist.' He was for chastity and moderation in love.

"She was sobbing and lamenting when she came to the next session and told the analyst that the night before she had three attacks surpassing in severity any she had ever undergone.

"Even while she was talking, she kept on gasping, swallowing, clicking her tongue and spitting mucus. She could hardly speak. She broke out in tears and cried: 'I am suffocating.' Then she fell into a brief spell. After a few convulsive quivers and gasps, she calmed down. She had tears in her eyes, breathed deeply a few times the way women do after an orgastic culmination.

"When she resumed talking, she told the analyst that on that parting night in Linz she had performed fellatio on the man. She remembered now that he had such a big organ that she used to call him a 'stallion.' She had nearly suffocated while performing the act.

"Her talk again turned on her girl friend who had been present that night in the hotel room. She admitted having had a homosexual relation with her. When she was sixteen, the girl friend performed cunnilingus on her and caused her to experience a strong orgasm. The two girls went on for a time stimulating each other. It was this girl friend who instigated her petting with men. Thereafter the relationship between the two girls was stopped.

"It became apparent how that the reliving of the fellatio episode was tied up with the presence and participation of the girl friend during the sexual scene. It had been a pluralistic act.

"The following day she appeared to be in better spirits. She had had only a brief spell. According to her husband's account she wanted to exchange kisses all the time. She had actually kissed him once. We knew that the kisses were not meant for him. The pressure in her chest and the feeling of a strange object in her throat were less acute.

"By then, we interpreted the obstruction in the throat as both the penis and (symbolically) the story she could not tell.

"As her throat irritation gradually diminished, she was able to take up singing lessons again. When she became sick she had to give up singing. She had lost her voice. Of course, it had meant symbolically that she could not talk about the things that went on in her mind.

"Another chain of memories revealed that the first spells, which occurred also in daytime, used to come on during the meals (displacement from below upward). Her favorite dishes at the time were spaghetti and sausage.

"She remembered being neurotic even in her childhood. She flew into a rage easily and lost her temper over trifles. When she was nine, she slept in a little bed which stood between the beds of her parents. She could not see anything, but she often heard that something was going on. Although she did not know what her father was doing to her mother, she was angry and she begrudged her mother the privilege of having her father in bed. She had a greater fondness for her father at the time. Not until his death had she turned her affection over to her mother.

"In her family, sex had been a thing wrapped in silence and mystery. Her friends at school provided her with some vague information, destroying the stork illusion in the process. Complete enlightenment came through the aforementioned girl friend. Whatever she learned and knew and did, she had to keep a secret from her parents, and she felt very guilty about it.

"At the time, it had struck her as being very strange that her parents' death could not make her cry, although she knew she loved them. Obviously, she had wished death upon them subconsciously, because they had exercised great restraint on her. Indeed, the restraining influence was so effective that even after her marriage she did not succumb to her weakness of petting with other men as long as her mother was still alive. Her state of gloomy depression after her mother's death was, to a great extent, a reaction to her suppressed death wishes.

"She reported the following dream:

Something gets stuck in my throat, and I suffocate. I think it's a sort of long intestine, and I am scared. I pull at it, and it stretches and stretches, until it becomes as thin as a thread and finally breaks.

"The functional meaning of the dream (to use Silberer's term) appeared to us to be far more significant than its material content. The fellatio configuration was used to represent the analysis, the 'pulling out.' She certainly had the intention of breaking up both the analysis and the thread of memories.

"She began begging for permission to have at least one man friend beside her husband. She argued that her girl friend indulged every now and then in extramarital relations without ever getting neurotic for all that. She was admonished to try to do without it.

"It was hardest on her to give up the elderly gentleman friend. He had a big genital, and she liked holding it in her hand. She mentioned again and again that she was missing it.

"She professed to be glad that she now responded to her husband. She now believed that he had been restraining himself merely on moral grounds.

"She improved considerably, and decided to get her child back. She wanted to be a good mother from now on. She also wished to become a better wife. She has succeeded in making her husband warmer and more tenderly playful. He was now doing things on his own initiative. She reported the following dream:

I am being chased by a stranger and run into the patio of a little restaurant. There's a snowdrift in a corner of the yard. I climb up on it, but my feet sink into the snow. I pull myself out and escape.

"The dream contained indications of her inner conflicts. It was hard on her to give up her gentlemen friends, yet she thought she could get well only if she concentrated all her desires on her husband.

"She showed continuous improvement. She resumed singing and played on her piano, read newspapers and books, and had no trouble reaching orgasm in sexual intercourse. In three months she has not had a single seizure.

"Her headaches disappeared. With the stabilization of her domestic life, she began indulging in little extraneous pleasures, previously forbidden by her doctors. She drank beer, swam, went dancing. Even the compulsive twist of her head leftward—the symbolic presentation of her side glance toward the Linz 'stallion' —was gone.

"She gave up completely her girl friend whom her husband intuitively hated so fiercely.

"Then suddenly came a terrific setback. The discharged patient returned, and was taken over by Dr. Stekel who suggested searching for deeper, infantile sources."

Here ends my assistant's report. I took over the treatment of the woman, saw her at first only once a week, and then changed to daily sessions.

At the very first session she went through a spell and all the known manifestations. I discovered that her elimination was not urine at all. I had before me a so-called *hydrorrhea ex libidine* (described by me in my volume on frigidity).

The analysis produced certain findings which I shall resume here briefly.

After the previous, partially successful, analysis she attempted another repression because she was unable to renounce her pluralistic desires (secondary repression).

The pluralistic tendency was endemic in her family and in the circle of her friends. Her brother married a girl with the stipulation that her father be present 'all the time.' Beginning with the wedding night, the father-in-law shared the bed with the couple.

Two brothers with whom she was acquainted lived with the same woman. When the woman died, the two men looked around until they found another woman willing to be the wife of both, although legally she married the older brother. The last time, the younger brother was the official husband.

My patient also remembered that as a child she used to sleep in a crib standing between the beds of her parents, and that she overheard many things. Her pluralistic tendencies were rooted in infantile experiences.

She reluctantly admitted at a later stage that the two brothers who shared the same wife were the brothers of the fateful girl friend of hers. The patient herself had had a relation with one of them even before her Linz experience. It had been this brother of her girl friend who had deflowered her. She could not remember whether her girl friend had been present at the act. Anyway, the Linz episode, as it turned out, was only a repetition of a much earlier one.

The patient's pitiful state was further illuminated when it was found that she had a pathological fixation upon her own brother. The Linz "stallion" was only a transfer of attachment. In fact, when he was lodging with her family he and her brother were close friends. The large penis she always saw in her fantasies was that of her brother on whom she had performed fellatio when she was a child.

Her brother still lived in the house in which she and her husband occupied an apartment. She and her brother were joint owners of the house. Her brother often complained of domestic troubles, and she was obsessed by the idea that if her husband died she could then live with her brother.

Significantly, her child was being raised somewhere in the country. When her first child had died, her brother encouraged her to be glad that the "papoose" was dead. At a later time, referring to the second child, he used to say, "Why do you have to have children? They only cost money and cause a lot of trouble."

It became clear why she once had a relapse after visiting with her child in the country. The recent deterioration also coincided with a reunion with the child.

When she had shown improvement during the first treatment I advised her to take her child back home, and with a burst of wakened motherhood she passed on the suggestion to her husband. He made it clear to her that he could do so only if he had a business of his own, and that they ought to sell her share of the house to raise the needed money. Her brother, however, was against the whole plan, which, he said, would ruin him financially.

She came into an acute conflict situation, and the death of the child looked like the only solution to the dilemma. If the child died, she would divorce her husband, her brother would divorce his wife, and she and her brother could at long last fulfill their old mutual promise to live together.

She had criminal fantasies in connection with her child begotten by an unloved husband. She resumed twisting her head leftward, toward her brother and the girl friend, and away from the "right" path.

The pluralistic setting in her fantasies was in essence the fulfillment of the infantile wish of petting with her brother in the presence of the copulating parents. And there is reason to believe that the configuration was not entirely unreal. Some of her dreams pointed at factual occurrences in the remote past. The patient began slowly remembering sexual games she had played with her brother.

But at this stage of the treatment, analysis was broken off by the patient, and I have never heard from her again.

Pluralistic episodes seem to exert such an influence on neurotics that they are unable ever to forget them. The neurotics only pretend to have forgotten the episodes, or allege to have experienced nothing but disgust at the time. However, analysis reveals that the experiences have been only repressed, and that they recur in the patients' daydreams.

The following case, analysed by my assistant, Mrs. Hilda Milko,[1] shows the determining and fatal influence of a pluralistic experience.

Case No. 118: Mrs. L.K., thirty-two, has been perturbed for years by a sense of weariness and by fear of insanity. She separated from her husband seven years ago, after a period of strained and unhappy marital life. He was highly neurotic, and he had tormented her constantly. He had also been unfaithful to her and he had dissipated her dowry. She was glad, she said, to have gotten rid of him. He had married a second wife, and she could only pity the poor woman.

The patient had undergone a gynecological operation in the first year of her marital life.

She complained of extreme loneliness. She looked upon herself as a person unwanted by any one in the world, especially since her mother died, some three years ago. "If I should pass away, no one will miss me. If I were not so cowardly, I'd put an end to my life, which is so barren of sense and joy."

She had to work to support herself, but what she really wanted was to sleep and sleep forever. She had to consume great amounts of coffee to stay awake. She'd give up her job, but then she'd be in a real predicament, and she was too proud to ask anything from her relatives, from whom she had pulled away somehow. It frightened her to think that she should go on like this, year after year. And here she was getting older all the time, and losing her bloom, and no man would ever be attracted by her. (Her appearance contradicted her words: she was a pretty, strikingly attractive person, with the face of a child.) She was not able to attract anyone's attention, even on the street. No man

---

[1] Later, Mrs. Stekel—*The Editor.*

tried to talk to her. She went completely unnoticed. She was thus condemned to loneliness, which she could not bear. She was craving for love and attention.

She had trouble in the office lately because she was inadequate for the job. She was incapable of a sustained effort; her thoughts were not on the job. She often had excruciating headaches, and at times she felt a pain in one half of her face. The latter discomfort she considered to be a neuralgia due to changes in weather conditions.

She regarded herself as very lazy. To change from a sitting to a standing position was, to her, an elaborate task. She had to exert herself every morning, because she loathed getting out of bed to start another day. Although she was a rather showy person, she lacked at times the energy to wash herself properly, much less to do any mending on her clothes.

She considered herself to be an inveterate daydreamer. At times, she threw herself into the corner of the couch with the deliberate intent of letting her fantasy ride. Her fantasies were protections from ugly reality. But she did not really have to exert any conscious effort. She fell into a daydream while walking the street or riding the streetcar. Not a day passed without her having dreamily forgotten something or other. Her propensity to daydreaming always increased toward her menses at which time she was in such a haze that everything seemed unreal.

She masturbated frequently and hated herself for her inability to give up the "harmful habit." She saw in it a contributory cause of her illness. Her husband had taught her the habit, and she still loathed him for it. Moreover, he had made her masturbate in his presence.

Normal intercourse brought her no orgasm; only cunnilingus gave her complete gratification. After her divorce she had a few shortlived affairs with men, and it was she who always put an end to the romance which invariably failed to give her sexual gratification. She had had many admirers. One man, a friend of her ex-husband, wanted to divorce his wife and marry her. She liked him, too, and yet she treated him so rudely that he was deeply hurt. But it was not her fault that she had been so mean: her husband had made her so.

At this point, the patient revealed, to the great surprise of the analyst, that she had maintained relations with her husband after the divorce. For a while they had continued with their intimacies. He was so fond of her he wouldn't give her up, while she continued being under his influence to such an extent that he supervised the interior decoration of her apartment.

As recently as three years ago, on the day of her mother's death, he happened to telephone her, and, distressed as she was, she asked him to come over. He accepted her invitation and was very sympathetic.

He hoped she would come back to him after her mother's death, but she could not think of living with him again, and he finally gave up seeing her. Shortly afterward she received his wedding announcement.

She learned, through common friends, that his appearance had deteriorated and that he had financial difficulties. She wondered why she still took such an interest in his life, why it pained her to hear of his precarious situation.

Her loneliness, after that final break with the ex-husband, became complete. She has never since paid any attention to men.

As analysis progressed, it became apparent that she still clung to her husband and lived with the idea that he would return to her. She ignored the fact of his second marriage. Her own chastity served the purpose of showing him that she loved only him. All her dreams revolved around his person.

These hidden wishes required quite a feat of repression, since she was consciously through with him and would not even think of living with him again. The fear of insanity was really her fear of those hidden thoughts breaking through to the surface. Every evening when she came home from work she wrapped a towel around her forehead. Her head was bursting with pain. In reality, she was gripped with fear that her thoughts would burst into the open.

Gradually, insight could be gained into the misery of her marital life and of her illness.

She had been sixteen, and a high school senior, when she had first met her husband. Soon afterward they became engaged. She was very much in love with him, but she kept on asking herself whether she should marry him. At times she hesitated. Step by step, he taught her all sorts of sexual perversions. He made her both passionate and completely subservient to him. Simultaneously, her ethical ego rebelled against him.

One occurrence made her most unhappy. A few days before their marriage, he deflowered her in a brief attack upon her in standing position in a corner of the house.

Everybody envied her her beau. The couple seemed destined for happiness, as both were young, handsome, and rich. Yet the wedding night was a disappointment. Under the pretext of exhaustion, the groom hardly spoke to her and avoided touching her.

From then on, through the days and weeks that followed, she suffered more and more. He refused to work, stayed in bed till noon, and spent money recklessly. He got himself involved in business failures and soon they had financial worries.

Yet she was strongly attached to him because he was very clever and she enjoyed talking to him.

When they were married for about two years they made a trip, and she had a terrifying experience. He picked up a prostitute on the street, brought her to their hotel room and slept with her in the patient's presence. Then he ordered the two women to perform a homosexual act. Although the patient was, and is, a pronounced homosexual, she refused to obey.

This pluralistic episode had the effect of a shock on her. Presumably she had felt nothing but disgust at the time, and felt nothing but shame now. She thought that no man could ever love a woman who had had such an experience. And all the time she had no one to whom she could unburden herself, while the memory of the episode kept tormenting her.

Her domestic life went from bad to worse. She, herself, was not the faithful type, and she often flirted with adolescent boys. She has always had a weakness for very young boys, and she allowed them many frivolities, although it never came to intercourse with any of them. Her husband knew what was going on, but he was not jealous. In his turn, he had a mistress, and he used to tell his wife of his dates with the other girl. He wanted to hurt her. He engaged in intimacies with the patient in the presence of friends, brought visitors into the bedroom when she was in bed, and finally went so far as to invite his friends to witness their sexual intercourse.

The friends were indignant and urged her to divorce him. Many of them also argued that he was ruining her financially. She went through a protracted inner struggle until she finally decided on separation. Her husband tried to hold her. Among other things, he used to tell her that she could never hope to attract any other man. Apparently these words had sunk in, for later on she behaved in a way that certainly displeased every man who came near her.

She was completely broken in spirit and in flesh when she at last left her husband. He had shaped her life for her for all the days to come. She had been sexually subservient to him, although her mind had rebelled against him. Consciously, she had known that he was dragging her down. In different circumstances, in company of another man, this fine, high-minded young woman could have developed into something quite different.

Yet her husband had been able to exercise such power over her only because the downward tendency was within her.

She has always felt a predilection for the ordinary and vulgar. When she was thirteen, she fell in love with a country postman. She dreamed of living with him and being his wife. She cried when vacation was over and the family went back to Vienna.

It was not so much love for her husband that made her long for him as the memory of a sexual life full of paraphilias. It was specifically the memory of the pluralistic episode and the hidden longing for a repetition of it.

Of course, her sensations at the time of the occurrence had been complex; they had contained hatred and lust, disgust and desire. But it was such a complex sensation that it was often capable of producing orgasm. Many women find satisfaction only when their innermost inhibitions are overwhelmed in the act of love.

The future of the patient depended on her ability to overcome the power of her fantasies. As long as they were effective she would long for her former husband because he was the only man who was both able and willing to fulfill them.

There was every reason to believe that the patient was on the way to understanding and liberation.

The two cases just cited have one thing in common: both neuroses came in the wake of a gynecological operation. I have made the observation that gynecological operations under general anesthesia often induced a neurotic state. The narcotic dream seems to include the element of rape fantasy. A gynecological operation is a traumatic experience. The woman lies there, naked, in front of many men and women, while someone is manipulating her genitalia.

The spells in Case No. 117 were a clear reproduction of a narcotic state. (Young analysts should be aware of the fact that all seizures have multiple determinants.) The woman in question stirred convulsively, kicked with her arms and legs violently, gagged, and ejaculated mucus. Even the twist of her head leftward seemed to be a mnemonic fixation on the anesthetist who had held her head turned to the left when the narcosis had made her vomit.

The state of anesthesia tends to become identified with the pluralistic and exhibitionistic wish-fulfilment.

In another severely neurotic case the patient's post-ex-cochleational pluralistic fantasies emerged as the source of her disturbance. She remembered the warm feeling of the flushing and other sensations of the narcotic state. She also remembered having protested against those sensations with, "I don't want it. Leave me alone!"

When a neurosis, characterized by a disturbance of sex functions, had emerged after a gynecological operation, the analyst must always be on the lookout for pluralistic fantasies. They may be at times superimposed on very early infantile fantasies, and at other times they can be traced to genuine traumatic experiences in adult life.

Chapter Nine

RETROSPECT AND PROSPECT

Chapter Nine

RETROSPECT AND PROSPECT

At a time when mankind is yearning for freedom, it is important to point out that the way to external freedom leads over internal roads. Only those are truly free who have overcome the imperatives of their past. Only those are properly armed in the struggle for existence who have conquered the internal enemy who represents the demands of childhood and thwarts the individual's adjustment to reality.

We have shown that many people seek their happiness in the perpetuation or revival of their childhood. They appear to hunt for the new, but in reality the new is a replica of the old—the old something which should have been long forgotten and buried.

We have seen that some of our infantile experiences do not yield to the influence of time. They are repeated in countless variations in the patient's daydreams and fantasies and show all the earmarks of a world that was. In many cases one or a few infantile experiences form a nucleus around which a neurosis crystallizes. It is sometimes very hard to progress in analysis sufficiently to reach this nucleus.

Our most important educational task is to guide the patient

out of his fantasy world into that of reality. The fantasy world has, as a rule, very little chance for realization; in some cases the coefficient of reality equals zero.

The first attempt to replace the fantasy world by reality should be made by the school, which should utilize the child's imagination to draw his attention gradually away from his infantile reveries. At first the reveries must obtain the higher reality value so that they may form a transition to a sober and efficient adaptation to the tasks of every day living. Since attention, according to Bleuler, is an affective process, education designed to replace the affects of daydreaming must also be affective. The child clings to his pleasure currency and yields it only under protest.

Only those individuals can overcome their fantasies who have learned to recognize and utilize pleasures of reality. Every moment offers new pleasure potentials; and if the individual is not fixed to his childhood enjoyments, he will find the proper transition to reality, with all its inherent gratifications. Most of our patients see, feel, and suffer once only. What follows are only carbon copies of the first impressions. It is a secret of successful living to be able to overcome the first impressions, to correct them under the impact of a constant reality—to see them for the second time from another perspective. If we can induce our patients to see their past with the eyes of adults and to depreciate it, we have done the most important part of our therapeutic re-education.

Often we are misled into believing that by revealing to the patient the details of his innermost complexes we have destroyed the crystallization point of his neurosis. Unfortunately many of our patients simulate recovery in order to preserve their treasure, their neurosis. In many cases a new crystallization forms around the undamaged nucleus. The fantasies grow, become more clandestine, better masked, more thoroughly split up from the patient's consciousness. We can say that as a rule the tendency to hide a fantasy is the greater the more unrealistic it is. The patient is ashamed of his daydreams. And yet he sacrifices to them the happiness of this world. If, as a result he is inefficient, unsuccessful in his pursuits, it is because he has devalued them in favor of his hidden fancies. He is like the dog in Aesop's fable who drops a substantial piece of meat into the water in which he sees the image of a far bigger piece.

It is interesting to observe some of our patients' pursuits. They are often archeologists, or connoisseurs of antiques or old paintings. They have a sentimental attachment to their home country and suffer from nostalgia whenever they are away from it. They are archconservatives, or overcompensate this conservatism by an equally exaggerated urge for the new and unusual.

Without exception they are unable to love. If they enter love relations they often experience serious internal tragedies. They then decide to live a double life. Alongside their love their infantilism marches as a constant threat always ready to destroy their love. Many of these patients do not realize that while they are engaged in passionate embraces they are committing acts of infidelity, inasmuch as in their accompanying fantasies, figures from their childhood are constantly intruding. Often these figures are arbitrarily recalled in order to increase the stimulus value of the embrace. This is a dangerous technique which sooner or later leads to the collapse of the love relationship.

Only a real love which stands on its own merits can save the infantilist. He must be ready and willing to sacrifice his infantile fantasies for the sake of the beloved person. However, since the fantasies are closely interwoven with the patient's total personality, he may be afraid to sacrifice them and thus lose his own personality. This fact shows the difficulty the therapist faces in his attempt to rehabilitate the psychosexual infantilist.

There is also another and perhaps more dangerous internal

enemy against whom the struggle of both the patient and the psychiatrist must be directed. It is narcissism. In order to get well the patient must overcome his feeling of omnipotence, self-overestimation, and self-admiration. He must recognize his mistakes through an impartial self-criticism. The affect of self-love blinds all of us. Our patients suffer from an unconscious pathological over-estimation of themselves, a feeling that is kept in balance by conscious violent inferiority complexes. Both feelings are unrealistic, and hence are unable to help the patient to appraise himself correctly.

Because of his daydreams the infantilist conveys the impression of being lazy. Work disturbs his daydreams. Artists, who mold their daydreams into creative works, are fortunate. They work with and through their fantasies. The neurotics, however, must be trained to work. It is a secret of all training to seek out that type of work which is capable of replacing the lost pleasures.

One of the curses of the war is that it keeps entire populations from the constructive occupation that is so necessary as a social form of adjustment. During the war the soldiers whose time is not occupied constructively fall back on playful daydreaming activities through which they help themselves over many an empty hour. They compensate for the otherwise distressing present by the pleasure contents of infantile revery. After the war many men can not return to reality and they destroy their marriages through the loss of joy that is inherent in every constructive occupation. As things look now, we must assume that infantilism as a mass phenomenon will increase and the present generation will fall back emotionally more and more on childhood patterns of pleasure. Many parents whose own lives were built on sweat and toil, harm their children emotionally when they foster in them infantile patterns of dependency with the rationalization that "at least their children's lot might be easier." Youth, which has not been trained to derive pleasure from work, in reality will have more difficulty and suffer more hardships than their overconsiderate parents have foreseen. Hardships for which the individual has not been prepared are often the causes of regression to the unforgettable pleasures of childhood.

One of the causes of infantilism is the one-child system with the concomitant pampering and overprotection. However, I have also observed cases of psychosexual infantilism in families with many children. As previously stated, infantilism is on the increase.

War represents such an infantilism. Mature people argue and settle their differences by agreement. Immature people fight. It is obvious that the one who wins is not always the one who is right. War is a regression which throws nations back thousands of years into cultural infancy. All peaceful pursuits are designed to bring peoples closer together. All the inventions, the steamships, the railroads, the telegraph and telephone, the radio and the airplanes serve the purpose of overcoming the distance in space between the peoples. War stops communications, disrupts connections, closes the borders, and with the closed borders also the hearts of the peoples are closed to the rest of humanity. Man undergoes a curious metamorphosis—he becomes ruthless and selfish. Dog eats dog. Crime rises. The idea of short-term profit overshadows considerations of human needs and human misery. The animal in man awakens, and the foundations of our moral and ethical ideals are threatened. All the sadism and cruelty of childhood return.

Modern art reflects this psychosexual infantilism of the masses. In contemporary paintings and music we notice definite regressive, archaic trends. We rediscover old Egyptian and Phoenician designs, and primitivisms celebrate their resurrection in "the new style." Some of the modern paintings show a remarkable resemblance to the drawings of children and psychotics—we are dealing here with regressions and infantilisms. The poetry of the supermodern writers is in part a ludicrous stammering and toying with words. Modern dance has many features of regression. The dance patterns borrowed from primitive peoples, the African Negro rhythms, and the body contortions styled according to some tribal dance rituals come more and more to the fore. The dance has always represented an erotic enjoyment—the erotism however, was formerly better masked. The dance today has dropped the controls and become more openly suggestive.

All the unfortunates described in this book are victims of hypocritical sexual morals. Prophylaxis would entail a total reform of our entire social life. I have attempted to show in my books life as it really is. What we read in novels are caricatures and fantastic elaborations of life. Where is the writer who dares to depict life with complete frankness? Even the diaries of great poets and writers which have reached the public eye have been toned down out of consideration for the morals of the public. (Hebbel, Goethe, Tolstoy, Dostoyevski.) Some of the diaries were suppressed against the testamentary wishes of the authors. In my work on *Disorders of Instinct and Emotion,* I have unfolded the painful history and the suffering of humanity which spends itself in the futile struggle between instinct and inhibition, between drive and culture, between impulse and morals. An unhappy world creates unhappy people, and unhappy people create an unhappy world. A vicious circle. In thinking about the cause of this course of events I cannot but feel that the denial of love is humanity's greatest weakness. All great constructive works are creations of love. We need an education for love. We must be trained in overcoming our hatreds; we must be shown how we can turn our love toward our fellowman, how we can develop with and through our fellowman, and thus prepare a happier future for all of us.

INDEX

INDEX

Abasia, 74

Abdomen: father's, 36; mother's, 50

Abortion, 82

Abraham, 53, 54, 303

Abreaction, 249

Absence, reproduced in play, 24-25

Act: sexual, 42, 46, 104, 164, 166, 167, 170, 267, 360; impulsive, 74, 172, 179, 180 note, 181; compulsive, 182, 246, 268 (see also Compulsion); unconscious, 192; visual, 164

Adler, 15, 86, 199, 319

Adolescence, 69

Adolescent: the eternal, 138 ff.; desire to be an, 141; neurotic, 299; attacks on, 180 note

Adoration, excessive, of a child, 291

Adults: sexual activity observed by child, 24, 49, 97, 105, 109, 118, 165, 166, 193, 218, 228, 359, 360, 373, 376; bed-wetting by, 231, 232, 234, 235, 297, 367; genitalia of, observed by child, 44, 45, 57, 272; attacked by child, 47, 48, 121; sex relations between adult and child, 48, 291, 296; observed by child, 44, 49, 164; imitated by child, 14, 35; tested by child, 26, 28, 50, 51, 56; deceived by child, 14; with predilection for eliminations, 43

Adulthood, 69, 70

Aerophagia, 251

Affair: love, 95, 106, 340; sexual, 89, 379, 352

Affect: transfer of, 191 note, 192; displacement and distortion of, 181, 275, 276, 346; floating, 192; affective charge in enuresis, 235; domination by 357; manifestations of, 265

Affectedness, 309

Age: fear of growing old, 28, 72, 73, 125, 309; old, 72, 235; pedophilia in old, 286

Aggression, 136, 272; in child, 12, 47, 48; discharge of, 150; in exhibitionism, 174

Agoraphobia, 240, 241, 294, 295, 317, 318

Alcoholics, 180, 180 note, 191, 193, 197

Alone, being: fear of, 88, 241; dislike of, 94, 361

Ambition, 132, 205

Amnesia, 369; and neurosis, 55, 63 (see also Memory)

Analysis, 102, 115, 125, 138, 144, 149, 158, 159, 203, 242, 350, 387; in dream, 200, 202

Analyst, 383; patient's relation to, 125, 208 (see also Transfer)

Anesthesia, 113, 383

Anger: in child, 12, 19, 134, 373; provoked by child, 51, 232; in adult, 150, 196; fear of, 365 (see also Rage)

Anilingus, 101, 203, 240, 242, 361; in children, 48, 239, 241

Animals: child's interest in, 12, 26, 35, 54, 55, 277; maltreatment of, 49, 262; sexual abuse of, 258, 265-7, 277; as objects of emotional catharsis, 149, 150, 257; identification with, 75, 267, 278; mating of, observed by child, 260, 261, 277; lovers of, 257, 279; in fantasy, 165, 257-279 (see also Zoophilia, Cat, Dog, etc.)

Animism, child's belief in, 26, 30

Annulment: of an experience, 34; of time, 75; mechanisms of, 152

Anorexia, 54; hysterical, 14

Anosexuality, 115, 237, 239, 240, 244; and creative ability, 244 (see also Erotism)

Antheim, 71

Anus, 71, 115, 119, 154, 155, 238, 239, 240, 243, 247, 254, 262, 272, 355; as erogenous zone, 41, 71,